Fundamentals of

Microwave Electronics

INTERNATIONAL SERIES IN PURE AND APPLIED PHYSICS
LEONARD I. SCHIFF, CONSULTING EDITOR

Allis and Herlin   Thermodynamics and Statistical Mechanics
Becker   Introduction to Theoretical Mechanics
Bjorken and Drell   Relativistic Quantum Mechanics
Chodorow and Susskind   Fundamentals of Microwave Electronics
Clark   Applied X-rays
Collin   Field Theory of Guided Waves
Evans   The Atomic Nucleus
Finkelnburg   Atomic Physics
Ginzton   Microwave Measurements
Green   Nuclear Physics
Gurney   Introduction to Statistical Mechanics
Hall   Introduction to Electron Microscopy
Hardy and Perrin   The Principles of Optics
Harnwell   Electricity and Electromagnetism
Harnwell and Livingood   Experimental Atomic Physics
Harnwell and Stephens   Atomic Physics
Henley and Thirring   Elementary Quantum Field Theory
Houston   Principles of Mathematical Physics
Hund   High-frequency Measurements
Kennard   Kinetic Theory of Gases
Lane   Superfluid Physics
Leighton   Principles of Modern Physics
Lindsay   Mechanical Radiation
Livingston and Blewett   Particle Accelerators
Middleton   An Introduction to Statistical Communication Theory
Morse   Vibration and Sound
Morse and Feshbach   Methods of Theoretical Physics
Muskat   Physical Principles of Oil Production
Present   Kinetic Theory of Gases
Read   Dislocations in Crystals
Richtmyer, Kennard, and Lauritsen   Introduction to Modern Physics
Schiff   Quantum Mechanics
Seitz   The Modern Theory of Solids
Slater   Introduction to Chemical Physics
Slater   Quantum Theory of Matter
Slater   Quantum Theory of Atomic Structure, Vol. I
Slater   Quantum Theory of Atomic Structure, Vol. II
Slater   Quantum Theory of Molecules and Solids, Vol. I
Slater and Frank   Electromagnetism
Slater and Frank   Introduction to Theoretical Physics
Slater and Frank   Mechanics
Smythe   Static and Dynamic Electricity
Stratton   Electromagnetic Theory
Thorndike   Mesons: A Summary of Experimental Facts
Tinkham   Group Theory and Quantum Mechanics
Townes and Schawlow   Microwave Spectroscopy
White   Introduction to Atomic Spectra

The late F. K. Richtmyer was Consulting Editor of the series from its inception in 1929 to his death in 1939.   Lee A. DuBridge was Consulting Editor from 1939 to 1946; and G. P. Harnwell from 1947 to 1954.

Fundamentals of
Microwave
Electronics

Marvin Chodorow

*Professor of Applied Physics
and of Electrical Engineering
Director, Microwave Laboratory
Stanford University*

Charles Susskind

*Professor of Electrical Engineering
University of California, Berkeley*

McGraw-Hill Book Company

New York   San Francisco   Toronto   London

Fundamentals of Microwave Electronics

10778

To Leah and Terry

Preface

This book is the outgrowth of a first-year graduate course taught by one of us almost every year at Stanford University, and by the other occasionally at the University of California in Berkeley, for over a decade. The course at Stanford was actually initiated by W. W. Hansen (1909–1949) and was possibly the first formal college course in microwave electronics taught anywhere. Over the years in which the material in this book has been used, more than 300 students have attended the course, not a few of whom have gone on to important research in microwave electronics. Interaction with them has served to clarify many of the ideas and to affect the treatment of various topics in a most beneficial way.

The organization of the text has grown out of the conviction that the several books on particular tube types that have been published since the now-classic M.I.T. Radiation Laboratory Series volumes on "Microwave Magnetrons" and on "Klystrons and Microwave Triodes" (McGraw-Hill, Inc., 1948), including recent books containing detailed theoretical treatments of individual tubes, aim at specific details and often fail to set forth the basic principles of microwave electronics in a general manner. By contrast, the present text places relatively little emphasis on circuit design or details of field configurations, but stresses instead electron motion and the various methods of treating interaction between electrons and circuits.

Microwave electronics is above all concerned with problems that involve the simultaneous treatments of electron motion and of electromagnetic fields; to a large extent, the solution of any problem consists of finding compatibilities between the requirements of Newton's equations and Maxwell's equations. We have tried to emphasize—sometimes even at the cost of some redundancy—the constant interplay between these two requirements. In keeping with this objective, we have largely confined our treatment to simple geometric configurations. We feel that the reader should not be hindered in his understanding of the subject because he cannot immediately recall the recurrence relations for Bessel functions or some other specialized technique.

Although many of the problems in microwave electronics can be formulated as field problems (with electrons represented by fluid-mechanics equations and electromagnetic fields by the appropriate Maxwell's equations), we have tried to avoid presenting the theory merely as an exercise in the solution of such field equations. As a result, the reader will find relatively few formal solutions of boundary-value problems—the standard approach to any field problem. The authors have never felt that the process of marching from boundary to boundary and providing continuity of the appropriate field components at each boundary is a particularly illuminating process, even though in principle it may be the way in which exact answers are obtained. Solutions to some problems in microwave electronics can be obtained in this manner, notably problems associated with space-charge waves between smooth conducting walls of various shapes; but this exception apart, useful solutions to interaction problems have been rarely obtained by rigorous field methods. The more approximate (and in a sense more evasive) methods associated principally with the names of W. W. Hansen and J. R. Pierce have been much more productive of new ideas and real physical insight.

One topic that has been omitted altogether is noise, which has two principal aspects. The first (and most difficult) concerns the statistics of electron motion near the cathode, which determines noise currents and velocities at the anode and beyond. This remains a very active and by no means settled research problem that requires a specialized analysis different from anything that has been included in the text; no proper understanding of the subject could therefore be conveyed at anything approaching the level of the rest of the book. The second aspect of noise theory is the straightforward application of space-charge-wave theory to the propagation of noise beyond the anode. Various chapters in the present volume adequately prepare the reader for this specialized subject.

Among the aforementioned students who have received their first introduction to microwave electronics in courses based on the present treatment, many have made specific contributions to its development. A few can be singled out who have had a particularly strong influence on the development of the material, not only as students but also later as colleagues: C. K. Birdsall, D. A. Dunn, Hubert Heffner, G. S. Kino, P. K. Tien, Glen Wade, D. A. Watkins, and L. T. Zitelli, among others. We are particularly indebted to Prof. C. K. Birdsall of the University of California in Berkeley, who read the entire manuscript and made detailed criticisms and suggestions that have served to turn the volume into a much clearer and more useful one than it would have been otherwise.

Finally, we should also like to acknowledge the profound influence on our own interest in microwave electronics of such pioneers as W. W. Hansen, Russell and Sigurd Varian, and E. L. Ginzton.

Marvin Chodorow

Charles Susskind

Contents

Preface   *ix*

1   General Principles   1

1.1   Some Microwave Tubes   *4*
1.2   General Properties of Microwave Tubes   *10*

2   Electron Beams   16

2.1   Electron Emission: Emission-limited Diodes   *17*
2.2   Space-charge-limited Diodes   *19*
2.3   Design of Electron Guns   *30*
2.4   Space-charge Spreading   *37*
2.5   Beam Focusing   *42*
2.6   Scaling   *52*
2.7   Additional Considerations   *55*

3   Basic Concepts of Interaction between Electrons and Fields   58

3.1   Elementary Theory of Velocity Modulation   *59*
3.2   General Current Equations   *62*
3.3   Transfer of Energy   *66*
3.4   Induced Currents   *68*
3.5   Total Current   *70*
3.6   Electron Motion in a High-velocity Gap   *72*

4   Space-charge Waves   81

4.1   Space-charge Waves: Particle Equations   *84*
4.2   General Equation of Space-charge Waves   *90*

xi

4.3   Solutions of the Space-charge-wave Equation   *96*
4.4   Double-beam case   *103*
4.5   Space-charge Waves with Transverse Motion   *112*

5   Llewellyn Diode Equations   120

5.1   Introduction   *120*
5.2   Equation of Motion   *122*
5.3   D-C Solution   *125*
5.4   R-F Solution   *127*
5.5   Space-charge Factor   *132*
5.6   Diode Equations   *134*
5.7   Multielement Tubes; Other Applications   *139*

6   Traveling Waves   141

6.1   Interaction of Traveling Waves with the Electron Beam   *142*
6.2   Transmission Line Theory Approach   *144*
6.3   Gain Parameter C *154*
6.4   Coupling Impedance   *157*
6.5   Space-charge Effects   *158*
6.6   Normal-mode Expansion   *163*
6.7   Generalization of the Normal-mode Expansion   *173*

7   Backward-wave Interactions   178

7.1   Qualitative Description   *178*
7.2   Oscillation Conditions   *181*

8   Electron Motion in Two-dimensional Systems   189

8.1   Motion through a Nonplanar Gap   *190*
8.2   Calculation of Velocity Modulation   *192*

9   Coupled-mode Analysis   205

9.1   Small-signal Kinetic-power Theorem for Longitudinal Electron Beams   *207*
9.2   Kinetic Power in Space-charge Waves   *213*
9.3   Application of the Power-flow Theorem to the Properties of Amplifiers   *214*
9.4   Coupled-mode Equations   *216*
9.5   Application of Coupled-mode Theory   *222*

9.6 Application of Coupled-mode Theory to the
Traveling-wave Tube   *227*

9.7 Other Applications of the Coupled-mode Approach   *228*

10   Crossed-field Interactions   230

10.1 General Considerations   *230*

10.2 Motion of an Individual Electron in Static Crossed Fields   *232*

10.3 Effects of Space Charge on D-C Motion   *236*

10.4 Crossed-field Amplification   *241*

10.5 Traveling-wave Interaction When Space Charge Is Negligible   *244*

10.6 Interactions with Space-charge Fields Considered   *269*

Appendix 1   Lagrangian and Eulerian Hydrodynamics   283

Appendix 2   Induced Currents—General Configuration   286

Index   289

1

General Principles

In the third and fourth decades of the present century it became apparent that conventional electron tubes were reaching their limits with regard to frequency and that existing theoretical analyses of such tubes were inadequate near these limits. To some extent, the theory developed to explain the behavior of space-charge-control tubes such as triodes is perhaps epitomized by the use of the word "valve" to describe a thermionic tube. In this concept, the action of an electron tube is pictured as essentially analogous to that of a hydraulic on-off valve, without much regard for the details of the flow. This concept serves to explain many of the simpler phenomena that take place in a space-charge-control tube, but it is inadequate when electron velocities have to be taken into account.

As far as performance is concerned, with increasing frequency it is found that the elements of the tube and leads become comparable in size with the wavelength and represent impedances that load the tube so as to affect its operation, usually adversely.

Moreover, the spatial limitations curtail power dissipation and lead to radiation losses. Equally important, when the electron transit time between electrodes becomes comparable with an appreciable portion of the cycle at the operating frequency, it becomes necessary to take the detailed motion of the electrons into account, particularly since these effects are likewise usually deleterious to tube operation. Despite attempts to minimize all of these factors by reducing the electrode spacings and the size of tubes and leads, such considerations limited widespread use of conventional space-charge-control tubes to frequencies below the microwave range.

To circumvent these difficulties, attention turned to radical changes in spatial configurations, as in the "lighthouse tube," in which the tube elements were actually made parts of the external circuits. New analyses, summarized in the publications of F. B. Llewellyn in 1941, were put forward. Also during those years, wholly new principles were investigated and some configurations that had been proposed much earlier were reinvestigated. Several devices that could overcome the above-mentioned frequency limitations were proposed and constructed, although the frequency range of more conventional tubes also continued to be increased and was ultimately extended to the microwave range.

Of the new devices that have been proposed, three have enjoyed the greatest technological success: the magnetron, the klystron, and the various traveling-wave tubes. The general features of each are described in this chapter; the remaining chapters are devoted to the fundamental principles of these tubes (some of which are common to all microwave tubes), rather than to their technical details.

Magnetrons date back to A. W. Hull's 1921 investigation of electron trajectories in a cylindrical diode with an axial magnetic field. Laboratory oscillators based on various modifications of this "smooth-bore" configuration were constructed by A. Žáček in Prague and E. Habann in Jena in 1924, K. Okabe and H. Yagi in Sendai (Japan) in 1928, and C. E. Cleeton and N. H. Williams in Michigan in 1936. These oscillators operated at the cyclotron frequency, with the ratio of anode potential to the square of the magnetic field adjusted for a value near cutoff of the anode current. If the magnetic field is considerably increased above cutoff, oscillations are observed (in a version of the magnetron in which the anode cylinder is split into two or more segments) that result from an effective negative resistance of the tube, as investigated by G. R. Kilgore in 1936. At intermediate values of the magnetic field, a third type of oscillation is observed, the so-called traveling-wave oscillations investigated by K. Posthumus in 1935. However, none of the devices developed in the course of these investigations proved to be of much technological significance. The modern magnetron, which depends on the third type of oscillation, had to await the introduction of the cavity resonator to be successful.

Research leading to the development of the *klystron* and other velocity-modulated tubes had its beginnings in three independent publications on velocity modulation: the publication of A. Arsenjewa-Heil and O. Heil in 1935, that of W. C. Hahn and G. F. Metcalf in 1939, and that of R. H. Varian and S. F. Varian in 1939. The result of the last, the klystron, became the subject of intense development most promptly, probably owing to the availability of a basic theory by D. L. Webster and of the cavity-resonator analysis of W. W. Hansen. The velocity-modulated klystron incorporating a cavity resonator represented the first major breakthrough beyond the frequency limitations of conventional electron tubes. Modern klystrons are direct descendants of this development.

With the outbreak of the World War II, the magnetron received renewed attention. Two Soviet investigators, N. F. Alekseev and D. D. Malairov, published a description of experiments utilizing a cavity magnetron in 1940. Similar configurations had been patented by inventors in the United States (1936), Britain (1938), and Germany (1938). But the major advance occurred when J. T. Randal and H. A. H. Boot designed a traveling-wave cavity-resonator 10-cm magnetron, in Birmingham in 1939–1940, that yielded pulsed-power outputs several orders of magnitude larger than any magnetron tested previously. Because of the urgent need for just such an oscillator in the radar defense of Britain against air attack, the magnetron received intense development, far overtaking the klystron in terms of output power. However, the klystron also came into wide use in radar service, notably in the form of the reflex klystron, which served as a local oscillator in superheterodyne operation. But the development of multicavity klystrons that equaled (and eventually overtook) magnetrons in output power did not come until after the war, with the need for high-power microwave amplifiers in such applications as particle-accelerator power sources and television transmitters.

Various schemes embodying the principle of electron interaction along distributed circuits were patented by a number of investigators in the late thirties. A principal objective of these schemes was to obtain amplification over a wide band, since the bandwidth of resonators (whether LC-circuit or resonant-cavity) is inherently limited. In 1944 R. Kompfner at Oxford completed a series of investigations on a prototype *traveling-wave tube* that he had studied with a view to improving the efficiency of interaction between beam and circuit of klystrons, which is limited to the necessarily short distance across the interaction gap. This investigation, continued after the war with the help of a sound theoretical foundation provided by J. R. Pierce and his associates (later including R. Kompfner), led to devices in which velocity and current modulation is produced by continuous interaction between the electrons and a "slow-wave" circuit (such as a helix) extending over some distance. Because the circuit can be nonresonant, the resulting bandwidths are astonishing: octave (2:1) ratios between end frequencies are not uncommon.   A number of variants of this basic type have been devised.   The most important is the backward-wave oscillator, explained in 1952 by R. Kompfner and by B. Epsztein and his associates, in which the group velocity is directed opposite to the phase (and beam) velocity; the resulting device can be tuned in frequency electronically (i.e., simply by varying a voltage) over a very wide range.

In the following sections, we shall give a brief description of several types of microwave tube.   It is useful to consider what electronic processes are common to all tubes; but before we enumerate these processes, we shall present a qualitative discussion of some of the more usual tube types for the benefit of those readers who are approaching the subject for the first time.   This procedure will enable us to refer to these types as illustrative examples in subsequent discussions of the fundamental processes involved.

1.1   Some Microwave Tubes

Perhaps the simplest microwave tube, from a pedagogical point of view, is the two-cavity klystron.   It has the useful property that the various electronic processes (to be described in Sec. 1.2) take place in separate portions of the tube, rather than overlapping as in some of the more elementary tube types.   Therefore, the klystron will be described first.

a. Klystron

In one form of klystron (Fig. 1.1), the beam emitted by the cathode is accelerated by the d-c potential of the anode and passes through a gap in the anode into a region between a pair of closely spaced grids, across which an r-f voltage exists, into a *drift space*, and then through another pair of grids to the collector.   It is quite accurate to describe these grids as forming the capacitance of a tuned resonant circuit, of which the inductance can be a coil, as shown in the figure.   (Resonant cavities are in fact used in klystrons in place of the *LC* equivalent circuit shown in the schematic representation, but this circumstance does not affect the description that follows.)

An electron is either accelerated or decelerated by the r-f field in the gap, depending on the part of the cycle during which it crosses the gap.[1]

---

[1] It is assumed that the transit time across the gap is so nearly zero as to be negligible compared with a period at the frequency of operation.   The case of appreciable transit time across the gap will be treated in the exact formulation of the theory.

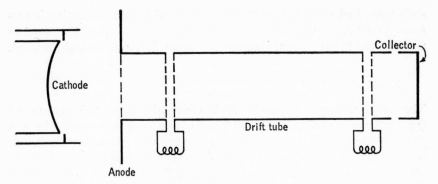

Fig. 1.1 Schematic diagram of two-cavity klystron.

Some electrons pass through at zero field, and hence suffer no change in velocity. They are preceded by electrons which have been decelerated and followed by those which have been accelerated. In the drift tube beyond the first modulating gap, then, the electrons drift with whatever velocity they had after leaving the gap, and the fast electrons overtake the slow ones, so that variations in density are produced by this drifting action. This phenomenon, commonly known as *bunching*, is a consequence of the velocity modulation produced at the first gap. When the electrons arrive at the second gap, they are no longer uniformly distributed in space or time; rather, they are arranged in bunches as a result of the action just described. These bunches then constitute a fluctuating component of current passing through the second gap, and in particular there is a component of current at the modulating frequency of the first gap. Figure 1.2 gives an approximate representation of the current passing through the second gap as a function of time. If voltage at this frequency exists across the second gap, properly phased relative to the arriving current pulses (so that the field is retarding for the bunches), then most of the electrons lose energy in crossing the gap. This energy appears in the form of power delivered to the external circuit. The simplicity of a klystron, already mentioned, is a result of the fact that in each separate region—cathode-anode region, input gap,

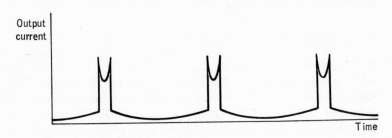

Fig. 1.2 Output current of klystron.

drift tube, and output gap—a single simple elementary function is performed on the electron beam or by the electron beam; and therefore, as we shall find in subsequent chapters, the analysis is quite straightforward.

b. Triode and tetrode

The second tube type on our list is the conventional space-charge-control (or density-modulation) tube, which exists in various forms.   The two simplest forms, and the only ones we need describe here, are the triode and the tetrode.   Additional electrodes and more complicated forms of space-charge-control tubes perform useful but (from the viewpoint of electronic behavior) nonessential functions, and they will not be discussed.

Consider first a tetrode, with an input circuit between cathode and grid and an output circuit between screen and plate.   An r-f voltage is applied between the grid and cathode, superimposed on any d-c voltage that might exist, positive or negative.   This fluctuating component of the field at the cathode then causes a variation in the number of electrons starting from the cathode toward the grid.   Depending on the transit time in this region and on the magnitude of the d-c and r-f voltage, some, all, or none of these electrons get through the grid, and there is a fluctuating component of current passing through the grid at the same frequency as that of the r-f voltage applied between grid and cathode, all at low power.   One can apply any d-c voltage between the grid and the screen that one chooses; this voltage merely accelerates all electrons uniformly.   Fluctuating components of current, now at higher velocity, passing into the region between the screen and the plate now drive the circuits across these grids in exactly the same fashion as in the klystron described previously.   One can, if one wishes, also apply a d-c voltage between the screen and plate for further increase in power; and such a potential difference could also be applied in the klystron case described previously.

The triode may be considered as a special case of the tetrode with the screen and control grid coinciding, thus eliminating the possibility of applying any d-c voltages between grid and screen and also eliminating the transit time between them.

c. Barkhausen oscillator

A third type of tube to be described here, less commonly known, but with certain virtues of simplicity, is the Barkhausen oscillator.   One form consists of a cathode and plate, both at the same potential, and a grid that is at a positive potential.   In addition to the d-c voltage, an r-f voltage is assumed to exist between the grid and the other two (symmetrically placed) electrodes.   Electrons starting from the cathode are accelerated by the potential difference between the cathode and the grid; and upon reaching the grid, they pass through it, except for the small fraction that is intercepted.   In general, however, the small r-f voltage causes electrons passing through the grid to have an energy that does not correspond to the d-c grid potential but is slightly greater or smaller, depending on their starting phase and the transit angle through the cathode-grid region.   If the transit angle in each region is approximately half a cycle, then an electron which has "seen" a retarding r-f field on the average in transit from cathode to grid will (to a first-order approximation) also see a retarding r-f field in transit from grid to anode, because of the reversal in field polarity.   Consequently, this electron cannot quite reach the anode (which is at cathode potential), since it has lost some energy as a result of the retarding action of the r-f field.   The electron therefore stops short of the anode, reverses, and goes through the grid again.   But in the meantime, the field polarity will have reversed, and the electron again loses a little energy to the r-f field and falls short of hitting the cathode (by a somewhat larger margin than in the preceding region).   Under these circumstances the electron keeps oscillating back and forth between the two regions, losing energy continually, until finally it is swept from the field by some extraneous process such as interception by the grid, having continuously transferred energy from the d-c field to the r-f field.

Conversely, an electron which on the average sees an accelerating r-f field during its first transit from cathode to grid also sees on the average an accelerating field during the transit from grid to anode, and it therefore arrives at the anode with a finite energy and is lost by impact at the anode without making further transits through the grid.   The net result is that electrons which gain energy during their first transit are lost, whereas those which lose energy to the r-f field continue to make multiple transits, continually losing energy and thereby providing a net transfer of energy to the r-f field and maintaining the oscillation.

d. Traveling-wave tube

A fourth type of tube, which is of great practical importance and demonstrates in the simplest form a very important kind of interaction, is the traveling-wave tube.   A large variety of traveling-wave tubes exist that differ from one another in the type of circuit used.   Basically, they can all be represented as shown in Fig. 1.3.   They all consist of a loaded transmission line, designed so that a wave travels along it (with the field lines as shown in the figure) at a velocity smaller than the velocity of light.   If electrons are injected along the axis of such a configuration with a velocity approximately equal to the wave velocity (actually slightly greater), such electrons travel with the wave and are acted upon

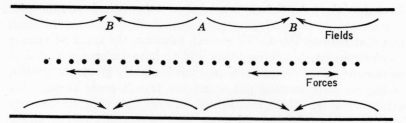

Fig. 1.3   Interaction of electron beam with traveling electromagnetic field.

by the fields.   As can be seen in the diagram, electrons near the zero-amplitude value are not accelerated at all; those in one half cycle are accelerated; and those in the other half cycle are decelerated.   The field obviously passes through zero at two points in each cycle.   At point A, electrons ahead of it are moving more slowly than the average and those behind it more rapidly, so that electrons tend to bunch themselves around this point.   The zero-field point B (180° away) has a corresponding decrease in density associated with it.   The action of the field is thus to produce bunching, just as in the klystron case, except that here the electrons travel with the field, so that the field continually acts to increase the bunching.   (Unlike in the klystron, drifting and bunching occur in the same region.)   If the average electron velocity is slightly greater than the wave velocity, then as the bunches are formed they tend to drift forward relative to the wave, i.e., into a decelerating portion of the field. Conversely, the regions of low density 180° away from the bunches are drifting into regions of accelerating field.   We therefore have a situation in which more electrons are in an accelerating region than in a retarding region; energy is lost by the electron beam and gained by the traveling wave, resulting in a growth of the field amplitude.

e. Magnetron

The last tube to be described in this section is the magnetron.   A simple form, the planar magnetron, is used in illustration.   Although this is a rather less common sort in practice, it has certain advantages as an illustrative example.   Figure 1.4 shows a cathode plane C and an anode plane A.   The anode plane is shown slotted periodically, with a resonant circuit assumed to be connected across each gap.   It should be pointed out that in practice the resonant circuit across this gap is most frequently a cavity, with adjacent cavities mutually coupled so as to form a traveling-wave circuit, similar in its electromagnetic behavior to the propagating circuits used in traveling-wave tubes—though the cavity may consist of nothing more than slots.   In any case, the configuration is electrically completely equivalent to a slow-wave circuit.   Moreover, it is the capacity across the slot that is most relevant to the operation of the magnetron, since it is the fringing field of this capacity that inter-acts with the electron stream.   A d-c potential is applied between cathode and anode, producing an electric field, and a magnetic field B is applied transversely (perpendicular to the plane of the paper).   Electrons start-ing from the cathode may behave in various ways, depending in a critical fashion on the space-charge conditions, initial thermal velocities, etc. Under such conditions it can be shown that the *average* electron velocity *parallel* to the anode depends on the ratio E/B, where the electric field E may include the effects of space charge as well as the applied field.   The requirement for useful interaction between electrons and fields is that this average velocity of the electrons should be close to that of the propagat-ing circuit.   It is not really necessary to describe the electron motion in detail.   This is to some extent still an unsolved problem.   However, a common feature of all the various theoretical arguments that have been employed in describing the motion of the electrons is this average velocity parallel to the anode.

If the electrons do move with this average velocity, then as they pass through the fringing field of the gap, they are either accelerated or decelerated (depending on their phase) by the action of this r-f field. If they are accelerated, it can be shown that the effect of the constant magnetic field is greater than that of the constant electric field, so that the electrons are pushed back toward the cathode and eventually strike it.   If they are decelerated by the r-f field, then the action of the com-bined electric and magnetic fields is to push the electron closer to the anode.   The electron is thus enabled to interact more closely with the fringing field (since it is closer to the gap), and also gains some energy from the applied electric field.   This process thus results in the separation of electrons into those which move closer to the anode and those which are returned to the cathode.   The electrons which move closer to the anode continue to lose energy to the r-f field and gain it from the d-c field.

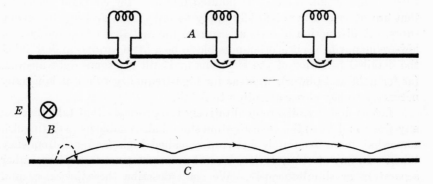

Fig. 1.4   Schematic diagram of planar magnetron.

The phase of the voltage at the various gaps and the velocity of the electrons from gap to gap must be properly synchronized, so that the electrons continue to behave in this fashion at successive gaps. This requirement and the resulting interaction are really the same as have been described for interaction of electrons in a traveling-wave tube. The major differences here are (1) that a sorting action occurs due to the steady electric and magnetic fields, which remove some of the electrons from the interaction; and (2) that transverse r-f fields play an important role. If the magnetron is operated as an amplifier, one gets growth just as in a traveling-wave tube. If the magnetron is operated as an oscillator, one gets feedback; one has a constant-amplitude field propagating at approximately the electron velocity; and there is a constant transfer of energy to this field from the electrons. The use of a magnetron of this kind as an amplifier is a much more recent development than the magnetron oscillator. However, the operation of a magnetron as an amplifier is probably simpler than operation as an oscillator, and it is therefore used here for illustration.

There is yet another class of tubes; it will be discussed later in some detail. The tubes of this class are the so-called space-charge-wave tubes, which have no external circuits at all, but depend for their operation on the interactions between the electrons themselves (or else with non-propagating circuits). It would be rather difficult to describe this tube type in any qualitative manner that would be simply related to the descriptions given above; it will be better to postpone the discussion until after space-charge effects have been analyzed in a later chapter.

1.2 General Properties of Microwave Tubes

Having described a variety of tubes, let us examine what properties they have in common. Also, let us see whether any distinction can be made between a so-called microwave or uhf tube and a low-frequency tube. First of all, it must be pointed out that the common principles that are described here actually apply to both high- and low-frequency tubes. A distinction of sorts arises from the fact that in the analysis of low-frequency tubes it is often possible to be a little careless in describing the detailed behavior of the electrons and still get some right answers (as for gain and power), whereas for high-frequency tubes, it is usually necessary to pay closer attention to detail.

Let us first investigate qualitatively the processes that take place in any electron device; this investigation should also enable us to distinguish somewhat more accurately between so-called high- and low-frequency tubes. In any electron device, several processes must take place, either separately or simultaneously. We shall describe these processes and refer to the tubes enumerated in Sec. 1.1 for illustrative examples.

a. Beam production

The first necessary process is the production of an electron beam, i.e., the employment of some method of obtaining a stream of electrons and making it follow trajectories (in a time-independent field) of the kind that is desired. The process of beam formation may involve configurations that range in complexity from a plane cathode faced by a plane anode (probably the most elementary form, depending on simple flow between two parallel electrodes) to more elaborate devices in which a very thin, pencil-like beam must be produced and directed through a very small aperture or required to perform motion that is more complicated than simple parallel flow. Although problems of beam production and focusing are in a sense outside the theory of microwave tubes proper, they are nevertheless so intimately tied in with the satisfactory performance of such tubes that they are very appropriately included in any discussion of tube behavior. Also included in our discussion of beam production will be details of the proper use of electrostatic and magnetic focusing, space-charge effects in a d-c beam, and allied topics.

b. Velocity modulation

The second process that must occur in any electron device is velocity modulation. The reader may conclude from the relatively recent dates of the various analyses of velocity modulation that the older tube types did not depend on such a process. This is a misconception. Velocity modulation does take place in conventional low-frequency tubes, although it may not be apparent as such when the transit time of the electrons is very small compared with the period of oscillation.

Velocity modulation means the application of r-f fields to the electrons as they move in their d-c trajectories under the action of static electric and magnetic fields, in such a way that the velocities of these electrons are varied in some periodic fashion. This variation of velocity is produced by voltages applied to suitably arranged electrodes (or possibly by suitable use of space charge, which is really a special form of electrode). Applying a-c fields to the electrons, and thus varying their velocity, provides a method of making electrons in different portions of the cycle move differently. It is then necessary to take advantage of this phase-dependent motion.

c. Conversion to density modulation

The third process, then, that must occur in a tube is the conversion of this variation in the motion of the electrons into a usable form. It is necessary to turn the variations in electron velocity into an r-f current, which can deliver energy to an electromagnetic field; i.e., the variations in velocity must be converted into density variations, which will then constitute an alternating current. The ways in which this conversion is brought about are numerous, and the distinguishing feature of many tube types lies in just this conversion mechanism.

It may be useful to illustrate processes *b* and *c* at this point to see how velocity modulation and conversion into density modulation take place in some of the tubes described in the preceding section.

In a two-cavity klystron, velocity modulation occurs in the first gap and the conversion to density modulation in the drift space. The variation of velocity yields a bunching of electrons, resulting in a beam with varying density, i.e., a current that has an a-c component capable of delivering energy to the electromagnetic field.

In a traveling-wave tube and in an *injected-beam magnetron amplifier*, both velocity modulation and bunching occur simultaneously and continuously along the entire length of the structure. Velocity modulation occurring at any one point continues to affect bunching at points beyond, with additional modulation being added as the beam moves along.

In triodes and multigrid tubes, the two processes cannot be so readily separated, because they occur in the same region. The r-f voltage between cathode and grid produces variations in electron velocities over a cycle. The faster electrons get through the grid, and the slower ones do not. The conversion to density modulation thus takes place by means of a *sorting* process. It is particularly difficult to make the distinction between velocity modulation and conversion to density modulation in low-frequency tubes, where the two processes take place almost simultaneously. Nevertheless, it should again be pointed out that velocity modulation takes place in all tubes. Whether or not an electron gets through the grid depends on the velocity which it acquires throughout the entire length of the preceding path. (That is, the velocity must be such that it does not become zero before the electron reaches the grid.[1])

Another type of tube in which the conversion takes place by a sorting process is the Barkhausen oscillator. The electrons speeded up during

---

[1] In this connection, it may be again remarked that although the term *tube* is not particularly descriptive of the large number of devices to which it is applied, it represents a happier choice than the term *valve* used in some countries. The latter term calls forth an image of a flood of electrons standing at a gate—the grid—ready to be released or shut off instantaneously. A better analogy might be a rotating bowl with sloping sides that contains small balls that climb up the sides as the speed of rotation is increased. Periodically increasing the speed until some of the balls spill over the rim yields a more satisfactory simple mechanical model of electron behavior in a triode.

the first transit from cathode to grid strike the plate and are lost; this process again depends on the velocity modulation produced by the r-f field. Those electrons which are slowed down do not quite reach the plate and therefore oscillate back and forth and lose energy, as described previously. Just as in the triode, a process therefore takes place by which (depending on the velocities given to the electrons by the alternating field) an electron is either removed or remains available for a later function, the later function being, of course, delivery of energy to the electromagnetic field.

In a reentrant magnetron oscillator, *both sorting and bunching* occur. Electrons that gain energy from the first transit through the r-f field return to the cathode with a finite velocity and are lost there; whereas those that lose energy on the first transit through the r-f field (i.e., those that suffer a decrease in velocity) are not returned to the cathode and continue their motions in the cathode-anode region. Under these circumstances, however, the electrons are also bunched in a way similar to those in a klystron. The result is first an initial sorting and then a final bunching of the remaining electrons.

d. Transfer of energy

The fourth process that must occur in an electron tube is energy transfer from the electron beam to the electromagnetic field, or (what amounts to the same thing) to a circuit. We have already alluded to this energy transfer in a general fashion in discussing some of the preceding processes. More explicitly, for the beam to transfer energy to the electromagnetic field, a beam with a variation in density must pass through the field. There are two ways of looking at the process. First, one can examine the electron motion in the electromagnetic field. If one finds that the electrons lose energy, then from the law of conservation of energy, the field must gain energy. The other way, which possibly gives a little more detailed insight into the process, is to calculate the current induced in electrodes and associated circuits by the passage of the beam near these electrodes and to calculate the energy transfer from the circuit characteristics. The first way of looking at this process postulates the existence of an established field with such a phase that electrons passing through it are on the average retarded and therefore lose energy. In the second method, it is not necessary to assume the existence of such a field; rather, one merely says that an electron passing near an electrode induces a current. This current, flowing through the circuit, therefore produces a voltage (and corresponding power). It will of course turn out that the voltage which is thus produced is in a direction such as to retard the electrons, and therefore the two methods yield the same answer. We shall return to these distinctions in a later chapter and discuss them at much greater length.

e. Collection of electrons

A fifth process that must occur in the tube is that the beam has to be collected after delivering energy to the electromagnetic field (or producing an induced current in some related circuits). This is largely a practical problem and not greatly relevant to the theory of tube operation. The electrons have done all their useful work in passing through the electromagnetic field. An impact on an electrode thus merely produces heat and does no useful work as far as tube operation is concerned. A conventional triode, for example, in an arrangement such as shown in Fig. 1.5, would work as usual, even though all the electrons pass through holes in the plate. All the r-f current that these electrons produce will have been produced by the time they arrive at the plate, and therefore the impact on the plate is not an essential feature of tube operation. Collection can take place at reduced potential, however.

From this brief outline of the processes which occur in a vacuum tube it is apparent that we shall have to discuss in great detail the following three major topics:

1. Beam formation, including electrostatic focusing, magnetic focusing, d-c space-charge effects, and plasma oscillations
2. The interaction of electrons with fields, both for producing velocity modulation of the electrons and in the transfer of energy from the electrons to the fields (principally a discussion of the dynamics of electrons in alternating fields)

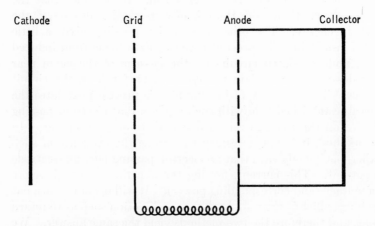

Cathode   Grid   Anode   Collector

Fig. 1.5   A triode with separate collector.

3. The conversion of velocity modulation to density modulation, where the two processes occur in separate portions of the tube, as in the klystron (i.e., problems relating to drift space or reflector space)

In topics 2 and 3 the interaction of the electrons with each other is often of great importance and must be considered. This discussion can be included under the general description of r-f space-charge effects.

2

Electron Beams

In the following sections we shall consider problems of electron emission, the behavior of electrons in the region between the emissive surface (the cathode) and the anode, and the behavior of the electrons after their initial acceleration by the anode. In many microwave tubes a fine, pencil-like beam at a relatively low voltage and high current density must be employed, and the problem of producing such a beam (i.e., of designing a suitable cathode-anode configuration), the problem of focusing the beam to a given diameter by means of electrostatic and magneto-static fields, and the problem of maintaining this diameter over a long path must be considered in some detail. These problems involve the consideration of electron motion in electrostatic and magnetostatic fields and of the effect of the space charge produced by the beam itself. We shall also investigate what restrictions apply to the focusing properties of such fields, i.e., whether limiting values of voltage, current, and beam dimensions can be specified. A great part of the chapter, therefore, will be devoted to the discussion and maintenance of long, thin beams. An analysis of the motion of electrons in crossed electric and magnetic fields is given in Chap. 10. This is the configuration of static fields which is used in a magnetron, and the motion of the electrons in such fields is an essential characteristic of magnetron performance.

2.1 Electron Emission: Emission-limited Diodes

Electrons escape from an electrode surface when it is heated, when light impinges upon it, when it is bombarded by other particles, or when it is subjected to the force exerted by a very strong electric field. These methods of liberating electrons are respectively known as thermionic, photoelectric, secondary, and field emission. Of these several methods only the first will be discussed in the present chapter.

Equations connecting emission current with cathode temperature were first obtained by Richardson.[1] The form most generally used is one which was later independently derived by Dushman;[2] it is known as *Richardson's equation:*

$$i = AT^2 e^{-b/T} \tag{1}$$

where i is the emission current density (usually in amp/cm^2), T is the absolute temperature (°K), and A and b are constants. Theoretically, the value of A should be the same for all metals, whereas b depends not only on the work function[3] of the material under consideration but on temperature as well. In most measurements of A and b both are considered constant; b is related to the voltage equivalent of the work function by

$$b = \frac{e}{k}\phi = 11{,}605\phi \qquad °K \tag{2}$$

where e is the electron charge (1.60×10^{-19} coul) and k is Boltzmann's constant (1.38×10^{-23} joule/°K). Under these conditions A is not related to the quantity which it was chosen to represent in the original derivation of Eq. (1), but merely appears as a factor in an empirical equation that has the same form as (1). The value of A for most metals, when measured in this manner, turns out to be 60.2 (amp/cm^2)/(°K)^2. For nonmetals, A may be as small as 10^{-3}.

Pure-metal cathodes, oxide-coated cathodes, and composite cathodes have all been employed in the construction of microwave tubes. Chief

---

[1] O. W. Richardson, On the Negative Radiation from Hot Platinum, *Proc. Cambridge Phil. Soc.*, **11**:286–295 (1901).

[2] S. Dushman, Electron Emission from Metals as a Function of Temperature, *Phys. Rev.*, **21**:623–636 (1923).

[3] The work function, usually expressed in terms of its voltage equivalent ϕ, is the energy required to free an electron from the parent body. Most metals have ϕ's of the order of a few volts.

among the pure metals used is *tungsten*, with its extremely high melting point (3370°C), good mechanical stability at high temperatures, and ability to withstand high-energy positive-ion bombardment.   However, tungsten has a high work function (ϕ = 4.5 volts) and hence a relatively low emission unless operated at very high temperatures.   Another pure metal used is *tantalum*, which has a lower melting point (3000°C), but an emission (over its more limited temperature range) which is at least 10 times higher than that of tungsten (ϕ = 4.1 volts).   On the other hand, emission from tantalum is more likely to be impaired by the oxides that form as the result of attack by even small traces of residual gases.

Very good emissive properties are obtained from *oxide-coated cathodes*.   The oxides of barium, strontium, and calcium all have ϕ's between 1 and 2 volts, and a combination of BaO and SrO has a ϕ = 1.0.   Oxide-coated cathodes are usually indirectly heated by a tungsten heater. They are widely employed in high-power pulsed microwave tubes because of their ability to produce very large emission currents for short pulses, although the high rate of emission cannot be maintained, and the cathode must be given time to "recover" before the next burst.   With a suitable duty cycle, pulsed oxide-coated cathodes can achieve emissions 100 or more times greater than those obtained in continuous operation.   The main disadvantages of oxide-coated cathodes are that they are very easily damaged or "poisoned" by various gases and vapors (e.g., oxygen and sulfur) and that they are subject to disintegration by positive-ion bombardment of even moderate intensity.

Among the composite cathode materials one that is frequently used is *thoriated tungsten*.   Thorium evaporates from tungsten at a lower rate than from itself, and a thin layer of thorium (ϕ = 3.4 volts) forms at the surface of the tungsten (ϕ = 4.5 volts).   The thorium forms a dipole layer (probably monatomic), partially neutralizing the electrostatic forces on the tungsten surface.   As a result, the work function of thoriated tungsten (ϕ = 2.6) is actually lower than that of pure tungsten *or* thorium.   The thorium which evaporates from the surface during operation is continuously replenished by diffusion from the inside.

Another composite cathode, originally developed in the Netherlands by Lemmens and his associates,[1] is the so-called *L cathode*.   The original design consisted of a pellet of barium-strontium carbonate (Ba-SrCO$_3$) mounted underneath a layer of porous tungsten.   The alkali metals and BaO diffused through the tungsten to the surface, where they formed a monatomic layer.   In an improved design,[2] a porous-tungsten or porous-nickel pellet is actually impregnated with an alkaline-earth

[1] H. J. Lemmens, M. J. Jansen, and R. Loosjes, A New Thermionic Cathode for Heavy Loads, *Philips Tech. Rev.*, 11:341–350 (1950).

[2] R. Levi, New Dispenser Type Thermionic Cathode, *J. Appl. Phys.*, 24:233 (1953).

metal compound.   This arrangement has been found to yield greater
emission and longer life.   The layer that forms on the surface again
reduces the work function and results in very high emissivity at the
relatively moderate temperatures (1000 to 1300°C) at which L cathodes
are customarily operated.

2.2   Space-charge-limited Diodes

The potential distribution between cathode and anode is affected by
the presence of electrons in that region.   In the simple case of parallel
electrodes of infinite extent (Fig. 2.1), the potential varies linearly
between zero and anode voltage in the absence of electrons (curve 1).
When the cathode is heated, the negative charge of the emitted electrons
depresses the potential in the interelectrode region (curve 2).   Further
increase in temperature (and hence emission) depresses the potential
even more, until a distribution that has zero slope at the cathode (curve 3)
is obtained.   If the cathode temperature is increased still further, the
slope at the cathode actually becomes negative (curve 4).   Not all the
emitted electrons, but only those which have sufficient velocity to overcome the retarding force, reach the anode.   Some electrons are turned
back and reenter the cathode.   Further increase in temperature does not
increase the anode current.   The anode current is limited to the value
obtained with the temperature corresponding to curve 3.

What is the relation between voltage and current under this condition?   We shall first show that for certain special cases, the relationship
is given by

$$i \sim V^{\frac{3}{2}} \tag{3}$$

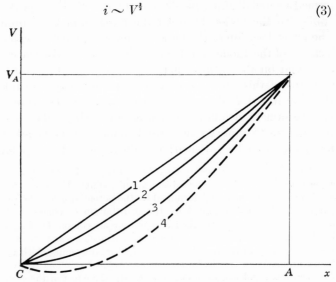

Fig. 2.1   Potential distribution between parallel plates.

and then show that this relationship holds generally for space-charge-limited emission. But the relationship will be first derived for three important cases: parallel planes, concentric cylinders, and concentric spheres. In the solution of each case, we must employ a combination of two equations. The first is the energy equation for the case when fields and velocities at any point are either independent of time or vary slowly with time and when relativistic effects are negligible:

$$\tfrac{1}{2}mv^2 = -eV \tag{4}$$

where m, v, and e are the electron mass, velocity, and charge, respectively, and V is the potential that determines the velocity. The second is Poisson's equation,

$$\nabla^2 V = -\frac{\rho}{\epsilon_0} \tag{5}$$

The problem consists in finding a solution that satisfies both the equation of motion and Poisson's equation.[1] We shall also need the relationship that defines current density,

$$i = \rho v \tag{6}$$

The ensuing analysis applies only under certain conditions and assumptions. The first condition is that the tube must be operated at a level of emission that corresponds to curve 4 of Fig. 2.1; that is, the number of electrons emitted must exceed the number that reaches the anode. Some electrons are turned back, and a potential minimum is formed a small distance from the cathode. Strictly speaking, the analysis applies to the region between the anode and this potential minimum. The exact location of the potential minimum and its value depend on the location of the anode and its potential, as well as on the cathode temperature, and on the ratio of actual current to saturation current. Exact analyses of this problem have been made; they also take into account that the initial velocities of all electrons emitted from the cathode are not the same, but follow approximately a Maxwellian distribution. For the analysis to apply to the cathode-anode region, an additional condition must therefore be satisfied: the distance and the potential difference

---

[1] This requirement occurs very frequently, and it might not be amiss to make some general remarks on the subject at this point. Equation (4) describes how the motion of the electrons is determined by the potential field, whereas Eq. (5) gives the potential field as determined by the distribution of charges. The actual motion obviously must be such that the two equations are compatible, i.e., the field established by the charges must make the charges move in such a way as to establish the field. A convenient way of referring to this twofold relationship, which arises in many electronic problems, is to call the Eq. (4) an *electronic equation* (the effect of the field on the electrons), and Eq. (5) a *circuit equation* (the effect of the electrons on the field). The resulting solutions are thus self-consistent.

between cathode and anode must be such that the distance from the cathode to the potential minimum is very small compared with the distance to the anode. In most applications the correction really is negligible, although there are some exceptions. (Examples are some high-frequency triodes, in which the control grid is approximately at the potential minimum, a few microns from the cathode.)

In addition to these two conditions (emission current greater than anode current and potential minimum very near the cathode), certain simplifying assumptions are made in the analysis, as follows:

1. The initial velocity of the electrons is zero. Actually, of course, the electrons have a whole range of initial velocities (with a Maxwellian distribution); but the average velocity of emission in most tubes corresponds to a potential of the order of 0.1 ev at the cathode, and even less at the potential minimum, so that neglecting this velocity represents a very small error.
2. The electric field (i.e., the gradient of the potential) is zero at the cathode. Actually, this assumption is exactly satisfied at the potential minimum; and since it has been stipulated that the analysis shall apply only to tubes in which the potential minimum virtually coincides with the cathode, the assumption of zero field at the cathode introduces only a small error, too.
3. The electrons are emitted in a direction normal to the cathode. The effect of electrons leaving the cathode at various angles with the surface actually puts a lower limit on the diameter into which a beam can be compressed by a focusing system (i.e., an upper limit on the maximum ratio of current density in the beam to current density at the cathode).[1] This effect is of considerable importance in electron optics (especially of cathode-ray tubes), but has very little influence on the results of the ensuing analysis.

a. Parallel planes

For this case, Eq. (5) reduces to

$$\frac{d^2V}{dx^2} = -\frac{\rho}{\epsilon_0} = \frac{i}{\epsilon_0} \sqrt{\frac{1}{2\eta}} V^{-\frac{1}{2}} \tag{7}$$

if we consider only variations with x and substitute from Eqs. (4) and (5). $\eta \equiv e/m$ is the electronic charge-to-mass ratio. One integration yields

$$\left(\frac{dV}{dx}\right)^2 = \frac{4i}{\epsilon_0} \sqrt{\frac{1}{2\eta}} V^{\frac{1}{2}} + C_1 \tag{8}$$

[1] J. R. Pierce, Limiting Current Densities in Electron Beams, *J. Appl. Phys.*, **10**:715–724 (1939).

the constant of integration C_1 being zero, since the gradient vanishes at zero potential. A second integration gives

$$\tfrac{4}{3}V^{\frac{3}{4}} = \sqrt{\frac{4i}{\epsilon_0}} \sqrt{\frac{1}{2\eta}}\, x + C_2 \tag{9}$$

The constant of integration (C_2) again vanishes, because zero distance (the cathode) corresponds to zero potential. Solution for the current per unit area gives finally

$$i = \frac{4\sqrt{2\eta}}{9}\, \epsilon_0 \frac{V^{\frac{3}{2}}}{x^2}$$
$$i = 2.331 \times 10^{-6} \frac{V^{\frac{3}{2}}}{x^2} \tag{10}$$

This is the $\tfrac{3}{2}$-power equation for parallel planes, or *Child's law*.[1] Thus the current density between a plane cathode and anode half a centimeter apart, with a potential of 1000 volts, is given by

$$i = 2.331 \times 10^{-6} \frac{10^{\frac{3}{2}}}{(0.5)^2} = 0.295 \text{ amp/cm}^2$$

The reader may easily derive the way in which the various quantities vary with distance (for fixed anode-cathode spacing d), as tabulated below.

Quantity	Varies as
V	$x^{\frac{4}{3}}$
v	$x^{\frac{2}{3}}$
ρ	$x^{-\frac{2}{3}}$
E	$x^{\frac{1}{3}}$

The last is the electric field, given by Eq. (8), the spatial gradient of potential.

b. Concentric cylinders

Poisson's equation for this case reduces to

$$\frac{d^2V}{dr^2} + \frac{1}{r}\frac{dV}{dr} = \frac{i}{\epsilon_0}\sqrt{\frac{1}{2\eta}}\, V^{-\frac{1}{2}} \tag{11}$$

This is a second-order differential equation of greater complexity than that obtained for the parallel-plane case. The solution involves a factor (proportional to the potential in the absence of space charge), $\gamma = \ln r/r_k$, that is, the logarithm of the ratio of the radial coordinate to cathode

[1] C. D. Child, Discharge from Hot CaO, *Phys. Rev.*, **32**:492–511 (1911).

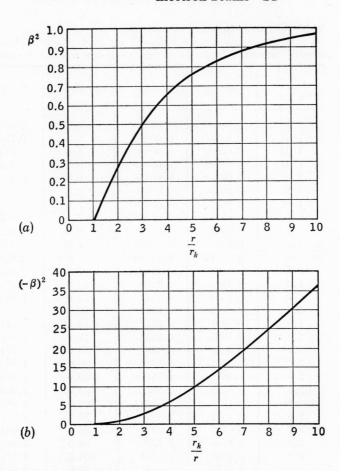

Fig. 2.2   Plot of β^2 as a function of radius.

radius.   The current per unit length is given by

$$\frac{I}{l} = \frac{8\sqrt{2\eta}}{9}\,\pi\epsilon_0\,\frac{V^{\frac{3}{2}}}{r\beta^2}$$

$$\frac{I}{l} = 14.648 \times 10^{-6}\,\frac{V^{\frac{3}{2}}}{r\beta^2} \tag{12}$$

where $\beta = \gamma - \frac{2}{5}\gamma^2 + \frac{11}{120}\gamma^3 - \frac{47}{3300}\gamma^4 + \cdots$ (13)

Values of β^2 have been calculated by Langmuir and Blodgett,[1] both for the case where the cathode is the inner cylinder and where it is the outer cylinder (Table 2.1 and Fig. 2.2).   The latter case, in which the appropriate function is designated by $(-\beta)^2$, applies in convergent-beam config-

[1] I. Langmuir and K. B. Blodgett, Currents Limited by Space Charge between Coaxial Cylinders, *Phys. Rev.*, **22**:347–356 (1922).

Table 2.1 β^2 as function of radius*

(r_k = radius of cathode; r = radius at any point P. β^2 applies to case where P is outside cathode, $r > r_k$. $(-\beta)^2$ applies to case where P is inside cathode, $r_k < r$.)

$\dfrac{r}{r_k}$ or $\dfrac{r_k}{r}$	β^2	$(-\beta)^2$	$\dfrac{r}{r_k}$ or $\dfrac{r_k}{r}$	β^2	$(-\beta)^2$
1.00	0.00000	0.00000	5.2	0.7825	10.733
1.01	0.00010	0.00010	5.4	0.7973	11.601
1.02	0.00039	0.00040	5.6	0.8111	12.493
1.04	0.00149	0.00159	5.8	0.8241	13.407
1.06	0.00324	0.00356	6.0	0.8362	14.343
1.08	0.00557	0.00630	6.5	0.8635	16.777
1.10	0.00842	0.00980	7.0	0.8870	19.337
1.15	0.01747	0.02186	7.5	0.9074	22.015
1.2	0.02875	0.03849	8.0	0.9253	24.805
1.3	0.05589	0.08504	8.5	0.9410	27.701
1.4	0.08672	0.14856	9.0	0.9548	30.698
1.5	0.11934	0.2282	9.5	0.9672	33.791
1.6	0.1525	0.3233	10.0	0.9782	36.976
1.7	0.1854	0.4332	12.0	1.0122	50.559
1.8	0.2177	0.5572	14.0	1.0352	65.352
1.9	0.2491	0.6947	16.0	1.0513	81.203
2.0	0.2793	0.8454	18.0	1.0630	97.997
2.1	0.3083	1.0086	20.0	1.0715	115.64
2.2	0.3361	1.1840	30.0	1.0908	214.42
2.3	0.3626	1.3812	40.0	1.0946	327.01
2.4	0.3879	1.5697	50.0	1.0936	450.23
2.5	0.4121	1.7792	60.0	1.0910	582.14
2.6	0.4351	1.9995	70.0	1.0878	721.43
2.7	0.4571	2.2301	80.0	1.0845	867.11
2.8	0.4780	2.4708	90.0	1.0813	1018.5
2.9	0.4980	2.7214	100.0	1.0783	1174.9
3.0	0.5170	2.9814	120.0	1.0726	1501.4
3.2	0.5526	3.5293	140.0	1.0677	1843.5
3.4	0.5851	4.1126	160.0	1.0634	2199.4
3.6	0.6148	4.7298	180.0	1.0596	2567.3
3.8	0.6420	5.3795	200.0	1.0562	2946.1
4.0	0.6671	6.0601	250.0	1.0494	3934.4
4.2	0.6902	6.7705	300.0	1.0440	4973.0
4.4	0.7115	7.5096	350.0	1.0397	6054.1
4.6	0.7313	8.2763	400.0	1.0362	7172.1
4.8	0.7496	9.0696	500.0	1.0307	9502.2
5.0	0.7666	9.8887	∞	1.0000	∞

*Taken from I. Langmuir and K. B. Blodgett, Currents Limited by Space Charge between Coaxial Cylinders, *Phys. Rev.*, **22**:347–356 (1922).

urations in which the cathode is a cylindrical sector. If θ is the half angle of the sector at the center of the cylinder, the current per unit length is given by

$$\frac{I}{l} = 14.648 \times 10^{-6} \left(\frac{\theta}{180°}\right) \frac{V^{\frac{3}{2}}}{r(-\beta)^2} \tag{14}$$

c. Concentric spheres

For this case, Poisson's equation becomes

$$\frac{d^2V}{dr^2} + \frac{2}{r}\frac{dV}{dr} = \frac{I}{\epsilon_0}\sqrt{\frac{1}{2\eta}}\ V^{-\frac{1}{2}} \tag{15}$$

The solution again involves $\gamma = \ln r/r_k$. The total current is given by

$$I = \frac{16\sqrt{2\eta}}{9}\pi\epsilon_0\frac{V^{\frac{3}{2}}}{\alpha^2}$$

$$I = 29.297 \times 10^{-6}\frac{V^{\frac{3}{2}}}{\alpha^2} \tag{16}$$

where $\qquad \alpha = \gamma - 0.3\gamma^2 + 0.075\gamma^3 - 0.0143182\gamma^4 + \cdots \tag{17}$

Values of α^2 have been likewise calculated by Langmuir and Blodgett.[1] The values for the case where the cathode is the outer sphere, and the function is designated by $(-\alpha)^2$, are given in Table 2.2 and Fig. 2.3. This is by far the more common configuration. It is widely used in

[1] I. Langmuir and K. B. Blodgett, Currents Limited by Space Charge between Concentric Spheres, *Phys. Rev.*, **24**:49–59 (1924).

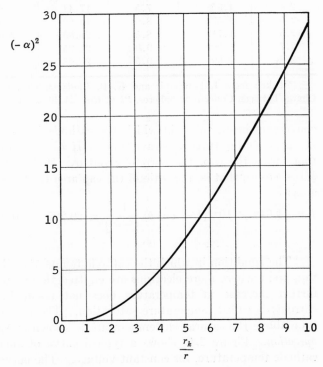

Fig. 2.3   Plot of $(-\alpha)^2$ as a function of radius.

Table 2.2 $(-\alpha)^2$ **as function of radius***
(r_k = radius of cathode; r = radius at any point P.)

$\dfrac{r_k}{r}$	$(-\alpha)^2$	$\dfrac{r_k}{r}$	$(-\alpha)^2$	$\dfrac{r_k}{r}$	$(-\alpha)^2$
1.0	0.0000	2.9	2.302	10.0	29.19
1.05	0.0024	3.0	2.512	12.0	39.98
1.1	0.0096	3.2	2.954	14.0	51.86
1.15	0.0213	3.4	3.421	16.0	64.74
1.2	0.0372	3.6	3.913	18.0	78.56
1.25	0.0571	3.8	4.429	20.0	93.24
1.3	0.0809	4.0	4.968	30.0	178.2
1.35	0.1084	4.2	5.528	40.0	279.6
1.4	0.1396	4.4	6.109	50.0	395.3
1.45	0.1740	4.6	6.712	60.0	523.6
1.5	0.2118	4.8	7.334	70.0	663.3
1.6	0.2968	5.0	7.976	80.0	813.7
1.7	0.394	5.2	8.636	90.0	974.1
1.8	0.502	5.4	9.315	100.0	1144
1.9	0.621	5.6	10.01	120.0	1509
2.0	0.750	5.8	10.73	140.0	1907
2.1	0.888	6.0	11.46	160.0	2333
2.2	1.036	6.5	13.35	180.0	2790
2.3	1.193	7.0	15.35	200.0	3270
2.4	1.358	7.5	17.44	250.0	4582
2.5	1.531	8.0	19.62	300.0	6031
2.6	1.712	8.5	21.89	350.0	7610
2.7	1.901	9.0	24.25	400.0	9303
2.8	2.098	9.5	26.68	500.0	13015

* Taken from I. Langmuir and K. B. Blodgett, Currents Limited by Space Charge between Concentric Spheres, *Phys. Rev.*, 24:49–59 (1924).

convergent-beam tubes in which the cathode is a spherical cap, as in klystrons and in traveling-wave tubes. If θ is the half angle of the cone that forms the cap, the current given by (16) must be multiplied by $\frac{1}{2}(1 - \cos \theta)$, that is, the ratio of the cap area to the total sphere surface area:

$$I = 14.648 \times 10^{-6}(1 - \cos \theta)\,\frac{V^{\frac{3}{2}}}{(-\alpha^2)} = 29.297 \times 10^{-6} \sin^2\left(\frac{\theta}{2}\right)\frac{V^{\frac{3}{2}}}{(-\alpha)^2} \tag{18}$$

The condition in which the cathode temperature has been increased to a point where more electrons are emitted than reach the anode (and further increase in temperature does not result in increased anode current) is called temperature saturation. The method of running the tube above the saturation temperature is known as *space-charge-limited operation*. Figure 2.4a shows a typical curve of anode current versus cathode temperature, for constant voltage. The curve follows Richard-

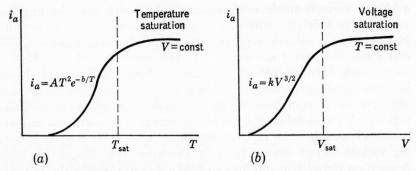

Fig. 2.4   Anode current as a function of (a) temperature and (b) voltage. The equations shown on each curve apply only under conditions corresponding to the flat portion of the other curve.

son's equation (1) up to the saturation temperature, where it becomes constant.   The break is gradual rather than abrupt, because saturation does not usually occur at the same temperature for all parts of the cathode surface.

If the temperature is kept constant and the voltage is increased, a similar effect is observed: above a certain voltage, the anode attracts all the electrons emitted from the cathode and a further increase in voltage does not increase the current significantly (since the number of electrons emitted is determined by the cathode temperature and is almost independent of the voltage).   This phenomenon is called voltage saturation, and running the tube above the saturation voltage is known as *temperature-limited operation*.   Figure 2.4b shows a typical curve for constant temperature: the curve follows the $\frac{3}{2}$-power law (3) up to the saturation voltage, where it breaks off gradually and becomes almost constant. The slight continued increase is due to a reduction of the work function by the external electric field, as predicted by Schottky.[1]

Richardson's equation gives the anode current only when all emitted electrons reach the anode, i.e., under temperature-limited operation; whereas the $\frac{3}{2}$-power law applies only when the supply of electrons exceeds the demand, i.e., under space-charge-limited operation.   In other words, the curved portion of Fig. 2.4a follows the appropriate equation only when the tube is being operated along the flat portion of Fig. 2.4b, and vice versa.

We have shown, for three particular geometrical configurations, that the space-charge-limited current density is proportional to the $\frac{3}{2}$ power of the applied voltage by actually solving the relevant equations.   We shall next demonstrate, by means of a simple dimensional analysis, the important property that this relationship applies quite generally for any

[1] W. Schottky, Über kalte und warme Elektronenentladungen, *Z. Physik*, **14**:63–106 (1923).

arbitrary cathode-anode configuration. We recall that for any configuration in which the current is limited by space charge, the potential just outside the cathode (approximately, *at* the cathode) has zero slope and starts from zero; moreover, i, V, etc., must be such that Eqs. (4) to (6) apply between cathode and anode. Now consider what changes in these variables result from a change in the anode potential, provided that the diode continues to operate under the space-charge-limited regime. We shall follow the essentially synthetic procedure of *assuming* certain changes in some variables and then determining how the remaining variables must change in order to ensure that the physical laws *imposed* on the system continue to hold. Let us describe the new situation, which corresponds to an applied voltage n times the old voltage, by primes; so that

$$V'_A = nV_A \tag{19}$$

If the new situation is to be physically possible, all the primed variables must satisfy equations of exactly the same form as Eqs. (4) to (6). The simple change in anode voltage described by Eq. (19) is obviously physically possible. We now *assume* that the potential everywhere in the diode increases by the same factor n, so that at each point

$$V'(x,y,z) = nV(x,y,z) \tag{20}$$

and we see whether it is possible to determine such changes in all the other variables that Eqs. (4) to (6) are satisfied. If Eq. (20) is to apply throughout the diode and a relation of the form of Eq. (4) is to hold for the primed quantities as well as for the unprimed, we must have

$$\frac{mv'^2}{2} = eV' = enV = n\frac{mv^2}{2} \tag{21}$$

Therefore, the velocities in the two systems must be related by

$$v'(x,y,z) = n^{\frac{1}{2}}v(x,y,z) \tag{22}$$

Moreover, if the potential is increased by n throughout the diode, all derivatives, first, second, third, etc., must also be increased by n; that is, for all Δx, Δy, or Δz,

$$\begin{aligned}
(\Delta V)' &= V'(x,y,z) - V'(x + \Delta x, y + \Delta y, z + \Delta z) \\
&= n[V(x,y,z) - V(x + \Delta x, y + \Delta y, z + \Delta z)] \\
&= n\,\Delta V
\end{aligned} \tag{23}$$

Therefore, in Poisson's equation (5) for the primed quantities,

$$\nabla^2 V' = \frac{\rho'}{\epsilon_0} \tag{24}$$

the requirement imposed by Eq. (23) on all derivatives also implies that the Laplacian in Eq. (24) can be expressed as

$$\nabla^2 V' = n \, \nabla^2 V \tag{25}$$

If Eq. (5) for the unprimed quantities and Eqs. (24) and (25) are to be simultaneously satisfied, we must have

$$\rho' = n\rho \tag{26}$$

Moreover, combination of Eqs. (22) and (26) yields for the primed current,

$$i' = \rho'v' = n\rho n^{\frac{1}{2}}v = n^{\frac{3}{2}}i \tag{27}$$

or

$$\frac{i'}{i} = n^{\frac{3}{2}} = \left(\frac{V'_A}{V_A}\right)^{\frac{3}{2}} \tag{28}$$

We see, therefore, that if all equations are to be satisfied under the new applied voltage, the ratios of the current densities everywhere must be related as the $\frac{3}{2}$ power of the applied voltage ratio.   This relationship has now been derived without reference to any particular geometrical configuration, but it applies quite generally from the above dimensional arguments.   If the anode voltage is increased by some factor, the current density everywhere (and therefore the total current) is increased by the same factor raised to the $\frac{3}{2}$ power.[1]

Note that the above argument uses the assumption that current is limited by space charge in both situations, so that the derivative of voltage is zero at the cathode in both cases, as required by Eq. (23).   But another, hitherto unstated, assumption is also implicit in the above proof: that the trajectories in both cases *have similar shapes*.   By satisfying Eqs. (4) and (21) we have ensured that certain dynamical restraints are satisfied, namely, that the correct total velocity at each point corresponds to the potential at that point.   That statement does not fully specify the details of the motion, but we can again resort to a synthesis technique to show that the trajectory shapes are the same.   The following relation between total velocity, instantaneous radius of curvature R of the trajectory, and field component $E_\perp$ transverse to the trajectory must hold at every point along the trajectory:

$$\frac{mv^2}{R} = eE_\perp \tag{29}$$

It is obvious that if this equation applies at each point of the trajectory,

---

[1] Strictly speaking, we have not proved this statement.   Rather, we have shown that, given a physically possible set of variables (i, V, v, ρ), we can construct an infinite number of other sets described by Eqs. (20), (22), and (26) to (28) that are also physically possible.   This construction is equivalent to the above statement, except for the absence of a proof of uniqueness.

with R changing from point to point, then an equivalent relation must apply when the potential is increased:

$$\frac{mv'^2}{R'} = eE'_\perp \tag{30}$$

The question then is this: are the two radii the same in both cases, as would be required if the trajectory shapes are to be the same? Evidently the answer is yes, since if all voltages had been increased by n according to Eq. (20), then the right-hand side of Eq. (30) is n times the right-hand side of Eq. (29), so that with the help of Eq. (22), we have

$$\frac{mnv^2}{R'} = enE_\perp \tag{31}$$

It is seen that Eqs. (31) and (29) are compatible if $R = R'$; therefore, the trajectories in the two cases are the same.

Although we have not so far discussed the effects of magnetic field on electron motion, it might be well to mention these effects briefly at this juncture, since the scaling requirements on the magnetic field can likewise be obtained very simply. The effect of a magnetic field may be most simply expressed by the following modification of Eq. (29):

$$\frac{mv^2}{R} = e(E_\perp + |\mathbf{v} \times \mathbf{B}|_\perp) \tag{32}$$

For the primed-voltage situation we then evidently have

$$\frac{mv'^2}{R'} = e(E'_\perp + |\mathbf{v}' \times \mathbf{B}'|_\perp) \tag{33}$$

so that $R' = R$ provided B' satisfies the relation

$$B' = n^{\frac{1}{2}}B \tag{34}$$

or

$$\frac{B'}{B} = \left(\frac{V'}{V}\right)^{\frac{1}{2}} \tag{35}$$

Equation (35) is thus the scaling relation that the magnetic field must obey when the applied voltage has been changed in an arbitrary way in a space-charge-limited flow. We shall see how this relation is actually used in connection with specific configurations in which magnetic fields are employed.

2.3   Design of Electron Guns

The configuration most commonly used in low-frequency tubes, as well as in magnetrons, is a cylindrical cathode surrounded by the other electrodes. However, in applications where a long, thin electron beam is required, as in cathode-ray tubes, klystrons, and traveling-wave tubes, the cathode more often takes the form of a disk or "button." The emitted electrons pass through a succession of grids or apertures in beam-forming, accelerating, and focusing electrodes and are formed into a narrow beam. The analysis of the type of electron gun used in most cathode-ray tubes is very difficult, even for the simplest configurations. Such guns are often designed empirically. A good deal of design information has accumulated over the years.

In those microwave tubes which require a long, thin electron beam, it is usually necessary to use much larger beam currents at relatively lower voltages than in cathode-ray tubes. In high-density beams, space-charge effects are by no means negligible. The effect of space-charge spreading owing to the mutual repulsion between electrons (Sec. 2.4) must be taken into account, both in the cathode-anode region, where the beam is produced and formed, and in the drift region, where the beam is merely being transmitted. Aberrations produced by surrounding electrodes and effects such as those of thermal and secondary electrons must be considered.

Most microwave tubes operate under the space-charge-limited regime described in the preceding section. (This mode of operation has the advantage that the beam current for a given configuration depends only on the voltage between cathode and anode; whereas in temperature-limited operation, the current is a very sensitive function of temperature as well.) The performance of an electron gun under space-charge-limited operation may be described by a figure of merit that is independent of the actual size of the configuration and depends only on the electrode shapes, the *perveance*, defined by

$$K = \frac{I}{V^{\frac{3}{2}}} \tag{36}$$

Thus an electron gun that yields 2 ma at 100 volts has a perveance $K = 2 \times 10^{-6}$ amp/volt$^{\frac{3}{2}}$. (The factor 10^{-6} is often omitted; one speaks of a "microperveance of 2.") It would be very difficult to obtain thin beams with perveances of this order of magnitude by purely empirical design. Fortunately, a method of obtaining rectilinear flow between electrodes of finite size has been developed by Pierce,[1] so that the solutions given in Sec. 2.2 may be applied in the formulation of a simple theory of electron-gun design. An electron gun designed by this method is known as a *Pierce gun*.

The method consists in employing configurations that are *segments* of infinite parallel planes, concentric cylinders, or concentric spheres. Ordinarily, a beam originating from such a cathode segment would spread (in an undesirable fashion) as a function of distance. The beam would diverge as a result of repulsive space-charge forces, which are all balanced

[1] J. R. Pierce, Rectilinear Flow in Beams, *J. Appl. Phys.*, 11:548–554 (1940).

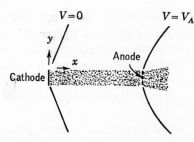

Fig. 2.5   Pierce cathode configuration for rectangular beam.

out in the "complete" configuration (e.g., in rectilinear flow between infinite planes, or between complete cylinders or spheres).   The method developed by Pierce (based on a principle originally established by Wehnelt) depends on supplying compensating forces in the cathode-anode region along the edge of a bounded beam by placing electrodes of certain shapes and potentials just outside the beam.   If the electrodes are so adjusted that the field distribution along the beam edge is the same as that inside a beam of a complete configuration, then rectilinear flow inside the segment is obtained.

Another way of stating the principle is to say that a potential must be established which satisfies Laplace's equation $\nabla^2 V = 0$ in the charge-free region outside the beam, reduces to the correct value along the edge of the beam, and gives the correct electric field (potential gradient) normal to the boundary, $E_\perp = (-\nabla V)_\perp$.   (For Pierce guns, $E_\perp = 0$.)

For a rectangular ("strip") beam that originates from a cathode extending a long distance at right angles to the paper (Fig. 2.5), the potential along the beam edge (i.e., at $y = 0$) is given from (9) by

$$V(x,0) = \left(\frac{9i}{4\epsilon_0 \sqrt{2\eta}}\right)^{\frac{2}{3}} x^{\frac{4}{3}} \tag{37}$$

Pierce has shown that a potential distribution which satisfies Laplace's equation outside the beam, reduces to (37) along the beam edge, and satisfies $\partial V/\partial y = 0$ is given by

$$V = \left(\frac{9i}{4\epsilon_0 \sqrt{2\eta}}\right)^{\frac{2}{3}} [\text{Re } (x + jy)^{\frac{4}{3}}] \tag{38}$$

Substitution of various values of constant V yields the shapes of the equipotentials outside the beam region.   The zero equipotential, for instance, is a plane whose intersect with the xy plane is given by

$$y = x \tan 67.5° \tag{39}$$

The angle of 67.5° ($\frac{3}{4} \times 90°$) arises out of the exponent $\frac{4}{3}$ which occurs in Eq. (37).   The other equipotentials are given by

$$(x^2 + y^2)^{\frac{2}{3}} \cos \frac{4}{3}\theta = \text{const} \tag{40}$$

where $\theta = \tan^{-1} (y/x)$.

To obtain rectilinear flow between a plane cathode and anode, then, it is only necessary to enclose the region by metal surfaces shaped according to (40). For convenience, the two surfaces which are customarily chosen are those corresponding to the cathode and anode potentials (Fig. 2.5). The external electrode at cathode potential is usually separated from the cathode by a small gap to improve the thermal efficiency and to provide for the possibility of a fine adjustment by a biasing potential if desired.

In a great many applications it is desired to obtain a beam of *circular* cross section.[1] For a parallel-flow beam, the cathode is disk-shaped. If r is the distance from the beam axis and z is the distance from the cathode, the conditions to be satisfied at $r = r_b$ (the beam surface) are now

$$\frac{\partial V}{\partial r} = 0 \tag{41}$$

$$V = kz^{\frac{4}{3}} \tag{42}$$

where k is a constant.

In addition, the potential must, of course, satisfy Laplace's equation in the region outside the beam. The solution of this problem is considerably more difficult than in the rectangular case. A convenient experimental approach, developed by Pierce, is based on an electrolytic-tank technique originally suggested by Bowman-Manifold and Nicoll.[2] In its simplest form, the method consists in representing a thin wedge of the beam by means of a tilted electrolytic tank (Fig. 2.6). The edge of the electrolyte represents the axis of symmetry, and the edge of the beam is represented by a strip of insulating material. The strip allows no current to enter the "beam" region, and it therefore correctly represents the condition that the potential gradient should be zero at the surface as specified by Eq. (41). Metal probes are inserted into the strip, and the potential distribution along the "beam surface" is measured by means of several voltmeters connected to the probes. Thin metal strips are used as the external electrodes; their shape is adjusted until the prescribed distribution along the edge of the beam is obtained. Since the angle of the electrolyte wedge is usually small (5° or less), it is permissible to use singly curved surfaces for the external electrodes and the insulating strip. The electrode strips, therefore, need not be portions of surfaces of revolution, but may be cut from plane metal sheets bent to the shape of longitudinal sections of the actual electrodes.

The above method counteracts the effect of the beam spreading only

---

[1] The beam of circular cross section is often called a *cylindrical beam*. An effort to avoid this expression has been made here in order to prevent confusion with a beam originating from a cathode which is a cylinder or a cylindrical segment.

[2] M. Bowman-Manifold and F. H. Nicoll, Electrolytic Field Plotting-trough for Circular Symmetric Systems, *Nature*, **142**:39 (1938).

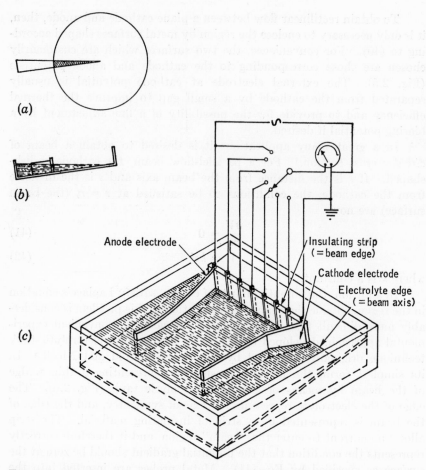

(a)

(b)

(c)

Anode electrode

Insulating strip
(= beam edge)

Cathode electrode

Electrolyte edge
(= beam axis)

**Fig. 2.6 Electrolytic tank used in the design of axisymmetric beams.
A thin wedge (a) of the beam is represented by a wedge of electrolyte in
a tilted tank (b). The electrode shapes are adjusted until the prescribed
voltage distribution along the insulating strip representing the beam
edge is obtained (c).**

within the axially accelerating (cathode-anode) region. Once the electrons reach the region beyond the anode, the repulsive forces are no longer counterbalanced, and it is necessary to resort to some form of focusing (Sec. 2.5). In addition, the anode aperture, which separates an accelerating region from a nonaccelerating (field-free) region, acts as an electrostatic lens with a considerable diverging effect. To obtain converging or parallel-flow beams in the region beyond the anode, electron guns that yield an initially converging beam are often used.

The rectangular strip cathode is then replaced by one that is part of a cylindrical surface. The potential distribution that must be achieved along the beam edge is that which exists *between segments of concentric cylinders,* as given by Eq. (14).   Appropriate electrode shapes may be obtained by an approximate analytical method,[1] or from the electrolytic tank.   The resulting wedge-shaped beam is focused along a line.   The electrons travel along radii until they reach the anode aperture, where they undergo a diverging action (Fig. 2.7).   In the region just beyond the anode, the beam then converges at a smaller angle, becomes parallel to the axis, or diverges from the axis, depending on the configuration. The problem of obtaining and maintaining a beam parallel to the axis is discussed in Sec. 2.5.

In the more important case of an initially converging beam of circular cross section, the disk cathode is replaced by a spherical cap.   The flow is now a segment of flow *between concentric spheres,* and the potential distribution along the beam edge is given by Eq. (18).   The external electrode shapes necessary to attain this distribution may again be obtained by means of the tilted electrolytic tank.   The insulating strip representing the beam surface is set at an angle to the beam axis (the edge of the electrolyte) equal to the spherical-cap cone half angle.   The distribution along the beam edge is proportional not to $x^{\frac{4}{3}}$, but rather to $\alpha^{\frac{4}{3}}$, where α is the factor defined by Eq. (17) and tabulated in Table 2.2. The quantity $\alpha^{\frac{4}{3}}$ is plotted in Fig. 2.8.   The abscissa in this plot is the fractional distance from the cathode,

$$\frac{R_C - R}{R_C} = 1 - \frac{R}{R_C}$$

where the R's are the spherical radii (Fig. 2.9).   Once the ratio of anode to cathode radius is specified, the curve to the left of that point represents the voltage distribution on an arbitrary scale.   For instance, if $R_A/R_C = 0.55$, then $1 - (R_A/R_C) = 0.45$ and the corresponding value of $\alpha^{\frac{4}{3}}$ (Fig. 2.8) is 0.649.   To obtain the voltage distribution at arbitrary points between cathode and anode, we need only multiply the value of

---

[1] Pierce, Rectilinear Flow in Beams, *op. cit.*   See also A. L. Samuel, Some Notes on the Design of Electron Guns, *Proc. IRE,* **33**:233–240 (1945).

Fig. 2.7   Converging flow between cylindrical segments. (*After Samuel.*)

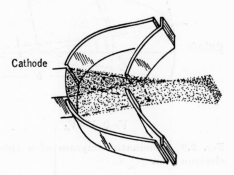

Cathode

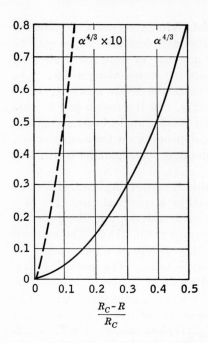

Fig. 2.8   Plot of $\alpha^{\frac{4}{3}}$ vs. fractional distance from the cathode.

$\alpha^{\frac{4}{3}}$ corresponding to each point by the ratio of the cathode-anode potential difference to 0.649.   If the location of these points is taken to coincide with the position of the probes in the insulating strip, the prescribed potential at each probe may thus be easily calculated.

The prescribed voltage distribution along the beam edge may be approximated in the electrolytic tank with a large variety of electrode shapes, and practical design tends toward shapes that are easily fabricated.   Figure 2.10 shows the cathode-anode configuration for a high-power klystron with a spherical-cap cathode.   The metal surface sur-

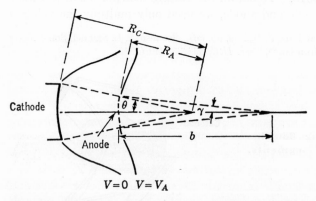

Fig. 2.9   Schematic diagram of a spherical-cathode electron gun.

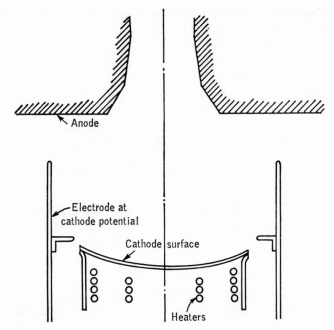

Fig. 2.10 Actual configuration used in a high-power klystron.

rounding the anode aperture is extended to form the external electrode at anode potential. The external electrode at cathode potential is a simple cylinder with an annular disk affixed near the cathode edge. This configuration gives a good approximation to the prescribed $\alpha^{\frac{4}{3}}$ voltage distribution along the beam edge almost all the way to the anode.

2.4 Space-charge Spreading

Electron beams tend to spread because of mutual repulsion between individual electrons. In a converging beam of circular cross section, for instance, the outward space-charge force increases as the radius is decreased and electrons are packed in tighter and tighter. The beam reaches a minimum diameter and then diverges. For a general current distribution, the shapes of the trajectories of electrons originating from different initial positions may not be similar (i.e., the trajectories may cross). The behavior of each electron depends on all the other electrons; and in an exact calculation, one must calculate all the trajectories simultaneously. However, an approximate solution may be found for a special case of considerable practical interest, namely, for a converging beam with a uniform current density over the cross section. To obtain this approximate solution, we have to assume that the axial velocity is also uniform over the cross section (and hence that the volume charge density is uniform).[1] In that case, the radial velocity of any electron is initially directly proportional to its distance from the axis, and this condition is preserved in the subsequent motion (i.e., all trajectories are similar, and the analysis of the outermost electron's trajectory will apply to any electron within the beam as well). We then speak of a *laminar beam*. For a beam that is not converging too rapidly, we may consider the radial electric field to be like that of an infinite cylinder of charge. The equation of motion is given by

$$m\ddot{r} = eE = e\frac{\rho_l}{2\pi\epsilon_0 r} \tag{43}$$

where E is the field due to a charge ρ_l per unit length. The charge per unit length is here a constant independent of the beam width and is related to the charge density per unit volume by the equation

$$\rho_l = A\rho \tag{44}$$

where A is the cross-sectional area of the beam.[2]

One integration of Eq. (43) yields the following equation:

$$\frac{m\dot{r}^2}{2} = \frac{e\rho_l}{2\pi\epsilon_0}\ln\frac{r}{r_m} \tag{45}$$

where r_m is the minimum radius attained by the beam ($\dot{r} = 0$ at $r = r_m$). If we take the origin at the point of minimum radius, Eq. (45) may be put into the form

$$\int_{r_m}^{r} \frac{dr}{\sqrt{\ln(r/r_m)}} = \int_0^t \sqrt{\frac{\eta\rho_l}{\pi\epsilon_0}}\,dt \tag{46}$$

Let

$$R \equiv \frac{r}{r_m} \tag{47}$$

Then Eq. (46), after integration of the right-hand side, becomes

$$\frac{1}{R}\int_1^R \frac{dR}{\sqrt{\ln R}} = \frac{t}{r}\sqrt{\frac{\eta\rho_l}{\pi\epsilon_0}} = \frac{z}{r}\sqrt{\frac{\eta\rho_l}{\pi\epsilon_0 v^2}} \tag{48}$$

provided we also make the substitution $z = tv$, where v is the velocity and

[1] In general, since the beam contains negative charge, a potential variation occurs inside the beam and results in the axial velocity also being a function of radius (lowest on the axis), at least in the absence of a confining magnetic field. The reduction in axial velocity depends on charge density and may be disregarded in the first approximation over a range of values of perveance of practical interest.

[2] Note that for electrons inside the beam (since ρ_l is proportional to r^2), the force on each electron is proportional to r, yielding similar trajectories, as was stated.

Table 2.3

R	$\int_1^R \dfrac{dR}{\sqrt{\ln R}}$	$\dfrac{1}{R}\int_1^R \dfrac{dR}{\sqrt{\ln R}}$
1.0	0.000	0.000
1.1	0.637	0.580
1.5	1.469	0.979
2.0	2.145	1.073
2.35	2.543	1.082
3.0	3.200	1.067
3.5	3.658	1.044
4.0	4.102	1.025
4.5	4.508	1.001
5.0	4.920	0.984

z is the distance.   Now let

$$w \equiv \sqrt{\ln R} \tag{49}$$

or $R = e^{w^2}$ and $dR = 2we^{w^2}\, dw$.   Then

$$\frac{1}{R}\int_1^R \frac{dR}{\sqrt{\ln R}} = \frac{2}{R}\int_0^w e^{w^2}\, dw \tag{50}$$

Values of the integral which appears on the right-hand side of Eq. (50) have been tabulated by Jahnke and Emde.[1] For easy reference, a few values of the integral and of the complete expression are shown in Table 2.3.   Note that the maximum of the function tabulated in the last column occurs at $R = 2.35$.

At low values of w, a few terms of the expansion

$$e^{w_2} = 1 + \frac{w^2}{1!} + \frac{w^4}{2!} + \frac{w^6}{3!} + \cdots$$

may be used to compute the value of Eq. (50), as follows:

$$\frac{1}{R}\int_1^R \frac{dR}{\ln R} = \frac{2}{R}\left[w + \frac{w^3}{3(1!)} + \frac{w^5}{5(2!)} + \frac{w^7}{7(3!)} + \cdots \right] \tag{51}$$

The substitutions

$$\rho_l = \frac{I}{v} \tag{52}$$

$$v = \sqrt{2\eta V} \tag{53}$$

[1] E. Jahnke and F. Emde, "Tables of Functions," 4th ed., p. 32, Dover Publications, Inc., New York, 1945.

may be used to simplify Eq. (48) as follows:

$$\frac{1}{R}\int_1^R \frac{dR}{\sqrt{\ln R}} = \frac{z}{r}\sqrt{\frac{I}{V^{\frac{3}{2}}}\frac{1}{2\pi\epsilon_0}\frac{1}{\sqrt{2\eta}}} = \frac{z}{r}\sqrt{3\times 10^4 K} \qquad (54)$$

The constant under the radical is very nearly 3×10^4, and K is the perveance defined by Eq. (36).

The *beam-spreading curve* for an initially parallel beam may be calculated by means of Eq. (54) from the initial (minimum) radius, r_m. The beam-spreading curve may be more conveniently plotted in terms of another form of Eq. (54), namely,

$$\frac{z}{r_m}\sqrt{3\times 10^4 K} = \int_1^R \frac{dR}{\sqrt{\ln R}} \qquad (54a)$$

The curve is symmetrical: the converging portion of the beam has the same shape as the diverging portion.

Another way of writing Eq. (48), for a solid beam, is to make the substitution

$$\rho_l = \pi r_m^2 \rho \qquad (55)$$

Then

$$\frac{1}{R}\int_1^R \frac{dR}{\sqrt{\ln R}} = z\frac{r_m}{r}\sqrt{\frac{\eta\rho}{\epsilon_0 v^2}} \qquad (56)$$

or

$$\int_1^R \frac{dR}{\sqrt{\ln R}} = \frac{\omega_p}{v}z = \beta_p z \qquad (57)$$

where we have defined a number called the *plasma frequency* ω_p and a plasma wave number β_p, as measured at the minimum diameter, by

$$\omega_p \equiv \sqrt{\frac{\eta\rho}{\epsilon_0}} \qquad (58)$$

$$\beta_p \equiv \frac{\omega_p}{v} = \frac{2\pi}{\lambda_p} \qquad (59)$$

where λ_p is the plasma wavelength. (The concepts ω_p, β_p, and λ_p will be discussed more fully in Chap. 4. These quantities are characteristic parameters that measure the magnitude of space-charge effects in the "plasma," i.e., the medium consisting of charged particles—here, the beam. It is always found that appreciable effects of space charge occur in a time of the order of $2\pi/\omega_p$, or a distance of the order of λ_p. These quantities are scale factors that crop up in any discussion of space-charge effects and are introduced here as the first example of such use.)

Equation (54) may be used to determine various limiting conditions for beam transmission through a cylinder. This equation relates beam radius r, perveance K, and distance z from the position of minimum beam radius r_m by means of a dimensionless parameter $R = r/r_m$. Thus, two

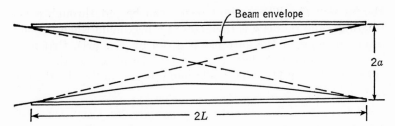

Fig. 2.11 Transmission of beam through a cylinder. Current is maximum when beam is "aimed" at center of tube.

beams of equal K with different values of r_m have the same z/r ratios at corresponding points. Since the function on the left-hand side of (54), which is tabulated in the last column of Table 2.3, has a maximum value of 1.082 at $R = r/r_m = 2.35$, this maximum value

$$\frac{z}{r} \sqrt{3 \times 10^4 K} = 1.082$$

determines the limiting conditions for various combinations of z, r, and K. For a fixed perveance K, for instance, the maximum value of z/r may be found giving the optimum length-to-radius ratio of a cylinder through which the beam of this perveance can be transmitted. Conversely, given a cylinder of length $z = 2L$ and $r = a$, we may obtain the maximum current that can be transmitted with the entering beam just grazing the opening:

$$\frac{L}{a} \sqrt{3 \times 10^4 \frac{I}{V^{\frac{3}{2}}}} = 1.082 \tag{60}$$

$$\frac{I}{V^{\frac{3}{2}}} = 38.6 \times 10^{-6} \left(\frac{a}{L}\right)^2 \tag{61}$$

The beam must enter at a specified angle. The slope may be obtained with the help of the relationship $dz = v\,dt$, which together with Eq. (45) yields

$$\frac{dr}{dz} = \frac{1}{v}\frac{dr}{dt} = \frac{1}{v}\sqrt{\frac{\eta \rho_l}{\pi \epsilon_0}}\ln \frac{r}{r_m} \tag{62}$$

which may be written, with the help of Eq. (48) and the substitution $L/a = z/r$, in the form

$$\frac{dr}{dz} = \frac{a}{L}\left(\frac{1}{R}\int_1^R \frac{dR}{\sqrt{\ln R}}\right)\sqrt{\ln \frac{r}{r_m}} \tag{63}$$

and has the value

$$\frac{dr}{dz} = \frac{a}{L}(1.082)(0.924) \approx \frac{a}{L} \tag{64}$$

at $r/r_m = 2.35$.   The current which can be put through a cylinder of length $2L$ and radius a is therefore at a maximum when the slope of the beam envelope at the entrance is given by Eq. (64), that is, when the beam is so directed that it appears to be aimed at the center of the cylinder (Fig. 2.11).   The minimum beam radius is then given by $r_m = a/2.35$.

2.5   Beam Focusing

In long, thin beams of very high density, space-charge spreading becomes so large that it must be counteracted by some electron-optical method. The various means that have been employed to accomplish that goal are loosely spoken of as "beam focusing," although the aim is usually to maintain some prescribed cross section of the beam rather than bring it to a focus.

Among the methods that have been proposed to offset space charge is its *neutralization by positive ions* such as are produced by collisions between electrons and gas molecules.   Such molecules are present to some extent even at the relatively "hard" vacuum used in ordinary commercial practice.   Because the ionization time (i.e., the time required before a degree of ionization that is sufficient for neutralization is achieved) is of the order of several microseconds, the molecules may cause a difference between the pulsed and c-w operation of a tube and lead to a false indication of satisfactory performance in c-w testing of a tube intended for pulsed operation.   But neutralization schemes in which the production of positive ions in the electron beam is deliberately fostered have found little favor: not only do the positive ions tend to be continually drained out by being attracted to the most negative electrode (the cathode, which they damage if it is of the oxide-coated type), but they also lead to oscillations and other instabilities that have an adverse effect on tube performance.

The most common method of maintaining the cross section of the beam is to subject it to a *magnetic field* parallel to the direction of motion. The effect of a magnetic field on moving charged particles may be summarized as follows: the paths remain *unchanged* by a magnetic field parallel to the path; the paths become *circular* when they enter a magnetic field perpendicular to the path; and the paths become *helical* if the magnetic field and the path intersect at an intermediate angle.

A simple way to maintain, say, a long beam of circular cross section is thus to employ what we shall term *immersed flow*, in which the entire tube is surrounded by a solenoid that produces a finite axial magnetic field.   As an initially parallel beam spreads owing to space-charge repulsion, each electron intersects magnetic field lines and begins to follow a complex helical path about the axis.   The projection of the path on a plane normal to the axis may be described qualitatively as a cycloid superimposed on a circle. This motion results from the interaction of each particle with the magnetic field (cf. Chap. 10), modified by the presence of the space charge of the entire beam. Broadly speaking, the excursions from the equilibrium radius are inversely proportional to the magnitude of the magnetic field. The electron's axial velocity remains unchanged, since the velocity component that gives rise to the force on the electron (and hence to the cycloidal path) is perpendicular to the magnetic field, which can thus change neither the kinetic energy nor the speed of the electron but only the direction of its motion.

The simple immersed-flow method has the disadvantage that an infinitely large magnetic field would in theory be required to reduce the radial excursions to zero. Although such an infinite field is sometimes assumed for analytical purposes (in what is termed *confined flow*), it cannot, of course, be attained in practice. In fact, the mere assumption of an infinite field may lead to difficulties of a theoretical nature in some cases. (However, focused flow is possible with a uniform magnetic field at reasonable magnitudes.)

There are other variations of immersed flow in which this theoretical difficulty is avoided, but they are subject to difficulties of a practical nature. These variations all involve having both electron beam and magnetic flux converge in the cathode-anode region (and possibly beyond it), so that some crossing of flux lines by electrons takes place. It is possible to arrange the several design factors in such a way that the combination of space-charge forces, centrifugal forces caused by angular electron motion, and magnetic forces caused by the interaction between the axial fields and the angular motion are all balanced and a cylindrical beam of constant radius can be maintained. Small departures from the correct conditions result in beam "scalloping," with the magnitude of the scallops (i.e., departures from an equilibrium radius) inversely proportional to the magnetic-flux density at the cathode—obviously a useful property. This relationship may be described in terms of beam "stiffness."[1]

The disadvantage of these designs is that the basic Pierce gun design method does not allow for the presence of a magnetic field, unless the magnetic field lines are aligned with the trajectories. Such alignment is quite easy in nonconvergent beams, but a fairly complex additional design procedure must be undertaken in convergent beams to ensure that the magnetic field lines and the trajectories coincide. Nevertheless, many high-power microwave tubes are designed according to such a procedure because of the greater beam stiffness. Nonconvergent immersed flow is often used precisely because it *is* simple and because

[1] J. L. Palmer and C. Susskind, Stiffness of Electron Beams, *J. Electron. Control*, **10**:365–373 (1961).

the design of certain guns (such as those intended for particularly low-noise operation) can be carried out by alternate methods only with great difficulties.

An alternate scheme, which requires a magnetic field considerably smaller than that employed in practical immersed-flow designs and which is not limited to nonconvergent beams, is called *Brillouin flow.*[1]   Here the electron gun is shielded from the magnetic field that surrounds the rest of the tube; the electrons, in passing from the shielded to the unshielded region, acquire an angular velocity about the axis that again results in a helical trajectory about the beam axis.   The rotation produces an inward radial force owing to the interaction with the axial magnetic field, as well as an outward centrifugal force.   If the magnitude of the magnetic field is so adjusted that the inward force just balances the combined outward forces (centrifugal plus space-charge forces), a beam of constant diameter is maintained.

Brillouin flow (zero magnetic field at the gun) and immersed flow (full magnetic field at the gun) are actually special cases of the more general aforementioned phenomenon that may be termed *space-charge-balanced flow,* in which the magnetic fields in the gun region and the remainder of the tube are in general different.   Before we discuss this general case, we shall derive an important theorem of electron optics that determines the angular velocity $\dot\theta$.   We shall refer to the successive regions of a beam-type microwave tube as the *electron-gun, transition, interaction,* and *collector regions;* and we shall restrict the discussion to cases in which the magnetic field is axially symmetric (i.e., independent of θ).

In the transition region, the magnetic field **B** has in general a radial component (Fig. 2.12).   A particle moving with a velocity **v** interacts with **B** to produce a force $\mathbf{F} = e(\mathbf{v} \times \mathbf{B})$ that (for a point in the plane of the paper) is directed out of the paper.   The angular velocity $\dot\theta$ resulting from this force causes the particle to interact with the axial magnetic field in the interaction region to produce an inward ("focusing") force.   (The interaction region is so designated because electrons interact there with r-f waves.)   The angular velocity also produces an outward centrifugal force, which actually reduces the focusing force.   In this region, **B** is parallel to the axial component of velocity and no interaction with that velocity results.

To compute $\dot\theta$, we recall that the rate of change of angular momentum equals the moment rF_θ of the angular force:

$$\frac{d}{dt}\,(mr^2\dot\theta) = re(-\dot r B_z + \dot z B_r) \tag{65}$$

[1] L. Brillouin, A Theorem of Larmor and Its Importance for Electrons in Magnetic Fields, *Phys. Rev.,* **67**:260–266, 1945.

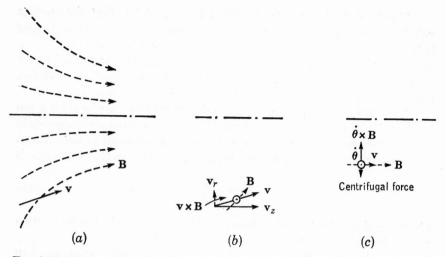

Fig. 2.12 Interaction of magnetic field with particle velocity in Brillouin-flow electron gun. (*a*) and (*b*) refer to transition region, (*c*) refers to uniform-flow region.

Multiplication by $2\pi \, dt$ yields

$$2\pi \, d(mr^2\dot{\theta}) = -e[2\pi r(B_z \, dr - B_r \, dz)] \tag{66}$$

But dr and dz are the components of the electron trajectory during the time dt, and in terms of these components we may define a vector area $\mathbf{dA} = r \, d\theta(\mathbf{a}_z \, dr - \mathbf{a}_r \, dz)$ generated by rotating this trajectory element through an infinitesimal angle $d\theta$. (The $\mathbf{a}$'s are unit vectors.) The *magnetic flux* through this element is $\mathbf{B} \cdot \mathbf{dA}$, and the total flux crossing the bounding strip at this value of r,z is the integral of this quantity over 2π, or $2\pi r\mathbf{B} \cdot (\mathbf{a}_z \, dr - \mathbf{a}_r \, dz)$, which is just the term in brackets on the right-hand side of Eq. (66). We designate this flux by $d\psi$ and integrate Eq. (66) between the initial point of the trajectory (at the cathode) and any arbitrary point along the trajectory to obtain

$$\int d(mr^2\dot{\theta}) = -\frac{e}{2\pi} \int d\psi = -\frac{e}{2\pi}(\psi - \psi_c) = (mr^2\dot{\theta}) - (mr^2\dot{\theta})_c \tag{67}$$

where the subscript C refers to the value in the electron-gun region (at the cathode). In most applications, $\dot{\theta} = 0$ there, which determines the lower limit of the integral and yields

$$\dot{\theta} = \frac{\eta}{2\pi r^2}(\psi - \psi_c) \tag{68}$$

This equation is known as *Busch's theorem*.

The important property described by Eq. (68) is that the angular velocity of any electron at any point depends only on the *difference* between the total fluxes linked by the charge rings at the two electron positions, the initial (at the cathode) and the final (at the point under consideration). The angular velocity is independent of the detailed trajectory between these two points.[1]

The various cases of space-charge-balanced flow can be designated by the ratio $K \equiv \psi_c/\psi$. The magnetic flux arising from a constant-field configuration with rotational symmetry (e.g., a solenoid) is the product of cross-sectional area and magnetic field, $\psi = \pi r^2 B$, so that this ratio is

$$K = \frac{\psi_c}{\pi r_0^2 B} \tag{69}$$

where the denominator refers to an equilibrium radius in the interaction region, in which there is a uniform magnetic field B.[2] For immersed flow $K = 1$; for Brillouin flow, $K = 0$. For the latter case, $\psi_c = 0$; and from Eq. (68) the angular velocity $\dot\theta$ becomes equal in magnitude to the *Larmor precession frequency*[3]

$$\omega_L = \tfrac{1}{2}\eta B \tag{70}$$

The equation of motion for the general space-charge-balanced flow $(0 \le K \le 1)$ is

$$m\ddot{r} = mr\dot\theta^2 + er\dot\theta B + \frac{e\rho_l}{2\pi\epsilon_0 r} \tag{71}$$

where the three terms on the right-hand side respectively represent the centrifugal force, the focusing (or $\mathbf{v} \times \mathbf{B}$) force arising from the cross product of angular velocity and axial magnetic field, and the space-charge-spreading force. For a beam in which the charge density is uniform over any cross section, the charge ρ_l per unit length may be related, according to Eq. (44), to the charge density ρ_0 per unit volume and the radius r_0 by

$$\rho_l = \pi r_0^2 \rho_0 \tag{72}$$

Equation (72) of course holds for any value of radius (and the corresponding charge density), and in general the beam radius varies with z. It is convenient, however, to write the equations in terms of a particular value of radius (and charge density), namely, that radius at which the

---

[1] If electron motion in a magnetic field is described in terms of the Hamiltonian form of dynamics, the definition of generalized angular momentum involves the magnetic field and Busch's theorem actually represents conservation of this angular momentum.

[2] If the magnetic field B_C in the cathode region is constant (e.g., in a nonconvergent-beam case), $\psi_c = \pi r_c^2 B_C$ and $K = r_c^2 B_C / r_0^2 B$.

[3] Brillouin, *op. cit.*

three forces in Eq. (71) just balance each other.   This is the value that shall be denoted by r_0.   The equation of motion thus becomes, with utilization of Eqs. (68) to (71) and of $\omega_L = n\psi/2\pi r^2$,

$$\ddot{r} = r\dot{\theta}^2 + \eta r\dot{\theta}B + \frac{\eta\rho_0}{\epsilon_0}\frac{r_0{}^2}{2r} = -r\omega_L{}^2\left[1 - \left(\frac{\psi_C}{\psi}\right)^2\right] + \omega_p{}^2\frac{r_0{}^2}{2r} \qquad (73)$$

The plasma frequency $\omega_p = (\eta\rho_0/\epsilon_0)^{\frac{1}{2}}$ introduced here—as defined in Eq. (58)—represents the effects of space charge.   We see at once that if the magnetic flux is greater at the cathode than in the interaction region ($\psi_C > \psi$), the right-hand side of Eq. (73) is positive ($\ddot{r} > 0$), so that the net force is outward and no focusing can result.[1]

A special case of practical interest, previously discussed, arises when the cathode is immersed in the same magnetic field that exists in the interaction region.   An initially parallel beam, for instance, diverges owing to space charge; the electrons, in crossing magnetic field lines, produce focusing of the type described earlier in this section.[2]

Thus, if $B = B_C$,

$$\psi = \pi r^2 B_C \qquad (74)$$
$$\psi_C = \pi r_C{}^2 B_C \qquad (75)$$

where r_C refers to the initial (cathode) value of the trajectory radius. Then (71) becomes

$$\ddot{r} = -r\omega_L{}^2\left(1 - \frac{r_C{}^4}{r^4}\right) + \frac{e\rho_l}{2m\pi\epsilon_0 r} \qquad (76)$$

$$\ddot{r} \approx -4\omega_L{}^2(r - r_C) + \frac{e\rho_l}{2m\pi\epsilon_0 r} \qquad (76a)$$

where we have made the approximation that $r + r_C \approx 2r$.   In this case, therefore, the magnetic field contributes an inward (focusing) or outward force depending on whether r is greater or smaller than r_C, respectively. (It should be noted that the focusing force increases with ω_L, i.e., with the magnetic field.)

In general, for $\psi_C < \psi$, a perfect balance is obtained by definition when $\ddot{r} = 0$ at $r = r_0$.   If we recall that $K = \psi_C/\psi$, we have for the

---

[1] It is important to recall that ρ_0 here corresponds to a beam of radius r_0; however, one cannot speak of an "equilibrium" radius when $\psi_C > \psi$, since there is no value at which $\ddot{r} = 0$ in this case.

[2] The same situation would arise in a converging beam (such as is obtained from a spherical-cap cathode) if the magnetic field lines were arranged to converge in such a way as to coincide with the electron trajectories that would exist in the absence of all magnetic focusing.   The electron trajectory then remains unaffected by the magnetic field as long as the trajectory follows the field line ($\mathbf{v} \times \mathbf{B} = 0$), but as soon as the trajectory deviates (owing to space-charge spreading) from the field line, the same type of focusing as described above results.

equilibrium condition

$$\omega_L{}^2(1 - K^2) = \tfrac{1}{2}\omega_p{}^2 \tag{77}$$

Since ω_L is proportional to B, we see that the case for which the required magnetic field is minimum for a given r_0 occurs when $K = 0$; that is, Brillouin flow, in which the electron-gun region is completely shielded from the magnetic field in the interaction region. This case is therefore of particular theoretical interest. For this case, from Eq. (77), $\omega_L{}^2 = \tfrac{1}{2}\omega_p{}^2$ and Eq. (73) becomes

$$\ddot{r} = \frac{\omega_p{}^2}{2}\left(-r + \frac{r_0{}^2}{r}\right) \tag{78}$$

We see at once that the flow is stable for all perturbations from r_0; for if $r > r_0$, the acceleration is negative (inward), and if $r < r_0$, the acceleration is positive (outward).

Let us compute the value of B required for Brillouin flow, which we shall designate by B_{Br}. The equilibrium condition for Brillouin flow, $\omega_L{}^2 = \tfrac{1}{2}\omega_p{}^2$, can be rewritten with the help of Eqs. (52) and (53) as

$$\left(\frac{\eta B_{Br}}{2}\right)^2 = \frac{\eta\rho_0}{2\epsilon_0} = \frac{\eta\rho_l}{2\pi r_0{}^2\epsilon_0} = \frac{(\eta/2)^{\frac{1}{2}}}{2\pi r_0{}^2\epsilon_0}\frac{I}{V_a{}^{\frac{1}{2}}} \tag{79}$$

or

$$B_{Br} = \frac{8.30 \times 10^{-4}}{r_0}\left(\frac{I}{\sqrt{V_a}}\right)^{\frac{1}{2}} \tag{80}$$

in mks units.[1]   That is the magnetic field required for Brillouin flow in a beam with uniform charge distribution.

It should be noted that we have introduced a potential V_a corresponding to an assumed common axial velocity for all the electrons. At the beginning of Sec. 2.4, we mentioned that the axial velocities of all electrons in the absence of a magnetic field were not the same, but rather depended on radius (as did the potential). For Brillouin flow, we shall presently show that all electrons do travel with the same axial velocity regardless of radial position. However, this potential is only approximately equal to the accelerating (anode) potential V_A when the perveance is low. More generally, the potential V at any radius r inside the beam differs from the anode potential because of the charge contained in the beam, which depresses the potential. (This potential depression gives rise to a phenomenon, not restricted to Brillouin flow, known as the *limiting current* or *critical current*, at which the potential is so low that a solid beam cannot be maintained.)

---

[1] If length is measured in centimeters and magnetic field in gauss (with I in amperes and V_a in volts),

$$B_{Br} = \frac{830}{r_0}\left(\frac{I}{\sqrt{V_a}}\right)^{\frac{1}{2}} \tag{80a}$$

To calculate the potential V at any radius r, we utilize Poisson's equation $\nabla^2 V = -\rho/\epsilon_0$, or

$$\frac{1}{r}\frac{\partial}{\partial r}\left(r\frac{\partial V}{\partial r}\right) = -\frac{\rho}{\epsilon_0} \tag{81}$$

which for a constant charge density[1] $\rho = \rho_0$ reduces to

$$V = -\frac{\rho_0 r^2}{4\epsilon_0} + V_a \tag{82}$$

since $V = V_a$ at $r = 0$. Outside the beam, we must add the logarithmic expression for the potential outside a cylinder of charge:

$$V = V_a - \frac{\rho_0 r_0^2}{4\epsilon_0} - \frac{\rho_0 r_0^2}{2\epsilon_0}\ln\frac{r}{r_0} \tag{83}$$

where r_0 refers to the equilibrium radius of the outermost electron. The anode potential V_A (corresponding to the potential of a metal wall of radius r_A) is therefore related to that on the axis, V_a, by

$$V_A = V_a - \frac{\rho_0 r_0^2}{4\epsilon_0}\left(1 + 2\ln\frac{r_A}{r_0}\right) \tag{84}$$

The error made when V_A instead of V_a is used in Eq. (80) may usually be neglected in an approximate calculation of B_{Br}.

To prove that all electrons move with the same axial velocity, corresponding to V_a, we use the equation of conservation of energy,

$$\dot{r}^2 + (r\dot{\theta})^2 + \dot{z}^2 = 2\eta V \tag{85}$$

where V is again the potential at any point in the beam. For Brillouin flow, $\theta^2 = \omega_L^2$ and $\dot{r} = 0$; so that we have, if we write v for $\dot{z}$,

$$V = \frac{\omega_L^2 r^2}{2\eta} + \frac{v^2}{2\eta} \tag{86}$$

But for constant charge density, we have from Eq. (83)

$$V = -\frac{\rho_0 r^2}{4\epsilon_0} + V_a = \frac{\omega_p^2 r^2}{4\eta} + V_a = \frac{\omega_L^2 r^2}{2\eta} + V_a \tag{87}$$

since for Brillouin flow, $\omega_L^2 = \frac{1}{2}\omega_p^2$ by virtue of Eq. (77). A comparison of Eqs. (86) and (87) then shows that the radial variation in potential is

---

[1] The current density emitted from a cathode is normally constant over the cross section of the beam. The assumption of a constant charge density ρ_0 thus implies the assumption that velocity is constant over the cross section—which we are trying to prove. Our proof is therefore one that merely shows self-consistency, i.e., that potential, charge density, and kinetic energy of angular motion are consistent with each other and with a constant axial velocity.

just exactly equal to the radial variation in kinetic energy due to angular motion, and therefore

$$v^2 = 2\eta V_a \tag{88}$$

i.e., that the axial velocity does not depend on radius, but is a constant and corresponds to the potential on the axis. This property does not hold for the general case of space-charge-balanced flow ($K \neq 0$), which is an important advantage of the Brillouin case.

We have shown that for the special case of a magnetically focused beam with no magnetic field at the cathode a particular combination of magnetic field, beam radius, beam current, and beam voltage can be found such that radial acceleration vanishes and there are no forces on the electrons. If the beam at this radius also has no *radial* velocities, a constant-radius beam would result. In practice, however, it is difficult to inject the beam from the cathode in such a way that at exactly the position along the beam where its radius satisfies the conditions (77), (79), or (80) the radial velocities are also zero and a constant-radius beam can be maintained. It is, therefore, also of interest to determine how the beam shape is modified if the radial velocities do *not* vanish at the value of the beam radius where the accelerations vanish. What results is a fluctuation in the boundary. The important question is whether this fluctuation is stable and, if it is, how large it is.

It is possible to obtain a good deal of information regarding this problem from the equations of motion. Equation (76) can be integrated once to yield

$$\dot{r}^2 - \dot{r}_i{}^2 = \omega_p{}^2 \left(\frac{r_i{}^2 - r^2}{2} + r_0{}^2 \ln \frac{r}{r_i} \right) \tag{89}$$

where certain initial conditions have already been introduced. The quantity $\dot{r}_i$ represents the initial radial velocity at some initial plane at which the beam radius was r_i. It proves to be more convenient to consider (with no loss of generality) the initial plane as that at which the fluctuating beam radius goes through either a maximum or a minimum. We designate this value, either maximum or minimum, r_m; and since the radial velocity vanishes at either position, Eq. (89) may be rewritten as

$$\dot{r}^2 = \omega_p{}^2 \left(\frac{r_m{}^2 - r^2}{2} + r_0{}^2 \ln \frac{r}{r_m} \right) \tag{90}$$

This equation obviously satisfies the condition that r_m is a maximum or minimum; and by setting the right-hand side equal to zero, one obtains another solution for r that represents the other extreme of beam excursion. Equation (90) therefore yields the maximum and minimum values of the beam radius; if we know one, we can find the other. Alternatively, if only the radial velocity and radius at some initial plane are known, Eq. (89) could be used in a similar way to find two values at which the radial velocity is zero, corresponding to the maximum and minimum radii. These integrations thus tell us nothing about the shape of the trajectory, the period of its oscillation, or indeed whether it is periodic at all; they merely enable us to calculate the maximum and minimum radii. In many cases, that is enough. However, it is possible to go a little further, at least when the departure of the beam radius from the equilibrium radius r_0 is small. In that case, Eq. (76) may be solved approximately and detailed information about the shape of the trajectory may be obtained.

For this purpose, we introduce a new variable Δ to represent a small deviation of the trajectory from the equilibrium radius, so that

$$r = r_0 + \Delta \tag{91}$$

and $\ddot{r} = \ddot{\Delta}$. Then Eq. (75) may be written as

$$\ddot{\Delta} = \tfrac{1}{2}\omega_p{}^2 \left[-(r_0 + \Delta) + \frac{r_0{}^2}{r_0 + \Delta} \right] \tag{92}$$

If we expand the denominator of the fraction on the right-hand side and assume that the deviation from the equilibrium radius is small, so that we may drop terms of higher than linear order in the deviation, we obtain an equation of simple harmonic motion,

$$\ddot{\Delta} \approx - \omega_p{}^2 \Delta \tag{93}$$

which has the solution

$$\Delta = r_i \cos \omega_p t + \frac{\dot{r}_i}{\omega_p} \sin \omega_p t \tag{94}$$

Here r_i represents the initial beam radius at some arbitrary initial plane and $\dot{r}_i$ the initial radial velocity. Accordingly, an electron on the beam boundary oscillates radially with a frequency equal to the plasma frequency ω_p and symmetrically around the equilibrium radius. It should be recalled that both of these statements apply, strictly speaking, only to small deviations, since we have dropped quadratic terms in the derivation of Eq. (92).

It is also possible to write Eq. (94) in terms of the axial distance, rather than time, to exhibit the periodic variations of the beam with distance, if we recall that $\beta_p = \omega_p/u_0$ and $u_0 t = z$, where u_0 is the common axial velocity of all electrons. Then Eq. (94) becomes

$$\Delta = r_i \cos \beta_p z + \frac{\dot{r}_i}{u_0 \beta_p} \sin \beta_p z \tag{95}$$

which is a description of the beam boundary as a function of axial distance. We note that it has a sinusoidal contour, with the magnitude, phase, and shape depending on initial conditions. It is also convenient to note that the coefficient of the second term on the right-hand side contains the slope of the beam at the entrance plane,

$$\tan \theta = \frac{\dot{r}_i}{u_0} \tag{96}$$

which is usually the quantity more directly known than $\dot{r}_i$.

2.6 Scaling

A problem that arises fairly often is the application of a successful electron-gun design to the design of a similar gun with different operating characteristics. For instance, we may want to change the dimensions of an existing electron tube so that it will operate at a different frequency, or change the voltage and current to obtain a different output power. In general, two requirements must be satisfied by the electrons of the scaled gun: (1) the shapes of their trajectories must remain the same and (2) they must traverse corresponding distances in the same fraction of a cycle of the operating frequency. We considered these concepts briefly in Sec. 2.2 in connection with the derivation of the generalized $\frac{3}{2}$-power law (Eq. 28), but we shall now derive scaling relations of a more general nature.

Suppose we consider two electron tubes with linear dimensions in the ratio

$$L \equiv \frac{l'}{l} \tag{97}$$

and which are to be operated at wavelengths in the ratio

$$\Lambda \equiv \frac{\lambda'}{\lambda} = \frac{\omega}{\omega'} \tag{98}$$

Then if the trajectory shapes and transit angles are to remain the same,

$$dl' = L \, dl \tag{99}$$

and since $\omega \, dt = \omega' \, dt'$,

$$dt' = \Lambda \, dt \tag{100}$$

Therefore,

$$\frac{dl'}{dt'} = \frac{L}{\Lambda} \frac{dl}{dt} \tag{101}$$

$$\frac{d^2l'}{dt'^2} = \frac{d}{dt'}\left(\frac{dl'}{dt'}\right) = \frac{1}{\Lambda} \frac{d}{dt}\left(\frac{L}{\Lambda} \frac{dl}{dt}\right) = \frac{L}{\Lambda^2} \frac{d^2l}{dt^2} \tag{102}$$

The equation of electron motion in the first gun is

$$m \frac{d^2\mathbf{l}}{dt^2} = e\left(\mathbf{E} + \frac{d\mathbf{l}}{dt} \times \mathbf{B}\right) \tag{103}$$

This equation may also be written in the form

$$m \frac{\Lambda^2}{L} \frac{d^2\mathbf{l}'}{dt'^2} = e\left(\mathbf{E} + \frac{\Lambda}{L} \frac{d\mathbf{l}'}{dt'} \times \mathbf{B}\right) \tag{104}$$

or

$$m \frac{d^2\mathbf{l}'}{dt'^2} = e\left(\frac{L}{\Lambda^2} \mathbf{E} + \frac{d\mathbf{l}'}{dt'} \times \frac{\mathbf{B}}{\Lambda}\right) \tag{105}$$

But the equation of motion for the second gun is

$$m \frac{d^2\mathbf{l}'}{dt'^2} = e\left(\mathbf{E}' + \frac{d\mathbf{l}'}{dt'} \times \mathbf{B}'\right) \tag{106}$$

A comparison of the last two equations shows that for the above relationships to be consistent when the wavelength and dimensions are changed in such a way as to preserve trajectory shapes and transit angles, the electric and magnetic fields in the scaled gun must be given by

$$E' = \frac{L}{\Lambda^2} E \tag{107}$$

$$B' = \frac{1}{\Lambda} B \tag{108}$$

Furthermore, since the electric field has the dimensions of potential divided by distance ($\mathbf{E} = -\nabla V$) and the distance ratio is L, the potentials of the scaled gun are related to those in the original gun by

$$\frac{V'}{V} = L \frac{E'}{E} = \frac{L^2}{\Lambda^2} \tag{109}$$

The ratio of current densities in the two guns is obtained by a consideration of Poisson's equation ($\nabla^2 V = -\rho/\epsilon_0$) and the relationship between charge density ρ and current density ($i = \rho v$, where v is the velocity). By an argument similar to that used in the derivation of $l' = (L/\Lambda^2)l$, the reader can quickly ascertain that

$$\frac{\rho'}{\rho} = \frac{\nabla^2 V'}{\nabla^2 V} = \frac{1}{\Lambda^2} \tag{110}$$

so that

$$\frac{i'}{i} = \frac{\rho' v'}{\rho v} = \frac{\rho'}{\rho}\left(\frac{V'}{V}\right)^{\frac{1}{2}} = \frac{1}{\Lambda^2}\left(\frac{L}{\Lambda}\right) = \frac{L}{\Lambda^3} \tag{111}$$

since the velocity is proportional to the square root of the voltage.

The ratio of currents, powers, and power densities may be obtained by applying simple dimensional considerations to the above results.

Table 2.4 Ratios used in scaling of electron guns; $L = \dfrac{l'}{l}, \Lambda = \dfrac{\lambda'}{\lambda}$

Quantity	General scaling	Proportional scaling, $\Lambda = L$	Dimension scaling, $\Lambda = 1$	Wavelength scaling, $L = 1$
Magnetic flux density, B'/B	$\dfrac{1}{\Lambda}$	$\dfrac{1}{\Lambda} = \dfrac{1}{L}$	1	$\dfrac{1}{\Lambda}$
Voltage, V'/V	$\dfrac{L^2}{\Lambda^2}$	1	L^2	$\dfrac{1}{\Lambda^2}$
Current density, i'/i	$\dfrac{L}{\Lambda^3}$	$\dfrac{1}{\Lambda^2} = \dfrac{1}{L^2}$	L	$\dfrac{1}{\Lambda^3}$
Current, I'/I	$\dfrac{L^3}{\Lambda^3}$	1	L^3	$\dfrac{1}{\Lambda^3}$
Power, P'/P	$\dfrac{L^5}{\Lambda^5}$	1	L^5	$\dfrac{1}{\Lambda^5}$
Power density, p'/p	$\dfrac{L^3}{\Lambda^5}$	$\dfrac{1}{\Lambda^2} = \dfrac{1}{L^2}$	L^3	$\dfrac{1}{\Lambda^5}$

The scaling ratios have been summarized in the *general scaling* column of Table 2.4. This column applies to tubes that have different dimensions *and* are operated at different wavelengths. It shows how the voltage, current, power, etc., in the scaled tube compare with corresponding quantities in the original tube. With the help of this tabulation, it is also possible to establish *scaling rules* which show at a glance how trajectory shapes and transit angles may be maintained by making appropriate changes in two or more operating characteristics. These scaling rules take the form of equations such as

$$\frac{V'}{B'^2 l'^2} = \frac{V}{B^2 l^2} \qquad \frac{V'^{\frac{3}{2}}}{i' l'^2} = \frac{V^{\frac{3}{2}}}{i l^2} \qquad \frac{V'^{\frac{3}{2}}}{I'} = \frac{V^{\frac{3}{2}}}{I}$$

and others, the method of making up a scaling rule being to obtain consistent equations when V'/V, B'/B, i'/i, etc., are replaced by the corresponding fractions in L and Λ from the general scaling column of Table 2.4.

The remaining three columns refer to special cases in scaling practice. In the very common case when the dimensions of an electron gun are changed in order to make operation at a different wavelength possible, the ratio of the dimensions is usually made equal to the ratio of the wavelengths ($\Lambda = L$); then the ratios in the *proportional scaling* column apply. Thus, the decrease of all dimensions by a third, to make the scaled tube suitable for operation at three times the frequency of the original tube, calls for a threefold increase in the magnetic field intensity. At the same time, the current density and the power density will each have been multiplied by 9. The extent to which proportional scaling may be carried out is thus limited by the current density which the cathode can supply and by the power per unit area which the tube is capable of dissipating.

If the scaled tube is intended for the same frequency and is merely changed in size (with an appropriate change in voltage to maintain the transit angle constant), the ratios of the *dimension scaling* column apply. For example, a tube which is doubled in size under this scheme will yield 32 times the power of the original tube. However, the voltage will have to be increased 4 times and the power density 8 times, so that scaling up on this basis is again limited by the allowable power dissipation as well as by the possibility of voltage breakdown.

Wavelength scaling ratios, given in the last column of Table 2.4, apply when a tube is to be operated at a different wavelength without a change in the dimensions. The constraints in this case are much too severe to allow any large variations: current density increases as the cube of the frequency, and power density as the fifth power of the frequency.

Scaling rules may, of course, be made up in the special cases characterized by the ratios given in the last three columns of Table 2.4 as well as in the general case, provided that the ratios given in one and the same column are used throughout the computation.

Finally, it is possible in some cases to resort to scaling in which only the shape of the trajectories is preserved but the transit angle is not. For example, it may not be very important whether the transit time across a klystron gap represents, say, one-twentieth of a wavelength or a slightly larger fraction. The scaling ratios used in this connection may deviate from those given in Table 2.4, but it is obviously not advisable to make the deviation very large.

2.7 Additional Considerations

The description of electron-beam behavior developed in the present chapter has been limited to the basic phenomena that are necessary for an understanding of the role that the electron beam plays in a microwave tube. In restricting the discussion to the fundamentals, we have omitted certain details that may be important to the designer but are, nevertheless, beyond the scope of the present treatment. Some of these additional considerations are briefly described below.

a. Curvilinear trajectories

The Pierce gun design technique depends on the assumption that electron flow is rectilinear at least part of the way from cathode to anode. This is a severe limitation in some cases, notably in the design of electron guns for crossed-field devices of the sort described in Chap. 10. The trajectories of electrons moving at right angles to mutually perpendicular electric and magnetic fields begin to curve as soon as the electrons leave the cathode. Methods of analyzing space-charge flow along curvilinear trajectories have been developed; they depend on the use of digital computers or of special electrolytic tanks in which currents are injected through probes arrayed along the bottom of the tank to simulate space charge. Resistance networks have also been successfully used in this connection.

b. Hollow beams

Radio-frequency interaction between a beam and a surrounding structure is strongest near the beam surface. This circumstance, together with several other practical considerations, has led to the employment of hollow beams in which an annular cross section is obtained from a similarly shaped cathode. For a convergent hollow beam, a solution utilizing space-charge-balanced flow is still possible, although the gun design is more difficult. In an alternate method known as Harris flow[1] a hollow beam originates from a shielded electron gun and is injected into the interaction region through a region of fringing magnetic field, where the beam acquires rotational motion. No magnetic field is required in the interaction region; instead, an inward force (to offset the two outward forces, space charge and centrifugal) is provided by a potential applied between the surrounding r-f structure and an electrode located along the axis, *inside* the hollow beam.

c. Thermal velocities

Electrons actually emerge from the cathode with nonzero velocities and at various angles, and their average velocity increases with temperature.[2] The assumption of laminar paths, implicit in all the above derivations, is thus violated by these thermal electrons, which cross the trajectories of other electrons and actually dictate the minimum diameter that a convergent beam may attain. In cases where the effects of thermal velocities are particularly severe, an alternate method of analyzing the beam shape has been developed: the problem is solved by means of an *optical model* of the electron beam. The observed periodic deviations from a smooth beam with a uniform charge density are accounted for with the help of the imaging phenomenon of optics.

[1] L. A. Harris, Axially Symmetric Electron Beam and Magnetic-field Systems, *Proc. IRE*, **40**:700–708 (1952).

[2] See, for instance, J. R. Pierce and L. R. Walker, "Brillouin Flow" with Thermal Velocities, *J. Appl. Phys.*, 24:1328–1330 (1953); and C. C. Cutler and M. E. Hines, Thermal Velocity Effects in Electron Guns, *Proc. IRE*, **43**:307–315 (1955).

d. Collectors

In its simplest form, the collection of electrons after the beam has passed through the interaction region is largely a problem of heat dissipation: electrons arriving at the collector, which is ordinarily at the same potential V_A as the accelerating anode and the r-f structure, represent power that must be dissipated, often by a water-cooled electrode. That power could be considerably reduced if the collector potential could be reduced, with a corresponding increase in over-all tube efficiency. The design of such practical *depressed collectors* is complicated by the fact that the velocities of electrons arriving in the collector region of a velocity-modulated tube are spread over a considerable range owing to the r-f signal, to say nothing of thermal velocities, so that not all electrons are decelerated to the same extent and some may be turned back. In most beam-type microwave tubes, the return of even a small portion of the electrons into the interaction region has a severe adverse effect on tube operation. Precautions must be taken to ensure that repelled electrons (as well as any secondary electrons originating in the collector region) are not returned into the interaction region. The solution usually requires the introduction of some deliberate asymmetry into the collector-region fields.[1]

[1] See, for instance, J. W. Hansen and C. Susskind, Improvement of Beam-tube Performance by Collector-potential Depression, and a Novel Design, *IRE Trans. Electron Devices*, **ED-7**: 282–288 (1960).

3

Basic Concepts of Interaction between Electrons and Fields

In this chapter some of the electronic processes that occur in high-frequency tubes will be discussed in an elementary fashion. As stated in the introductory chapter, several such processes generally occur in a high-frequency tube:

1. Velocity modulation of the electrons by an r-f field
2. Conversion of velocity modulation to density variation (i.e., into an r-f current) by some mechanism
3. Interaction of this r-f space current with an electromagnetic field in such a way as to retard the electrons and deliver energy to the field

Items 1 and 3 involve the interaction between electrons and electromagnetic fields and can conveniently be treated together. For item 2 the mechanism varies from tube to tube, and a somewhat different detailed treatment for each tube is therefore indicated. For items 1 and 3, various tube types differ only in configuration and in the extent of the region over which the interaction takes place; therefore, a more unified treatment is possible. For example, in klystrons and triodes the interaction usually takes place in a rather limited region, the dimensions of which are considerably smaller than a wavelength; whereas in the magnetron and the traveling-wave tube the interaction region may extend over a relatively large distance (several wavelengths).

In the following sections, we shall derive some of the general principles that govern the behavior of a beam of electrons in an electromagnetic field and the exchange of energy between the electron beam and the field. However, we shall restrict ourselves to applying the principles to the simplest configuration: the plane parallel gap. Many details which, though important, are not essential factors in the electron dynamics will be omitted. These details will be supplied in later chapters, where more complicated structures will also be considered. It will be convenient to derive some of these general principles by considering first the elementary and somewhat nonrigorous theory of a particularly simple electronic device and then using this theory as a framework for generalizing these principles. The klystron lends itself most readily to this kind of treatment, because the several electronic processes are clearly separated in the klystron. The various simplifications and approximations made in the analysis will be stated at appropriate places, and they will be reviewed at the end to establish what extensions must be made to make the analysis applicable to other tubes.

3.1 Elementary Theory of Velocity Modulation

Schematically, a klystron can be depicted as shown in Fig. 1.1. The two pairs of perforated plates form capacitances with an inductance connected across each pair, so that each combination forms a resonant circuit. As was stated in Chap. 1 such a diagram may be considered to be an actual representation of a circuit or a schematic version of a klystron cavity. (We prefer to leave out the cavity, since everything we shall say about electronic behavior is valid both for a lumped-constant circuit, such as shown here, and for a cavity. The cavity merely serves as a resonant circuit in a more efficient manner than a lumped-constant circuit at very high frequencies.) Let us imagine a beam, produced in the cathode-anode region and accelerated by a constant voltage V_0, passing through gap 1, which has across it a voltage $V_1 \sin \omega t$ (an r-f voltage unaffected by the beam). If we assume that the transit angle across the gap is zero, so that we may use the notion of an instantaneous voltage "seen" by the electron, then the electron, upon emerging from the gap at time t_1, has an energy given by

$$eV = eV_0\left(1 + \frac{V_1}{V_0}\sin \omega t_1\right) \tag{1}$$

Obviously, for any real tube (and particularly at high frequencies), the transit time across the gap is *not* zero. This fact must be taken into account in a more exact treatment. The relative magnitude of the transit time is most usefully specified not in seconds, but in fractions of a cycle of the frequency under consideration. Thus a transit of much less than one cycle can be considered as essentially equal to zero, whereas transit times corresponding to one-quarter of a cycle or more cannot be considered as negligible and must be taken into account. In what follows, however, we shall assume the gap spacing and frequency to be such that the transit time is a small fraction of a cycle and can be neglected.

The velocity v of the electron after it leaves the gap, under these restrictions, is given by

$$v = v_0 \sqrt{1 + \alpha \sin \omega t_1} \tag{2}$$

where v_0 is the injected velocity

$$v_0 = \sqrt{2\eta V_0} \tag{3}$$

and

$$\alpha \equiv \frac{V_1}{V_0} \tag{4}$$

The electrons enter a drift region and maintain the velocity they had upon leaving the gap. This simplification implies no interaction between electrons and a constant average potential in the drift region. If we assume that $\alpha \ll 1$, then (2) may be written as

$$v = v_0 \left(1 + \frac{\alpha}{2} \sin \omega t_1 \cdot \cdot \cdot \right) \tag{5}$$

Since successive electrons are not traveling with the same velocity when they leave the gap, bunching takes place: an electron which leaves the gap at a time corresponding to

$$\omega t = 2\pi n \qquad n = 0, 1, 2, \ldots \tag{6}$$

is preceded by electrons which have been decelerated and followed by electrons which have been accelerated. Therefore, a grouping of the electrons around this one takes place because of their relative velocities. From this simple description, it is obvious that the electrons do not arrive spaced uniformly in time at any subsequent position such as gap 2; rather, they arrive in groups or bunches which are periodic at the frequency of modulation existing at gap 1. To calculate the current flow at gap 2, we must know when the electrons arrive there, since the distribution of arrival times specifies the current. If a great many electrons arrive close together in time, a large current at that instant results; and conversely, when fewer than average arrive, the current is small. A diagram representing this nonuniformity in arrival times is quite illumi-

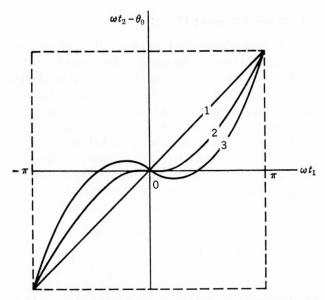

Fig. 3.1   Departure time of electrons from the first gap as a function of arrival time at the second gap.

nating (Fig. 3.1).   The arrival time of the electrons at the second gap is plotted as a function of the departure time from the first gap.   For convenience, the ordinate is $\omega t_2 - \theta_0$, where θ_0 is the average transit time for a nonmodulated electron from gap 1 to gap 2 and ωt_2 is the actual phase of its arrival.   If there were no modulation, $\omega t_2 - \theta_0$ would be equal to ωt_1, since the elapsed time between departure from gap 1 and arrival at gap 2 would be θ_0 (curve 1).   However, if there is modulation, then the picture is changed, as indicated by curve 2.   Electrons which left at a phase $\omega t_1 < 0$ arrive a little later than they would in the absence of modulation, that is, ωt_2 is larger.   Conversely, electrons which leave at a phase $\omega t_1 > 0$ (that is, electrons which are accelerated) arrive at the second gap earlier than in the absence of velocity modulation.   Curve 3 shows the same situation when the modulating voltage at the first gap has a still greater value than that for curve 2.   The spread in transit times from gap 1 to gap 2 is then greater.   Either curve 2 or curve 3 illustrates the bunching process described previously.   We see that in the neighborhood of $\omega t_1 = 0$ a large number of electrons which left over a wide interval of time arrive at the second gap in a much smaller interval of time; in other words, a large fraction of all the electrons leaving per cycle have arrived at the second gap in a much smaller fraction of time.   A plot that represents schematically the density of electrons arriving at the second gap as a function of ωt_2 is shown in Fig. 1.2.   This plot also illustrates the greater concentration around $\omega t_2 - \theta_0 = 0$.

3.2   General Current Equations

To calculate a numerical value for the current, we must compute the actual arrival time of the various electrons at gap 2. It can be seen that the arrival time must be somehow related to the current at the second gap, and we shall next try to express this relationship mathematically. The appropriate expression is formulated by means of the law of conservation of charge. All the charge that leaves gap 1 arrives at gap 2, but the amount of charge that passes through gap 1 during a given time interval dt_1 may take a larger or smaller time interval dt_2 to pass through gap 2, depending on the part of the arrival-time curves (Fig. 3.1) to which this charge corresponds. Quantitatively, we can say that during an infinitesimal interval of time dt_1, a total charge

$$dq = I_0 \, dt_1 \tag{7}$$

passes through gap 1 at a time t_1, where I_0 is the injected beam current. We follow the *same* particles (i.e., the same charge) through gap 2 at some later time t_2. These particles will pass through the second gap during an infinitesimal time interval dt_2, which may be shorter or longer than dt_1, depending on whether these particular electrons were in the bunch or half a cycle removed from it, respectively. In either case, the instantaneous current $I_2(t_2)$ due to this charge passing through gap 2 in the interval dt_2 is obtained from

$$dq = I_2 \, dt_2 \tag{8}$$

Obviously, the two charges are the same since we are following the same set of particles. Hence, due to this charge, there is a current through gap 2

$$I_2 = I_0 \frac{dt_1}{dt_2} \tag{9}$$

In addition to this compression or expansion of the time interval for the charges we are considering here, there may be several contributions to the current I_2 at the second gap at t_2 from different groups of charge with different t_1's that may have overtaken this particular group of charge in transit from gap 1 to 2. Therefore, the current I_2 at gap 2 must be summed over all the possible intervals dt_1 that may be contributing simultaneously to this current.

In using these equations for conservation of current, we are following specific particles from one region of space to another. Since, obviously, no particles are destroyed, we can make the statements about the current represented by these particles at two different positions (and at two different times). The treatment given here corresponds to the treatment of fluid flow using what is known as *Lagrangian* hydrodynamics. Equation (9) is the equation of continuity of charge in the Lagrangian formulation of hydrodynamics. There is another way of treating hydrodynamics, known as the *Eulerian* approach, in which one considers the flow of charge through fixed points of space and does not follow the same set of particles. In that case, one formulates the statement about the nondestruction of charge in other terms. As we shall see in later sections, this formulation may in many cases be a more convenient one. Appendix 1 describes the difference between these two formulations of hydrodynamics in somewhat greater detail.

It may be pointed out at this time that practically all that has been said so far is applicable to any tube, and not merely to the klystron used in the present illustration. Quite generally, in order to find the current at some position, we must know the arrival time of the electrons, and therefore Eq. (9) always applies. In a triode, for example, modulation occurs in the grid-cathode region, and one might be interested in evaluating the current as it flows past the grid by use of a relation such as Eq. (9). This relation also applies even if some of the electrons are turned back and never reach position 2; this condition would merely appear on a diagram such as Fig. 3.1 as a gap in the curve, corresponding to the nonarrival of electrons for a given initial starting phase.

Note also that Eq. (9) is an exact equation which applies under all conditions, including those of large r-f voltages and conditions under which the electrons pass each other in transit from position 1 to position 2. We shall find later, however, that in some cases one need not use this equation, but rather an equivalent expression which would apply under small-signal conditions and for noncrossing trajectories. Although the equations to be thus obtained are of more limited validity, they have the virtue of being simpler.

There is a close relation between the expression for the current given by Eq. (9) and the curves shown in Fig. 3.1. According to the equation, the current is large wherever the derivative is large. This statement agrees with our interpretation of the curves, since wherever the derivative is large, the curve is flat, indicating that the electrons which have left position 1 during a large interval of time arrive at position 2 in a much smaller interval of time and therefore give a large current at position 2. Indeed, there are places where the curve has a horizontal tangent, corresponding to an infinite derivative in the equation and an instantaneously infinite current density.[1] In terms of electron motion, infinite derivative means that faster electrons are just overtaking slower ones ahead of them. In curve 3, Fig. 3.1, there are two such positions of infinite derivative. They correspond to a situation in which electrons are passing one another just at the gap and in which a considerable

---

[1] No mathematical difficulty arises from this infinity, since the integral of the current density over any finite time interval results in a finite charge.

amount of overtaking has actually taken place for some electrons before reaching the gap.

We return now to consider not the general expression for the current, but rather its explicit form for the klystron. We are interested in this specific result not so much for its own sake, but rather as an illustration of the general method of using Eq. (9). As stated above, it is necessary to obtain an exact relation between t_2 and t_1. If an electron has velocity v when it leaves gap 1 and maintains this velocity, then its transit time to gap 2 is given by the expression

$$t_2 = t_1 + \frac{L}{v} = t_1 + \frac{L}{v_0 \sqrt{1 + \alpha \sin \omega t_1}} \tag{10}$$

where L is the distance between the gaps and v is given by Eq. (2). If we remember that $\theta_0 = \omega L / v_0$, and if we assume $\alpha \ll 1$, we may write approximately

$$\omega t_2 = \omega t_1 + \theta_0 \left(1 - \frac{\alpha}{2} \sin \omega t_1 \right) \tag{11}$$

This equation provides us with the relation between the arrival time t_2 at gap 2 for the particular group of charges which left gap 1 at the departure time t_1. If we were to substitute this relation (or rather its derivative) into Eq. (9), we should get the current at the second gap in a rather useless form, namely, as a function of t_1, which is the value of the time when the particular charges constituting the current left gap 1. Obviously, this is not the result in which one is interested. What is really of importance is the value of the current at gap 2 as a function of the time of its occurrence at gap 2, namely, t_2. It is possible to calculate this approximately for small values of α and θ_0 by differentiating Eq. (11) and substituting in Eq. (9). This procedure leads to

$$I_2 = \frac{I_0}{1 - \frac{1}{2}\alpha\theta_0 \cos \omega t_1} \approx I_0(1 + \frac{1}{2}\alpha\theta_0 \cos \omega t_1) \tag{12}$$

This equation is obviously still not in a useful form, since it also only gives the current at gap 2 in terms of departure times of the charges from gap 1. However, by using Eq. (11) again (to eliminate t_1) and using the fact that $\alpha \ll 1$, one can write approximately

$$I_2 = I_0[1 + \frac{1}{2}\alpha\theta_0 \cos (\omega t_2 - \theta_0)] \tag{12a}$$

where the terms that have been neglected in t_1 would have contributed only terms of the order of α^2 to the current I_2.

In the more general case where one wishes to calculate the current at the second gap without the limitations of small values of $\theta_0\alpha$, one can proceed in a somewhat different manner. It is obvious that what is required is a Fourier analysis of the current at the second gap as a function of the time at the second gap. Formally, one can write

$$I_2 = \sum_n (a_n \cos n\omega t_2 + b_n \sin n\omega t_2) \tag{13}$$

with the coefficients given by

$$a_n = \frac{1}{\pi} \int_{-\pi}^{\pi} I_2 \cos n\omega t_2 \, d(\omega t_2)$$

$$b_n = \frac{1}{\pi} \int_{-\pi}^{\pi} I_2 \sin n\omega t_2 \, d(\omega t_2)$$

The formal problem is to evaluate the integrals. Substituting for t_2 [from Eq. (11)] in the integrands would not result in a very useful form for the integrals, since t_1 and t_2 would both appear. However, a little consideration of the meaning of the integral for the Fourier coefficients simplifies the calculation. In performing the Fourier integration, each element of charge $I_2 \, dt_2$ is multiplied by the corresponding value of the cosine or sine for that particular value of time, t_2, and a summation over all elements of charge is carried out. This operation will obviously result in the same value for the integral regardless of whether t_1 or t_2 is used to label the various elements of charge in summing over all elements of charge. The cosine or the sine appropriate to the particular value of t_2 must be used, but the method of summing and indexing the various elements is not a unique one. Therefore, we can formally write a typical integral entirely in terms of t_1, which then reads

$$a_n = \frac{1}{\pi} \int_{-\pi}^{\pi} I_0 \cos n \left(\omega t_1 + \theta_0 - \theta_0 \frac{\alpha}{2} \sin \omega t_1 \right) d(\omega t_1) \tag{14}$$

where we have replaced $I_2 \, dt_2$ by $I_0 \, dt_1$ and the argument of the cosine by its value in terms of t_1. This substitution does not change the value of the integral but is merely a change of variables. Everything is now expressed in terms of a single variable. Furthermore, this substitution has the very important property that the integrand is a single-valued function of t_1, whereas if we had written the integral in terms of t_2, the integrand would have been in the general case a multiple-valued function of t_2. This fact was pointed out earlier and can be seen from curve 3 of Fig. 3.1. If we now expand this integral as follows,

$$a_n = \frac{1}{\pi} \int_{-\pi}^{\pi} I_0 \left[\cos n \left(\omega t_1 - \frac{\theta_0 \alpha}{2} \sin \omega t_1 \right) \cos n\theta_0 \right.$$
$$\left. - \sin n \left(\omega t_1 - \frac{\theta_0 \alpha}{2} \sin \omega t_1 \right) \sin n\theta_0 \right] d(\omega t_1) \tag{15}$$

the second term in this sum vanishes (because it is an odd function of t_1), and the first term yields $2I_0J_n(n\alpha\theta_n/2) \cos n\theta_0$, where J_n is the Bessel function of order n. An exactly parallel treatment for b_n yields $2I_0J_n(n\alpha\theta_0/2) \sin n\theta_0$. By combining terms of the same frequencies in Eq. (13), we obtain for the current at the second gap,

$$I_2 = \sum_n 2I_0J_n(nx) \cos n(\omega t_2 - \theta_0) \tag{16}$$

where

$$x \equiv \frac{\theta_0\alpha}{2} \tag{17}$$

It should be pointed out here that this method of evaluating the integral extends the validity of the result even to curves such as curve 3 in Fig. 3.1, which correspond to electrons having passed each other on their way to gap 2. That is, the analysis applies even to cases in which there are infinite densities at certain points in the beam. In making this calculation, however, we have completely neglected the interaction between the electrons, i.e., the space-charge forces in the drift tube. Actually, the motion of an electron in the drift tube is not merely a constant-velocity drift, as is implied in the derivation of Eq. (10); rather, there are changes in an electron's velocity due to the forces exerted by the other electrons. If the effect of these space-charge forces is considered, the calculation can still be made, but under much more restricted conditions than above. Moreover, the calculation cannot then be extended by any simple method to the case where electrons pass each other. If one neglects space-charge forces, however, then the above calculation is completely valid.

It should also be emphasized that the use of the relation between I_0 and I_2 is perfectly general, and the steps in making the Fourier analysis are perfectly general, even though for other kinds of structures an analytic evaluation may be much more difficult. However, if an equation corresponding to Eq. (10) for the t_2-t_1 relation can be obtained, a graphical Fourier analysis of the resulting curves is always possible. In a klystron, for example, if large signals exist at gap 1, so that $\alpha \ll 1$ no longer applies, Eq. (11) cannot be deduced from Eq. (10). Equation (10) may still be used to plot curves of t_2 versus t_1, however, and the current can be computed graphically.

3.3 Transfer of Energy

Having calculated the r-f current at the second gap, we must now calculate the effect of this current on the circuit that is connected across the gap. This calculation may be made by using the law of conservation of energy; i.e., the work done by the charges appears in the circuit. If the

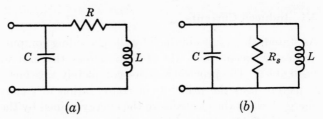

(a)   *(b)*

Fig. 3.2 Equivalent circuits illustrating energy transfer in electron tubes.

voltage across the second cavity is $V_2 \cos (\omega t_2 - \theta_0 - \beta)$, then work done by any charge q is given by

$$dW = qV_2 \cos (\omega t_2 - \theta_0 - \beta) = I_2 V_2 \cos (\omega t_2 - \theta_0 - \beta) \, dt_2 \quad (18)$$

Integration of Eq. (18) over a cycle yields for the power delivered to the circuit

$$P = \frac{1}{2\pi} \int_{-\pi}^{\pi} I_2 V_2 \cos (\omega t_2 - \theta_0 - \beta) \, d(\omega t_2) = \frac{V_2 [2I_0 J_1(x)] \cos \beta}{2} \quad (19)$$

Here again we have ignored the fact that the transit time of the electrons across the gap may not be negligible, so that one cannot really speak of an instantaneous voltage seen by a particular electron or group of electrons. This anomaly can be remedied, as we shall see later.

The expression we have just derived is the same as would be found for a resonant circuit across gap 2 driven by a constant-current generator (Fig. 3.2a) with current of magnitude $2I_0 J_1(x) \cos (\omega t_2 - \theta_0)$ and with a voltage $V_2 \cos (\omega t_2 - \theta_0 - \beta)$. Actually, a cavity or an LC circuit has losses (1) because of the resistance in the walls in the case of a cavity, or because of the coil resistance in the case of the lumped-constant circuit; and more importantly, (2) because of the useful load coupled to cavity or circuit. A more useful equivalent circuit would be that shown in Fig. 3.2b. If the series resistance is given by R, one can establish an equivalent shunt resistance given by $R_s = \omega^2 L^2 / R$. For such an equivalent circuit the definition of R_s is consistent only if the power dissipated in the circuit is given by $V^2 / 2R_s$. Since the power delivered is given by $I_0 J_1(x) V_2 \cos \beta$, the consequence of the above relations must be that the voltage is given by $V_2 = 2I_0 J_1(x) R_s \cos \beta$, and such an equivalent circuit therefore yields the correct answers.[1]

---

[1] Furthermore, just as in the circuit shown in Fig. 3.2b, the relative phase angle β between the voltage and the driving current is given by the phase angle of the impedance presented by the circuit at the frequency of the driving current: $\beta = \tan^{-1} (X/R_s)$. For the resonant circuit shown, the phase angle would be simply $\beta = \tan^{-1} [2Q(\omega - \omega_0)/\omega_0]$, where Q is the quality factor and ω_0 is the resonant frequency of the circuit.

3.4 Induced Currents

As stated, the result obtained by the preceding computation is completely accurate, except that transit time across the gap was assumed to be negligible. The procedure is not completely satisfactory, however, since it merely uses the principle of conservation of energy and equates the energy lost by the electrons to the energy gained by the circuit or electromagnetic field. It would be much more satisfactory if one could show the detailed mechanism of the interaction between the electrons and the circuit. There is an alternative method of calculation which gives the same result and at the same time shows what actually happens in the circuit when the electrons pass through the gap. This method[1] uses the concept of induced current, and is based on the fact that when a charge moves in the neighborhood of any electrode, a current flows to or from the electrode, depending on the details of the motion of the charge in its neighborhood. This flow of current follows in an obvious way from the fact that any charge in the neighborhood of an electrode induces charges on the electrode. As the external charge moves, a change in the induced charge, corresponding to a flow of current, is produced.

Some mention of the motion of a charge resulting in an induced current in the electrode was made in Chap. 1, where it was pointed out that in a triode the current in the plate circuit flows *during* the transit of the electron across the output gap, and not when the electron strikes the plate. However, in low-frequency tubes, because of the relatively short transit time and the relation of the induced current to the inducing charge, the conventional method (which tacitly assumes that the current flows when the electron strikes) nevertheless gives the right answer. Such an induced current will also flow in the input gap; i.e., if electrons move across the gap, they produce a current in the circuit. The presence of current in the input gap (if the transit time is considered to be finite) leads to a phenomenon called beam loading in klystrons and grid loading in triodes.

For the output gap, use of the induced-current concept leads to a more detailed picture of the exchange of energy. To determine how to calculate this induced current, we shall consider first what happens in a very simple configuration and then generalize the calculation to more complicated forms of electrodes.

Consider a pair of parallel planes a distance d apart, as shown in Fig. 3.3, joined by a conductor so that both are at the same potential. A sheet of charge containing a charge density q per unit area moves from plate a to plate b with a velocity v. A field E_1 exists between plane a

---

[1] W. Shockley, Currents Induced by a Moving Charge, *J.Appl.Phys.*, **9**:635–636 (1938), and S. Ramo, Currents Induced by Electron Motion, *Proc. IRE*, **27**:584–585 (1939).

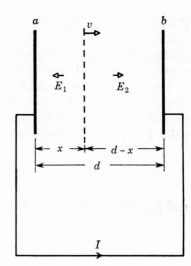

Fig. 3.3   Basic configuration for the calculation of induced current.

and the sheet, and a field E_2 between the sheet and plane b.   For negative charge, both fields are directed toward the sheet.   If the sheet is at a distance x from a (and $d - x$ from b), the following relationship exists for the plate potentials V_a and V_b:

$$V_a - V_b = E_1 x + E_2(d - x) = 0 \tag{20}$$

The charge density induced on plate a is $q_a = \epsilon_0 E_1$, and that on b is $q_b = -\epsilon_0 E_2$, with the additional relationship that

$$q_b + q_a = -q \tag{21}$$

Since

$$E_2 = -\frac{E_1 x}{d - x} \tag{22}$$

we have

$$q_b = \frac{q_a x}{d - x} \tag{23}$$

or

$$q_a = -q\,\frac{d - x}{d} \tag{24}$$

As the sheet of charge moves across at a velocity v, the distance x changes and hence the charges on each plate change, but in such a way that the potential difference between the two plates remains zero.   The rate of change of the charge on either plate must be equal to the current that flows in the connecting conductor.   In other words, since the total charge on the two plates is always constant and equal to the charge in the moving sheet, as expressed by Eq. (21), when charge leaves plate a, it must move to plate b·and thus provide a current I per unit area of the plates given by

$$I = -\frac{dq_a}{dt} = q\,\frac{d}{dt}\frac{d - x}{d} = -\frac{q}{d}v \tag{25}$$

since $v = dx/dt$. Equation (25) yields the value of the induced current produced by the moving charge q, in terms of velocity and of electrode configuration (spacing d), which are factors involved for *any* electrode configuration. It is convenient to put this equation in the same form as that derived for a completely general configuration in Appendix 2. If the electrode at d were maintained at a potential V_1' with *no* charge present between the plates, then the gradient of the potential V_p' at any point P between the electrodes would be $\nabla V_p' = V_1'/d$ or

$$\frac{1}{d} = \frac{\nabla V_p'}{V_1'}$$

and Eq. (25) can then be written as

$$I = -qv\frac{\nabla V_p'}{V_1'} \tag{26}$$

which is the general equation derived in Appendix 2.

3.5 Total Current

In discussing the flow of these currents to the electrodes, it is convenient to introduce at this point the notion of total current, or total current density. This is a very fundamental concept in any discussion of tube behavior. Two equations will be used in the derivation of total current. Let i represent the current density (or, more exactly, the convection current density) due to the actual motion of charges, either in space or in a conductor, and let ρ be the charge density. It should be pointed out at this time that in the ensuing analysis of current flow and charge density our point of view will change from the Lagrangian approach utilized in the earlier sections of this chapter to the Eulerian form of hydrodynamics (see Appendix 1). Previously, we have always followed a particular group of charges from one location to another and traced the manner in which the currents represented by *these* charges changed as we followed the group through space because of the changes (contraction or expansion) in the volume occupied by them and in their velocity. Now we shall consider the current density everywhere in space as a function of time, not following particular charges but examining the current as a function of the coordinates. That is, in talking about current at any point in space, the current is now constituted by different groups of charges passing through at different times. We no longer follow individual charges. The change from the Lagrangian to the Eulerian approach means that current and charge density are now field variables (i.e., functions of the coordinates and time) and not associated with particular charges. Keeping this change in point of view in mind, we can see that the equation that must be satisfied by i and ρ is

$$\nabla \cdot \mathbf{i} + \frac{\partial \rho}{\partial t} = 0 \tag{27}$$

where $\mathbf{i} = \rho \mathbf{v}$. This is the equation of continuity, which merely states that no charge is destroyed; it is the equivalent for Eulerian variables of Eq. (9) for Lagrangian variables.

The other equation that we need is

$$\epsilon_0 \nabla \cdot \mathbf{E} = \rho \tag{28}$$

This equation states how the total flux of field from an infinitesimal volume is related to the charge within that volume. If we take the time derivative of Eq. (28) and combine it with Eq. (27), we obtain the relation

$$\nabla \cdot \left(\epsilon_0 \frac{\partial \mathbf{E}}{\partial t} + \mathbf{i} \right) = 0 \tag{29}$$

By use of the divergence theorem for vector fields, Eq. (29) may be written

$$\int_\tau \nabla \cdot \left(\epsilon_0 \frac{\partial \mathbf{E}}{\partial t} + \mathbf{i} \right) d\tau = \int_s \left(\epsilon_0 \frac{\partial \mathbf{E}}{\partial t} + \mathbf{i} \right) \cdot \mathbf{ds} = \int_s \mathbf{i}_A \cdot \mathbf{ds} = 0 \tag{30}$$

The quantity i_A is known as the *total current density*. It contains two terms. The first is $i = \rho v$, the *convection current density*, and the second is $\epsilon_0 \, \partial E / \partial t$, which is known as the *displacement current density*. In differential form, the equation implies that there is no outward flow of the total current density from any volume. Stated (perhaps more usefully) in the integral form (29), the equation implies that for any closed surface, the net outward flow of the total current density is always zero. In other words, if we divide any *closed* surface into two singly connected portions by drawing a closed curve around the surface, the normal component of the current integrated over one surface must be equal and opposite to that over the other. For example, if we consider a sphere (Fig. 3.4) which is cut by a plane as shown, the outward currents across surfaces dS_1 and dS_2 must be equal and opposite. As a more pertinent example, consider two electrodes (Fig. 3.5) with some moving charges in the region between them. Across the surface S_1, through which the wire passes, there is a current I'. (This current is almost entirely convection current, since the displacement current in a conductor is very small.) Therefore, through the surface S_2, or S_3, or any similar surface, there must also be a current I'. This current may consist of displacement current, convection current, or both. In any case, the total current must be continuous.

How is this concept of total current related to the previous discussion

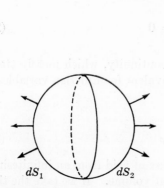

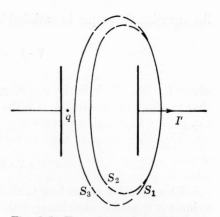

Fig. 3.4 Sphere cut by plane: total current flow through each portion is the same.

Fig. 3.5 Two electrodes with moving charge in between. Total current across any intersecting surface is the same.

about the induced current produced by moving charges? Consider the current I' in the wire, as shown in Fig. 3.5. Obviously, such a current may exist in the external circuit even in the absence of any charges moving in the space between the electrodes (e.g., there may be a current from an external generator). In addition, there may be a contribution to I' because of moving charges. It is this contribution that constitutes the induced current mentioned previously. In the region of space where the charge is *not* present, the contribution to total current due to this moving charge is in the form of displacement current. At a surface across which the charge is moving, such as S_3, there are in general two contributions: one owing to the moving charge itself (convection current) and another owing to the change in the electric field ($\epsilon_0 \, \partial E/\partial t$) caused by the motion of the charge (displacement current). That is, at a time t_1 the moving charge is on one side of the surface and at a time $t_1 + \Delta t$ it is on the other side. Therefore, during the time interval Δt, the total flux of E (owing to the charge) across the surface changes, and thus there is a contribution arising from this term also.

3.6 Electron Motion in a High-velocity Gap

Let us apply the notion of the total current to the simplest case of plane structure: a pair of parallel, plane electrodes of large enough area (compared with spacing between them) that fringing fields can be neglected. Then both convection currents and displacement currents depend only on x, the coordinate normal to the planes. The total convection current is given by $I = i_x A$, and the total displacement current by $\epsilon_0(\partial E/\partial t)A$, where A is the area. For this case, then, the theorem (29) for the continuity of total current may be written in the form

$$\frac{\partial}{\partial x}\left(I + \epsilon_0 \frac{\partial E}{\partial t} A\right) = 0 \tag{31}$$

or
$$I + \epsilon_0 \frac{\partial E}{\partial t} A = I_A \tag{32}$$

where I_A is the total current, independent of x but still dependent on t. This relationship also follows from the integral form for the conservation of total current if we use as the surface s any two planes s_1, s_2 plus the sidewalls joining them. Since both displacement current and convection current are zero across the sidewalls, by virtue of our original condition, it follows that the total current across each plane must be the same, independent of x.

If we solve Eq. (32) for I, integrate both sides from $x = 0$ to $x = d$ (where d is the distance between the planes), and divide by d, we obtain the relation

$$\bar{I} \equiv \frac{1}{d}\int_0^d I\, dx = I_A - \frac{A\epsilon_0}{d}\int_0^d \frac{\partial E}{\partial t}\, dx \tag{33}$$

which can be written in the form

$$\bar{I} = I_A + C \frac{dV}{dt} \tag{34}$$

since $A\epsilon_0/d = C$ is the capacitance of the capacitor formed by the two planes and the integral $-\int_0^d E\, dx$ is just the voltage V between the planes. The equation derived in this fashion is a very significant one, because it gives a rigorous relation between the current and voltage in the circuit and the space current between the electrodes. It can be represented by an equivalent circuit such as shown in Fig. 3.6, where $\bar{I}$ is the driving current delivered by the current generator, I_A is the current which then flows in the external circuit, and the current through the capacitor is $C\, dV/dt$.

It thus appears that part of the problem, for any gap, is to calculate this driving current $\bar{I}$ by solving the equation of motion of the electrons in the gap to get I and then averaging. However, Eq. (34) does not completely determine the whole problem. This equation involves two circuit

Fig. 3.6 Simple equivalent circuit of high-velocity gap.

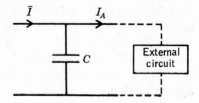

quantities, V and I_A. There is, however, another relation between V and I_A, determined by the external admittance: $Y = I_A/V$. Substitution of this relation in Eq. (34) yields

$$\bar{I} = VY + C\frac{dV}{dt} \tag{35}$$

This is a *circuit* equation stating how the voltage is determined by the space current. The space current in turn depends on the voltage across the gap, as expressed through a dynamical or *electronic* equation. The actual values of $\bar{I}$ and V must be compatible with both of these relationships.

The first problem in any gap, then, is to calculate the driving current; i.e., first calculate I and then the average value over the gap.   In general, I consists of three parts.   The first is due to the injected r-f current, and the second arises as a result of an r-f variation in the velocity at the entrance.   (These two terms may be grouped together as an "exciting" current due to sources outside the gap and independent of the gap voltage.)   The third part arises from the velocity modulation of the electrons by the gap voltage and is proportional, within the limits of a linear approximation, to the r-f voltage.

Having carried through the dynamical problem which determines the driving current, we may then substitute the results in Eq. (35) to determine completely all the operating conditions. We shall carry through a detailed calculation for the case in which there is no constant voltage across the gap.   (A similar calculation may be carried out for the case when either accelerating or decelerating d-c voltages are present.)   In this calculation, several approximations will be made; they can also be made in the more general case when accelerating voltages are present. First, this will be a small-signal theory in which we shall neglect all quadratic terms in r-f amplitudes.   Thus the final results involve functions of the d-c transit angles multiplied by r-f amplitudes; and the terms which are neglected in general arise from corrections in the transit time across the gap due to the r-f, multiplied by these same r-f amplitudes.   Moreover, we shall neglect space-charge effects. Since the r-f space current in the gap varies over the gap, an r-f field exists there because of the variations in charge density. Instead, we shall assume that the r-f field at any time is independent of x and has the same value at all points in the gap. This approximation means that only the contributions to the r-f field arising from charges on the plates are taken into account, and not those arising from space-charge effects. If the charge density is small enough (i.e., at sufficiently high velocities in the gap), this approximation is not bad; furthermore, as we shall see in Chap. 5, one can also perform a similar calculation without this approximation.

Let us now proceed with the calculation of the driving current.   (We shall make the calculation in terms of current densities.)   Consider a plane parallel gap with a voltage across the gap given by

$$V_2 - V_1 = V e^{j\omega t} \tag{36}$$

and a current density injected through plane 1 of the form

$$i_1 = i_0 + i' e^{j\omega t} \tag{37}$$

with initial velocity

$$v = v_0 + v' e^{j\omega t} \tag{38}$$

The field is given by

$$E = -\frac{V}{d} e^{j\omega t} \tag{39}$$

and the equation of motion of a charge e is

$$\ddot{x} = \eta \frac{V}{d} e^{j\omega t} \tag{40}$$

Integration, and the initial condition that $\dot{x} = v_0 + v' e^{j\omega t_1}$ when the electron enters at $x = 0$ (at $t = t_1$), yields

$$\dot{x} = j\eta \frac{V}{\omega d} (e^{j\omega t} - e^{j\omega t_1}) + v_0 + v' e^{j\omega t_1} \tag{41}$$

Another integration, and the condition that $t = t_1$ at $x = 0$, gives

$$x = \eta \frac{V}{\omega^2 d} [e^{j\omega t} - e^{j\omega t_1} - je^{j\omega t_1}(\omega t - \omega t_1)] + \frac{v_0 + v' e^{j\omega t_1}}{\omega} (\omega t - \omega t_1) \tag{42}$$

The above integrations involve no approximations. Before we proceed to the next step, let us recall again what it is that we wish to determine from this calculation. We are trying to find the convection-current density $i(x,t)$ at the plane x at the time t. To do so, we shall use the same relation for the current as was used in Sec. 3.2; it is based on the conservation of charge. At a time t, the charge passing through the plane at x in an interval dt is the same as the charge which passed through the plane at $x = 0$ at the time t_1 in an interval of time dt_1. If the current density at the plane $x = 0$ is i_1, the charge crossing this plane in an interval of time dt_1 is $i_1 dt_1$. At any other plane x, then,

$$i(x,t) \, dt = i_1 \, dt_1 \tag{43}$$

Therefore, to find the current at a plane x at the time t, it is necessary to find the relation between t and t_1 for the group of charge that we are following. However, this is exactly information given by Eq. (42), which can be considered as a relation determining the value of the arrival time t at the plane x of the electron that left the plane 0 at t_1.

Stated differently, if we *fix* the value of x, Eq. (42) gives us a relation for the time of arrival of successive electrons at x as a function of their time of departure from the original plane. That is, we must invert Eq. (42) and solve it for t as a function of t_1 at a fixed x, from which we can then find the necessary relationship to substitute into Eq. (43). This procedure is entirely analogous to that used in deriving Eqs. (10) to (12), except that here we are interested in finding such relations not only at one plane at some distance L but at all planes between the input and output planes of the gap.

It is difficult to perform the required inversion of Eq. (42) exactly, but one can make approximations that would be valid over a wide range of practical conditions and that would yield analytical results in a quite straightforward manner. The inversion is difficult because of the exponentials that involve the unknown value of t. All of these exponentials are multiplied, however, by the amplitude of the r-f voltage. For small amplitudes, we may neglect the modification in the transit time caused by r-f voltages and velocities in calculating the effect of the r-f voltage. This procedure amounts to using values of t corresponding to the d-c transit time in the exponentials. Further comments on the method follow the derivation of the final equation. Let us define

$$T \equiv \omega t \qquad T_1 \equiv \omega t_1 \tag{44}$$

$$\theta \equiv \frac{\omega x}{v_0} \qquad D \equiv \frac{\omega d}{v_0} \tag{45}$$

$$T - T_1 \equiv \theta + \delta \tag{46}$$

where θ is the d-c transit time to the plane x, D is the d-c transit time to the plane d, and $T - T_1$ is the transit time under r-f conditions. Thus δ is the small r-f quantity which represents the change in the motion resulting from initial r-f velocity and velocity modulation by the gap voltage. In terms of this notation, Eq. (42) can be written as

$$T - T_1 = \frac{\omega x}{v_0 + v'e^{jT_1}} - \frac{\eta V e^{jT}}{\omega d(v_0 + v'e^{jT_1})} [1 - e^{-j(\theta+\delta)} - je^{-j(\theta+\delta)}(\theta + \delta)] \tag{47}$$

The expansions

$$e^{-j\delta} = 1 - j\delta + \cdots \tag{48}$$

and

$$\frac{1}{v_0 + v'e^{jT_1}} = \frac{1}{v_0}\left(1 - \frac{v'}{v_0} e^{jT_1} + \cdots\right) \tag{49}$$

and the omission of all except linear terms in the r-f quantities yield

$$T - T_1 = \frac{\omega x}{v_0}\left(1 - \frac{v'}{v_0} e^{jT}e^{-j\theta}\right) + \frac{V}{2V_0 D} e^{jT}(1 - e^{-j\theta} - j\theta e^{-j\theta}) \tag{50}$$

Terms of the form $v'\delta$, $V\delta$, etc., have been omitted. The factor $V/2V_0D$

replaces $\eta V/\omega \, dv_0$ as a result of Eqs. (45) and the relation for the d-c velocity, $v_0 = (2\eta V_0)^{\frac{1}{2}}$, where V_0 is the d-c acceleration voltage.

It is to be observed that all terms involving δ on the right-hand side have disappeared. This is the result of the fact that in the original equation arising from the expansion of Eq. (47), δ depends everywhere on the r-f amplitudes and would have appeared multiplied by another r-f amplitude. The resulting quadratic correction may be omitted within the limits of our approximation; then all the terms on the right except the first $(\omega x/v_0)$ constitute the first-order value of δ.

According to Eq. (50), $T - T_1$ is determined by the original velocity plus a linear correction term owing to the r-f voltage. In computing the effect of this r-f voltage, the transit time that appears in this correction is the d-c transit time. This procedure yields a first-order correction to the d-c motion. If this first-order r-f correction were added to the transit time and the computation repeated, the resulting correction would be of the second order, and presumably very small. One could obtain such higher-order terms by successive approximations, but it is usually not necessary. The method may be justified by the following qualitative argument. The electron actually arrives at any plane x at a time depending on its original d-c velocity plus whatever r-f velocity it has picked up on its way to the plane x, either from the r-f field or because of an injection velocity. The effect of the r-f field should be calculated at the plane x at this proper arrival time. However, if the corrections to the arrival time owing to the r-f fields are very small, one can approximately calculate the effect of the r-f field as if the electron moved to the plane x with its original d-c velocity. This procedure results in omitting quadratic corrections to the velocity and to the transit time which, within our approximation, will be negligible. Even if they are not negligible, we can make the first-order calculation, add it to the original d-c calculation, and reiterate the process. This method is quite generally employed and yields useful results the validity of which depends essentially on how well the inequalities $v'/v_0 \ll 1$ and $V/2V_0D \ll 1$ are met.

From Eq. (50) we may obtain the derivative

$$\frac{dT_1}{dT} = 1 + j\theta \frac{v'}{v_0} e^{-j\theta} e^{jT} - j \frac{V}{2V_0D} e^{jT}(1 - e^{-j\theta} - j\theta e^{-j\theta}) \qquad (51)$$

and from the current-density relation (43),

$$i = (i_0 + i'e^{-j\theta}e^{jT}) \frac{dT_1}{dT}$$

$$i = i_0 + i'e^{-j\theta}e^{jT} + i_0 j\theta \frac{v'}{v_0} e^{-j\theta}e^{jT} - j \frac{i_0 V}{2V_0D} (1 - e^{-j\theta} - j\theta e^{-j\theta})e^{jT} \qquad (52)$$

Let us examine this equation term by term. The first term is the average current density, and the remaining terms represent the r-f convection-current density at the plane x. The second corresponds to the injected r-f current density. This component comprises the main part of the current density through the output gap of a triode, tetrode, or klystron, and it is the main source of power delivered to such a gap. The r-f portion of the injected current density is given by $i'e^{jT}$, multiplied by the phase factor $e^{-j\theta}$, to describe the transit time from the entrance plane to the plane x. In other words, the current density at x at the time $T_1 + \theta$ is the same as that at the entrance plane at the time T_1. The contribution to the *average* space-current density in Eq. (33) arising from this term (if we omit the factor e^{jT}) is given by

$$\bar{i'} = \frac{1}{d} \int_0^d i'e^{-j\theta}\,dx = \frac{v_0}{\omega d} \int_0^D i'e^{-j\theta}\,d\theta$$

$$= \frac{i'}{D} j(e^{-jD} - 1) = -\frac{i'}{D/2} e^{-jD/2} \frac{1}{2j} (e^{-jD/2} - e^{jD/2})$$

$$\bar{i'} = i'e^{-jD/2} \frac{\sin (D/2)}{D/2} = i'e^{-jD/2}M \tag{53}$$

where we have defined

$$M \equiv \frac{\sin (D/2)}{D/2} \tag{54}$$

This factor is called the *beam-coupling coefficient* (sometimes also designated as *gap factor* or *modulation factor*). It represents the reduction in the effect of the injected current owing to a nonzero transit angle. We can say that the effect of the injected current is the same as that in a zero-width gap, with a phase factor corresponding to the center of the gap but reduced by the factor M. This reduction factor arises from the fact that with a finite transit angle, r-f current components of various phases are present in the gap at all times, and the instantaneous effect of these components at any given time is somewhat reduced because they are not all in the same phase. The simplest example which illustrates this phenomenon is that in which the transit angle corresponds to a full cycle. In this case, all phases of the injection current are present in the gap at any time and one might expect that the average contribution to the driving current will be zero. Indeed, $M = 0$ for this case. For a transit angle corresponding to less than a full cycle, this factor is not zero, but it is still considerably reduced from unity.

The third term in Eq. (52) arises from bunching in the gap due to an r-f component of *velocity* at the entrance plane. This term is usually small; but for the sake of generality we include it, since it is as easily calculated as the other terms. Moreover, it may be readily correlated with the results of simple bunching theory (Sec. 3.1). The electron velocity in a beam velocity-modulated by a voltage $V \sin \omega t_1$ is given by

$$v = v_0 \sqrt{1 + \frac{V}{V_0} \sin \omega t_1} \approx v_0 \left(1 + \frac{V}{2V_0} \sin \omega t_1 \right) \tag{55}$$

In terms of our notation for r-f velocity,

$$v' = \frac{v_0 V}{2V_0} \tag{56}$$

The current density arising from velocity modulation at a distance x from the point of modulation is given by

$$2i_0 J_1 \left(\frac{\omega x V}{2v_0 V_0} \right) = 2i_0 J_1 \left(\frac{\theta V}{2V_0} \right) \tag{57}$$

and for small arguments, $J_1(z) \approx z/2$, so that

$$i_0 \frac{\theta V}{2V_0} = i_0 \frac{v'}{v_0} \theta \tag{58}$$

which is precisely the amplitude of the third term in Eq. (52). We shall not calculate the average current density due to injected velocity (which we might call $\bar{i_v}$), because it is usually not significant. It may be pointed out that this term is in quadrature with the r-f velocity which gives rise to it; this property is common to all currents arising from the velocity modulation.

The fourth term in Eq. (52) is proportional, within the limits of our linear approximation, to the gap voltage; the proportionality constant depends on the d-c conditions (current and voltage) and on the gap spacing. We find the space average of this term (again omitting e^{jT}) to be given by

$$\bar{i_V} = j \frac{G_0}{D} V e^{-jD/2} \left[\cos (D/2) - \frac{\sin (D/2)}{D/2} \right] \tag{59}$$

where we have defined

$$G_0 \equiv \frac{i_0}{V_0} \tag{60}$$

This factor is called the *beam conductance*. The effect which gives rise to the component given by Eq. (59) is sometimes called *beam loading* or *grid loading*. It arises from velocity modulation of the electrons by the gap voltage and the consequent bunching in the gap.

The average r-f driving-current density $\bar{i}$ may be therefore written as a sum of the average values of the three terms in Eq. (52):

$$\bar{i} = \bar{i'} + \bar{i_v} + \bar{i_V} \tag{61}$$

In terms of the equivalent circuit of Fig. 3.6 (with C redefined to represent capacitance per unit area), we can rewrite Eq. (34) as

$$\bar{i'} + \bar{i_v} + \bar{\bar{i_V}} = i_A + C\frac{dV}{dt} \tag{62}$$

from which we obtain

$$\bar{i'} + \bar{i_v} = i_A + C\frac{dV}{dt} - \bar{\bar{i_V}} \tag{63}$$

In this equation, the left-hand side represents the *exciting current density* from sources *outside* the gap; the last term on the right-hand side is proportional to the r-f voltage. We may therefore introduce an admittance per unit area defined by

$$-\bar{\bar{i_V}} \equiv Y_B V \tag{64}$$

so that Eq. (63) becomes

$$\bar{i'} + \bar{i_v} = i_A + C\frac{dV}{dt} + Y_B V \tag{65}$$

The gap may be thus represented by the equivalent circuit of Fig. 3.7, in which all the loading effects of the r-f voltage are contained in the admittance defined by Eq. (64). This admittance may be separated into real and imaginary components,

$$Y_B = G_B + jB_B \tag{66}$$

For the case under consideration, the conductance G_B and the susceptance B_B are obtained from a comparison of Eqs. (66) with (64) and (59):

$$\frac{G_B}{G_0} = \frac{1}{2}\frac{\sin{(D/2)}}{D/2}\left[\frac{\sin{(D/2)}}{D/2} - \cos{(D/2)}\right] \tag{67}$$

$$\frac{B_B}{G_0} = \frac{1}{2}\frac{\cos{(D/2)}}{D/2}\left[\frac{\sin{(D/2)}}{D/2} - \cos{(D/2)}\right] \tag{68}$$

Of these two terms, G_B represents a net power transfer from a d-c beam to the circuit. The r-f voltage across the gap produces, by velocity-modulating the electrons, a contribution $(\bar{i_v})$ to $\bar{i}$, and the component of $\bar{i_V}$ 0° or 180° out of phase with the voltage results in a power transfer to the beam. Note that this power can be positive or negative. In the latter case, oscillation is possible. B_B represents a related interaction corresponding to a reactive flow of power from the beam due to the component of $\bar{i_V}$ that is in quadrature with V.

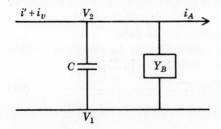

Fig. 3.7   Equivalent circuit of high-velocity gap, showing effect of beam loading.

4

Space-charge Waves

In this chapter, we shall consider the effects of the interaction between electrons. We shall consider principally space-charge effects in electron beams of a particular kind, namely, those in which the average velocity of the beam is constant, independent of its transverse or axial coordinates. This restriction corresponds to assuming that no constant electric fields are present or that the beam is so constrained that no acceleration or deceleration of the beam takes place in the absence of r-f modulation. This limitation leads to a relatively simple analysis of space-charge effects. The results, although related to those obtained by the different approach of Llewellyn and Peterson (Chap. 5), are in a different form and, for the special case considered, are valid over large ranges of the parameters.

The method is generally known as *space-charge-wave analysis*. Before performing any detailed computation, it is worthwhile to consider the basic phenomena that occur in electron beams of this kind. Under various special circumstances, these same phenomena lead to a wide variety of results and numerical characteristics.   It is easiest to describe the basic phenomena in terms of a stationary electron cloud.   If the electrons are moving at a steady velocity, the same phenomenon occurs in a coordinate system moving with the electrons, so that everything that is said about the stationary cloud applies directly to a moving stream.

For such an electron cloud, with suitable imposed conditions, a steady-state configuration thus exists, so that there is no net force on the electrons.   Such a condition may consist of the presence of a strong ("infinite") magnetic field, or of a neutralizing cloud of positive ions. In the former case the strong magnetic field would prevent any transverse motion that might arise from the electrostatic forces produced by the unneutralized space charge; in the latter case the average electric field is zero.   If the cloud is disturbed in any way, i.e., if the electrons are displaced from their normal position, this condition of zero force (zero electric field) no longer applies.   It turns out that the forces that do exist are such as to restore the electrons to their original position in the cloud.   These forces are proportional to the local (average) charge density of the beam, and they act in such a direction as to restore the electrons to their original position.   The restoring forces thus return the electron to its original position, but when it arrives there, its velocity relative to that position is no longer zero; therefore, the electron passes through the point and assumes a displacement in the opposite sense. Since the restoring force turns out to be proportional to displacement from the equilibrium position, an oscillation results; and since the proportionality constant in the force is proportional to the charge density, the corresponding frequency of the oscillation is proportional to the square root of the charge density.   The oscillation is known as a *plasma oscillation*, and the corresponding frequency as a *plasma frequency* (Chap. 2). This basic phenomenon is one which appears in various guises under various beam conditions and leads to a large number of important effects (both good and bad) in all electron-beam devices.

It should be noted that the basic phenomenon is a *local* oscillation. The electrons oscillate about their equilibrium positions, but there is no wave actually propagating through a stationary medium.[1]   However, most of the applications with which we are concerned here deal with moving electron beams, so that the steady-state (equilibrium) position of the electron is moving relative to the observer.   It turns out to be

---

[1] At least, not for the conditions considered in this volume.   It is known that a wave can propagate through a stationary *plasma* column.   [See, for instance, A. W. Trivelpiece and R. W. Gould, Space-charge Waves in Cylindrical Plasma Columns, *J. Appl. Phys.*, **30**:1784–1793 (1959).]   However, for modulating frequencies that are much higher than plasma frequencies, such as considered in this chapter, such propagation does not occur.

convenient, mathematically and otherwise, to describe the electron oscillation relative to a stationary observer; and since the medium is moving, the mathematical results have the form of waves in the medium. But it is important to point out that this wavelike behavior is the result of the motion of the *medium*, and not of waves propagating through the medium.   It follows that the velocity of propagation of the waves is approximately equal to the beam velocity.   However, depending on the configuration, the presence of d-c magnetic fields, the presence of other beams, etc., the oscillation frequency may vary somewhat.   In some cases, e.g., in the presence of metallic walls, the oscillation frequency of a particular electron depends on its distance from the wall; in the presence of other beams the oscillation frequency may have an imaginary component, etc.   The plasma frequencies differ for the various cases, and the propagation constants characterizing these space-charge waves therefore also differ from configuration to configuration.   The usual mathematical analysis aims at a calculation of the wave numbers or propagation constants for the particular configuration involved.   It is important to stress the basic aspect of space-charge effects as a *local oscillation* in a medium, especially since it is very often possible to understand the fundamental nature of the phenomenon in any particular problem in a more physical sense by considering this local oscillation rather than by considering the space-charge waves.   The formal approach of calculating propagation constants unfortunately sometimes results in obscuring the simple meaning of what is actually happening.

In some ways this difference in methods of attack (i.e., considering the local oscillation in a stream of electrons as against calculating space-charge waves propagating in space) corresponds to the difference between the Lagrangian and the Eulerian approach in hydrodynamics.   In the former, one calculates the motion of individual particles; and in the latter, one calculates quantities characteristic of a fluid as a whole, i.e., velocity, density, pressure, etc.   However, even in the latter case, the dynamical equations for the *individual* particles must be used as steps toward obtaining the field quantities characteristic of the fluid.   Just as in hydrodynamics, it turns out that the Lagrangian approach is much less flexible for calculating the properties of electron streams and that the Eulerian approach of calculating the quantities characteristic of the medium as a whole is much more convenient.   (See also Appendix 1.)

It should be pointed out, however, that for one simple case it *is* possible to calculate the results by finding the motion of the individual particles and then using these individual particle equations to translate the results into the more common language of waves in a medium.   Since this approach is in many ways more illuminating than the mathematical approach commonly used for more complicated problems, we shall actually start by treating this case first and then go on to more complicated cases, in which the medium approach is necessary.

Among the various cases that will be considered are a beam with an infinite cross section, a beam moving parallel to metal boundaries but under the action of a very strong magnetic field that effectively restrains all transverse motion, two electron beams moving with different velocities in the same space, a combination of an electron beam and a stationary cloud of positive ions, and, finally, a case which is common in practice, a beam of finite cross section moving within metal boundaries under the action of a magnetic field whose magnitude is adjusted to produce the so-called Brillouin flow (Chap. 2). In the last case, transverse motion due to r-f fields is possible and leads to some new effects.

It is also possible to treat a case that is really an exception to the condition stated at the beginning of this chapter (that there shall be no d-c electric field acting on the electron in steady motion). It turns out that one can treat the problem of an electron beam in a region *with* acceleration by methods analogous to those used here and get results that are equivalent to those of the classical analysis due to Llewellyn (Chap. 5).[1] The resulting solution does not correspond to plane waves (as for all the other special cases considered), but it is nevertheless appropriate that this case should be mentioned here, since the methods are analogous.

One additional restriction that applies to all the cases considered here should be mentioned. The region in which the electron beam is moving is invariably capable of propagating electromagnetic waves as well. In the present chapter we are dealing only with cases in which the phase velocities of such waves are quite different from the electron-beam velocities, and there is therefore no cumulative interaction between the electron beam and these so-called *cold* modes. If this condition does not apply (i.e., if the velocities *are* comparable), we have the problem of the traveling-wave tube. The method used here can be applied to traveling-wave tubes if the cumulative interaction between the electron beam and a cold mode which has a phase velocity close to that of the beam is taken into account. This type of problem will be reserved for Chap. 6.

4.1   Space-charge Waves: Particle Equations

We shall begin by considering a type of problem that lends itself to an analysis in terms of the motion of individual particles rather than in terms of quantities describing the state of the medium. This is the problem of a beam of infinite cross section (moving with constant velocity) that crosses a modulating gap and enters a space in which its average velocity remains constant. To maintain a constant velocity in such a region, it is

[1] L. D. Smullin, Propagation of Disturbances in One-dimensional Accelerated Electron Streams, *J. Appl. Phys.*, **22**:1496–1498 (1951).

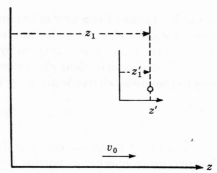

Fig. 4.1 Schematic diagram of electron motion, showing moving coordinate system.

necessary to neutralize the effect of space charge, which would otherwise create a depression of potential in the region and cause the particles to slow down. The usual assumption made in problems of this sort is that *positive ions* are present in the region and that their charge density is equal to that of the electrons. This is not a wholly artificial assumption. Indeed, a calculation of the number of ions produced by an electron beam in what is normally considered to be a good vacuum would indicate that such a situation can very well exist.

However, it is necessary to make an additional assumption of more limited validity: that the positive ions have a virtually infinite mass (in comparison with the electron mass), so that all positive-ion motion may be neglected. This approximation, which thus leads to a fixed distribution of positive charge through which electrons are free to move, is quite good for the purpose of determining electron motion, since the mass of the positive ion is indeed greater by a factor of the order of 10^4 than the electron mass. However, there are types of space-charge behavior in which the mass of the positive ions cannot be neglected and which lead to phenomena of an adverse nature.[1]

Let us therefore consider the essentially one-dimensional problem of a bunch of electrons moving in a region between infinite parallel plates (in which the space charge has been neutralized), with an average velocity v_0 (Fig. 4.1). In addition, each electron has relative motion (due to velocity modulation) with respect to the center of the bunch moving at v_0. A convenient way of describing this motion is to use a coordinate system z' that moves at a velocity v_0 with respect to the stationary coordinate system z. When a particular electron enters the region from the modulating gap, its initial position is z_1' in the moving system. If there were no modulation, the electron would remain stationary at z_1' in the moving system; in the stationary system, at a time t, it would have moved a distance from the gap $z_1 = v_0(t - t_1)$. With modulation, the particle

[1] J. R. Pierce, Possible Fluctuations in Electron Streams Due to Ions, *J. Appl. Phys.*, **19**:231–236 (1948).

is moving toward the center of the bunch, and at the later time t at position z' (or z) the charge that has accumulated since the time t_1 between the center of the bunch and z' is given by $\rho_0(z_1' - z')$, where ρ_0 is the average electron (and positive-ion) charge density; and the field at the electron due to the excess charge is given by the equation

$$E = \frac{\rho_0}{\epsilon_0}(z_1' - z') \tag{1}$$

The above argument contains the tacit assumption that no particle has overtaken another in moving from z_1' to z'. We may now describe the motion (with respect to the moving coordinate system) by means of the equation

$$\ddot{z}' = \frac{\eta\rho_0}{\epsilon_0}(z_1' - z') = \omega_p{}^2(z_1' - z') \tag{2}$$

where we have substituted for the plasma frequency $\omega_p = (\eta\rho_0/\epsilon_0)^{\frac{1}{2}}$, as defined previously. Now let

$$y \equiv z' - z_1' \tag{3}$$

Then $\ddot{z}' = \ddot{y}$, and (2) becomes

$$\ddot{y} = -\omega_p{}^2 y \tag{4}$$

This is the equation of simple harmonic motion, and it has the solution

$$y = z' - z_1' = A \sin(\omega_p t + \phi) \tag{5}$$

where A and ϕ are constants of integration. Evidently the electrons oscillate about an equilibrium position, the frequency of oscillation being the plasma frequency ω_p, which is proportional to the square root of the charge.

To evaluate the constants, we recall that $z' = z_1'$ at $t = t_1$; therefore, $\phi = -\omega_p t_1$ and

$$y = A \sin \omega_p(t - t_1) \tag{6}$$

Differentiation yields

$$\dot{y} = \dot{z}' = \omega_p A \cos \omega_p(t - t_1) \tag{7}$$

But $\dot{z}' = \dot{z} - v_0$; and at $t = t_1$, we may substitute for $\dot{z}$ from Eq. (3.5), so that

$$\dot{y} = \dot{z}' = \dot{z} - v_0 = v_0\left(1 + \frac{\alpha}{2}\sin \omega t_1\right) - v_0$$

$$= v_0\frac{\alpha}{2}\sin \omega t_1 = \omega_p A \tag{8}$$

and (6) becomes

$$y = z' - z_1' = \frac{v_0}{2}\frac{\alpha}{\omega_p}\sin \omega t_1 \sin \omega_p(t - t_1) \tag{9}$$

The modulation frequency ω thus enters into the expression for the displacement, as could be expected. It should be noted that maximum displacement (i.e., a maximum of charge) in the bunch occurs at $\omega_p(t - t_1) = \pi/2$. Therefore, no improvement in performance is obtained by increasing the transit time $(t - t_1)$ from the gap beyond the value corresponding to this maximum.

In order to enable us to compare the results of the present analysis with the results of the simple kinematic bunching theory (Sec. 3.2), it is necessary to describe the particle position in terms of the stationary coordinate system. We may then compare the position (as well as the current) with the position (and current) in the absence of space charge, and thus obtain a measure of the effect of space charge. Let us therefore rewrite (9) in terms of the stationary coordinate system, at the same time introducing the plasma wave number β_p defined by

$$\beta_p \equiv \frac{\omega_p}{v_0} = \frac{2\pi}{\lambda_p} \tag{10}$$

where λ_p is the plasma wavelength, i.e., the distance through which a particle travels during one cycle of the plasma frequency. We may thus write

$$\omega_p(t - t_1) = \beta_p v_0(t - t_1) = \beta_p z_1 \tag{11}$$

and if we recall that the displacement from equilibrium measured in either coordinate system is the same, i.e., $z' - z_1' = z - z_1$, we have in place of (9),

$$z = z_1 + \frac{v_0}{2} \frac{\alpha}{\omega_p} \sin \omega t_1 \sin \omega_p(t - t_1)$$

$$z = v_0(t - t_1) + \frac{v_0 \alpha}{2\omega_p} \sin \omega t_1 \sin \beta_p z_1 \tag{12}$$

or

$$t = \frac{z}{v_0} + t_1 - \frac{\alpha}{2\omega_p} \sin \omega t_1 \sin \beta_p z_1 \tag{13}$$

This is almost the desired form, except that it is necessary to eliminate the equilibrium coordinate z_1 (no modulation) and convert instead to the running distance z. Note that

$$\beta_p z_1 = \beta_p z - \frac{\alpha}{2} \sin \omega t_1 \sin \beta_p z_1 \tag{14}$$

and $\sin \beta_p z_1$ may therefore be expanded as follows:

$$\sin \beta_p z_1 = \sin \beta_p z \cos \left(\frac{\alpha}{2} \sin \omega t_1 \sin \beta_p z_1 \right)$$
$$- \sin \left(\frac{\alpha}{2} \sin \omega t_1 \sin \beta_p z_1 \right) \cos \beta_p z \tag{15}$$

Now if $\alpha \ll 1$, the cosine term containing α may be replaced by unity and the sine term by the argument, so that

$$\sin \beta_p z_1 \approx \sin \beta_p z - \frac{\alpha}{2} \sin \omega t_1 \sin \beta_p z_1 \cos \beta_p z \tag{16}$$

This expression is to be substituted in (13); but the second term of (16) would yield a term quadratic in α, and we may therefore omit it in a linear approximation. The result of the above expansion thus turns out to be that, for the purposes of the present analysis, $\sin \beta_p z_1$ in (14) may be replaced by $\sin \beta_p z$:

$$t = \frac{z}{v_0} + t_1 - \frac{\alpha}{2\omega_p} \sin \omega t_1 \sin \beta_p z \tag{17}$$

The current density at a fixed value of z is given from considerations of the conservation of charge (see Sec. 3.2):

$$i = i_0 \frac{dt_1}{dt} = \frac{i_0}{dt/dt_1} \tag{18}$$

Differentiation of (17) yields

$$\frac{dt}{dt_1} = 1 - \frac{\alpha \omega}{2\omega_p} \cos \omega t_1 \sin \beta_p z \tag{19}$$

This expression is next substituted into (18) to give

$$i = \frac{i_0}{1 - (\alpha \omega / 2\omega_p) \cos \omega t_1 \sin \beta_p z} \tag{20}$$

If we assume that $\alpha \omega / 2\omega_p$ is small compared with unity (which is equivalent to stating that velocity is single-valued and electrons do not overtake one another), then the expression for dt/dt_1 may be removed from the denominator by binomial expansion and

$$i \approx i_0 \left(1 + \frac{\alpha \omega z}{2v_0} \cos \omega t_0 \frac{\sin \beta_p z}{\beta_p z} \right) \tag{20a}$$

where we have also made the substitution $\omega_p = \beta_p v_0$.

This expression may be directly compared with the equations of Sec. 3.2, such as Eq. (3.12a), if it is remembered that the transit angle is given by $\theta = \omega z / v_0$. The added factor $(\sin \beta_p z)/\beta_p z$ that occurs above thus describes the extent to which space charge affects tube operation. As β_p^2 approaches zero, $(\sin \beta_p z)/\beta_p z$ approaches unity, so that the expression for the current density remains unaffected by space charge. At any other value of $\beta_p z$, the current is reduced; for instance, at $\beta_p z = \pi/2$ we have $(\sin \beta_p z)/\beta_p z = 2/\pi < 1$. The decrease in the second term of (20) has the same effect as if α were reduced; i.e., the result of increasing the space-charge density is equivalent to a reduction in the magnitude of the modulating voltage.

To find the corresponding expression for velocity in the laboratory frame, given by

$$v = \dot{z}' + v_0$$

we need only rearrange (9) and differentiate with respect to t:

$$v = v_0 + \frac{v_0 \alpha}{2} \sin \omega t_1 \cos \omega_p (t - t_1)$$

$$v = v_0 \left(1 + \frac{\alpha}{2} \sin \omega t_1 \cos \beta_p z \right) \tag{21}$$

where the replacement of z_1 by z may be justified by an argument similar to that employed in the derivation of (17). A comparison of the second (r-f) term inside the parentheses of (21) with the corresponding term in (20a) shows that the expression for r-f velocity involves a term $\cos \beta_p z$, whereas the r-f current density involves $\sin \beta_p z$. The r-f velocity thus turns out to be 90° out of phase (in space) with the r-f current. This fact has some interesting consequences (e.g., in low-noise traveling-wave tubes), and it is the basic phenomenon in a special device known as the *space-charge-wave amplifier*.[1]

The preceding analysis, carried out in terms of the motion of the individual particle, is very useful in describing the basic phenomenon of the local oscillation of charge. However, the behavior of electron streams in more complicated configurations can be best described by considering the local oscillation in the moving stream to be equivalent to wave motion. We shall be concerned with such space-charge waves throughout the remainder of this chapter. Before we go on to the general solution it is valuable, for the purposes of comparison, to express the solution of the simple case considered above in terms of such waves. To make this transformation, let us rewrite Eq. (20a) in complex notation, where the usual convention applies that the physical quantity can be represented by the real part. Then (20a) becomes

$$i = i_0 + i_0 \frac{\alpha \omega}{2 \omega_p} e^{j\omega t_1} \frac{e^{j\beta_p z} - e^{-j\beta_p z}}{2j} \tag{22}$$

But from (11)

$$t - t_1 = \frac{z_1}{v_0} \approx \frac{z}{v_0} \tag{23}$$

since the elapsed times represented by z_1/v and z/v are approximately

---

[1] P. K. Tien and L. M. Field, Space-charge Waves in an Accelerated Electron Stream for Amplification of Microwave Signals, *Proc. IRE*, **40**:688–695 (1952).

the same. Therefore

$$t_1 = t - \frac{z}{v_0} \tag{24}$$

and

$$i = i_0 + i_0 \frac{\alpha\omega}{4j\omega_p} e^{j\omega[t-(z/v_0)]} \left(e^{j\beta_p z} - e^{-j\beta_p z} \right) \tag{25}$$

Let us define a wave number β_e in connection with the modulating frequency ω,

$$\beta_e \equiv \frac{\omega}{v_0} = \frac{2\pi}{\lambda v_0/c} = \frac{2\pi}{\lambda'} \tag{26}$$

where λ' is a wavelength of the modulating frequency, i.e., the distance through which a particle travels in a cycle of the modulating frequency. Then

$$i = i_0 + i_0 \frac{\alpha\omega}{4j\omega_p} e^{j\omega t} [e^{-j(\beta_e-\beta_p)z} - e^{-j(\beta_e+\beta_p)z}] \tag{27}$$

The presence of space charge between infinite parallel plates thus may be said to manifest itself in the form of two sets of waves, called *space-charge waves*, with propagation constants corresponding to $\beta_e - \beta_p$ and $\beta_e + \beta_p$, respectively.

4.2 General Equation of Space-charge Waves

The foregoing analysis cannot be readily applied to more complicated structures. From a practical viewpoint, we are particularly interested in two configurations: the "strip" beam, bounded by finite, plane, conducting boundaries extending parallel to the direction of the flow, and the circularly symmetric beam, bounded by a tubular conductor whose axis coincides with the beam axis.

The solution of these and other cases may be obtained by a procedure that is quite different from that employed in the preceding section. In the ensuing analysis, we shall start from the basic considerations of the equation of continuity, Maxwell's equations, and the equation of motion and proceed by looking for solutions in the form of waves.

The equation of continuity is given by

$$\nabla \cdot \mathbf{i} + \frac{\partial \rho}{\partial t} = 0 \tag{28}$$

where the convection current density is given by

$$i + i_0 = (\rho + \rho_0)(v + v_0) = \rho v + \rho_0 v + \rho v_0 + \rho_0 v_0 \tag{29}$$

Note that all symbols without subscripts stand for r-f quantities. At this point we introduce the important assumption that the modulation voltage is much smaller than the d-c voltage ($\alpha = V/V_0 \ll 1$).   If this condition applies, it is permissible to neglect the first term on the right-hand side of (29), since it is the product of two r-f quantities and, as such, would lead to terms quadratic in α.   The *small-signal approximation* that allows us to omit this term is particularly useful, since it enables us to linearize the differential equations that follow.   On the other hand, the approximation obviously limits the validity of the analysis.

We also note that

$$i_0 = \rho_0 v_0 \tag{30}$$

so that finally

$$i = \rho_0 v + \rho v_0 \tag{31}$$

Maxwell's equations in free space are:

$$\nabla \times \mathbf{E} = -\mu_0 \frac{\partial \mathbf{H}}{\partial t} \tag{32}$$

$$\nabla \times \mathbf{H} = \epsilon_0 \frac{\partial \mathbf{E}}{\partial t} + \mathbf{i} \tag{33}$$

$$\nabla \cdot \mathbf{E} = \frac{\rho}{\epsilon_0} \tag{34}$$

$$\nabla \cdot \mathbf{H} = 0 \tag{35}$$

Next, multiply Eq. (33) by μ_0 and take its partial time derivative, take the curl of (32), and combine the results, at the same time making use of the vector expansion $\nabla \times \nabla \times \mathbf{E} = \nabla^2 \mathbf{E} - \nabla(\nabla \cdot \mathbf{E})$:

$$\nabla^2 \mathbf{E} - \nabla(\nabla \cdot \mathbf{E}) - \frac{1}{c^2}\frac{\partial^2 \mathbf{E}}{\partial t^2} - \mu_0 \frac{\partial \mathbf{i}}{\partial t} = 0 \tag{36}$$

where $c = 1/\sqrt{\epsilon_0 \mu_0}$ is the velocity of light in free space.   If we substitute from (34) and transpose, we obtain

$$\nabla^2 \mathbf{E} - \frac{1}{c^2}\frac{\partial^2 \mathbf{E}}{\partial t^2} = \frac{1}{\epsilon_0}\nabla\rho + \mu_0 \frac{\partial \mathbf{i}}{\partial t} \tag{37}$$

This will be recognized as a generalized form of the wave equation, with two "driving" terms on the right-hand side (replacing the zero which appears there in the more common case of a region free of charges and currents).   This is the fundamental equation that governs the operation of every electron device, in that it specifies the electric field resulting from any distribution of charges and currents.   However, it is seldom useful in the form given above, and the methods used to obtain the circuit fields from a given charge and current distribution are usually approximations to the exact solution of (37).

For the case under consideration, a solution may be obtained by combining this general circuit equation with the equation of motion of the electrons in order to eliminate $\mathbf{i}$ and ρ.   The equation of motion of an electron is given by[1]

$$\frac{d\mathbf{v}}{dt} = \eta\mathbf{E} \tag{38}$$

where dv/dt is the rate of change of the velocity of the *particle*.

We note that **i** is related to **v** through (31), so that the substitution for $\partial\mathbf{i}/\partial t$ in (37) actually involves $\partial v/\partial t$, which stands for the rate of change of the velocity of the *stream* at a particular point in space. This partial derivative is not equal to the derivative dv/dt that appears in the equation of motion. We thus require a relationship between the partial and total derivative. This is a relationship that occurs very often in fluid dynamics, and it may be stated as follows:

$$\frac{ds}{dt} = \frac{\partial s}{\partial t} + \mathbf{v}\cdot\nabla s \tag{39}$$

where s may be taken to stand for *any* quantity associated with the stream of particles, either a scalar or a component of a vector (e.g., electric field, current, velocity, density, etc.).

The total derivative ds/dt describes the variation in s seen by a *given* particle as that particle moves along its trajectory; it is sometimes called the *particle derivative*. The partial derivative $\partial s/\partial t$ describes the variation of s at a given point; it is associated with successive particles passing an observer stationed at that point, and it is called the *local derivative*. The second term on the right-hand side represents the contribution to the rate of change of s *as seen by* the particle due to its motion at velocity **v** through a region with a *spatially varying s*. In general, then, any particle in a time Δt, say, will see two contributions to the change in s: one because s is changing locally with time, and the second because the particle in changing its position moves from the value of s associated with one point of space to another value of s associated with a neighboring point. For a vector quantity, Eq. (39) would apply to each of its components.

As stated above, (39) holds for any of the particle properties. We may thus write for velocity,[2]

$$\eta\mathbf{E} = \frac{d\mathbf{v}}{dt} = \frac{\partial\mathbf{v}}{\partial t} + (\mathbf{v}\cdot\nabla)\mathbf{v} \tag{40}$$

---

[1] The magnetic field term $\mathbf{v}\times\mathbf{B}$ is omitted from the equation of motion. The force associated with this term is small compared with the electric force unless the particle velocity is a sizable fraction of the velocity of light; in that case the magnetic force and other (relativistic) corrections must be taken into consideration.

[2] In this equation we make a transition from v as a Lagrangian (or particle) variable to v as a Eulerian (or field) variable; in Eq. (40) and in what follows, v is on the same footing as E—a function of the coordinates and of time. The reader should not be confused by the fact that the velocity **v** appears in the general equation (39) for any s and that we shall apply Eq. (39) to the velocity as one particular fluid variable of interest.

If we consider $(\mathbf{v} \cdot \nabla)\mathbf{v}$ in terms of its components, say, in cartesian coordinates, we have, for instance, for the x component

$$[(\mathbf{v} \cdot \nabla)\mathbf{v}]_x = v_x \frac{\partial v_x}{\partial x} + v_y \frac{\partial v_x}{\partial y} + (v_z + v_0) \frac{\partial v_x}{\partial z} \tag{41}$$

since v_0 is assumed to be directed in the z direction. For small signals, all terms except $v_0 \, \partial v_x/\partial z$ may be neglected, since they involve the product of two small (r-f) quantities. Similarly, the y and z components yield only $v_0 \, \partial v_y/\partial z$ and $v_0 \, \partial v_z/\partial z$, respectively; so that with the approximation of small-signal theory, (40) becomes

$$\eta \mathbf{E} = \frac{d\mathbf{v}}{dt} = \frac{\partial \mathbf{v}}{\partial t} + v_0 \frac{\partial \mathbf{v}}{\partial z} \tag{42}$$

Let us assume now that solutions of (37) will be in the form of waves, with a time dependence and a space dependence given by $e^{j(\omega t - \beta z)}$, where β is the phase constant (to be determined). This assumption allows us to make the following substitutions:

$$\frac{\partial}{\partial t} \to j\omega \qquad \frac{\partial}{\partial z} \to -j\beta$$

$$\frac{\partial^2}{\partial t^2} \to -\omega^2 \qquad \frac{\partial^2}{\partial z^2} \to -\beta^2$$

Thus, (42) becomes

$$\eta \mathbf{E} = j(\omega - v_0\beta)\mathbf{v} \tag{43}$$

and (37) takes the form

$$\nabla^2 \mathbf{E} + k^2 \mathbf{E} = \frac{1}{\epsilon_0} \nabla \rho + j\omega\mu_0 \mathbf{i} \tag{44}$$

where we have also made use of the definition of the free-space wave number

$$k \equiv \frac{\omega}{c} = \frac{2\pi}{\lambda} \tag{45}$$

where λ is the free-space wavelength.

We are now able to eliminate ρ and $\mathbf{i}$ from Eq. (44). At this point let us limit ourselves to a special case in order to simplify the analysis. This is the case in which the r-f motion is also restricted to the axial direction; i.e., the transverse components of r-f velocity (and current) are negligible in comparison with the z component. This condition is, of course, exactly satisfied in the beam of infinite cross section (from symmetry); it is nearly satisfied even in beams of finite extent, provided a very strong confining magnetic field is applied. (A more general case, in which the condition does not apply, is discussed in Sec. 4.5.)

The effects of this condition are that the only nonvanishing component of **v** in Eq. (43) may be written as

$$\eta E_z = j(\omega - v_0\beta)v_z \tag{46}$$

and that the expression for the divergence of current may be replaced by its partial derivative with respect to z:

$$\nabla \cdot \mathbf{i} = \frac{\partial i_z}{\partial z} = -j\beta i_z \tag{47}$$

We may thus rewrite the equation of continuity, given by (28), as follows:

$$-\beta i_z + \omega\rho = 0 \tag{48}$$

But from (31),

$$i_z = \rho_0 v_z + \rho v_0 \tag{49}$$

Therefore

$$\rho = \frac{\beta\rho_0}{\omega - v_0\beta}\, v_z \tag{50}$$

$$i_z = \frac{\omega}{\beta}\, \rho = \frac{\omega\rho_0}{\omega - v_0\beta}\, v_z \tag{51}$$

In both equations, we may substitute for v_z its equivalent in terms of E_z from Eq. (46):

$$\rho = \frac{\eta\beta\rho_0}{j(\omega - v_0\beta)^2}\, E_z \tag{52}$$

$$i_z = \frac{\eta\omega\rho_0}{j(\omega - v_0\beta)^2}\, E_z \tag{53}$$

Thus (44) becomes

$$\nabla^2\mathbf{E} + k^2\mathbf{E} = \frac{1}{\epsilon_0}\, \nabla\left[\frac{\eta\beta\rho_0}{j(\omega - v_0\beta)^2}\, E_z\right] + \frac{\omega^2\eta\mu_0\rho_0}{(\omega - v_0\beta)^2}\, E_z\mathbf{a}_z$$

$$\nabla^2\mathbf{E} + k^2\mathbf{E} = \frac{\omega_p{}^2\beta}{j(\omega - v_0\beta)^2}\, \nabla E_z + \frac{\omega^2}{c^2}\, \frac{\omega_p{}^2}{(\omega - v_0\beta)^2}\, E_z\mathbf{a}_z \tag{54}$$

where we have also made the substitutions $\omega_p{}^2 = (\rho_0\eta/\epsilon_0)$ and

$$c^2 = \frac{1}{\epsilon_0\mu_0}$$

Note that $\mathbf{a}_z$, the unit vector in the z direction, has been introduced in the last term, which has only one component; the term involving ∇E_z has, of course, three components.

In order to solve Eq. (54), we must consider one component at a time. It is most convenient to start with the z component, since

$$[\nabla^2\mathbf{E}]_z = \nabla^2 E_z \tag{55}$$

$$[\nabla E_z]_z = \frac{\partial E_z}{\partial z} = -j\beta E_z \tag{56}$$

in both the cartesian and in cylindrical coordinate systems, so that the z component of (54) may be easily expressed in terms of E_z alone. Moreover, boundary conditions are usually expressed in terms of E_z (that is, the tangential component of the electric field vanishes at a conducting wall, etc.). Once the solution for E_z is known, the other components may be readily obtained by means of simple differentiations from equations similar to those which occur in the theory of propagation along waveguides.

If we, therefore, consider the z component of (54), we obtain the simple scalar equation

$$\nabla^2 E_z + \left[k^2 + \omega_p^2 \frac{\beta^2 - \omega^2/c^2}{(\omega - v_0\beta)^2} \right] E_z = 0 \tag{57}$$

In the cartesian and cylindrical coordinate systems (of any cross section), the Laplacian $\nabla^2 E_z$ may be further split up into a "two-dimensional" Laplacian,[1] designated by $\nabla_\perp^2 E_z$, plus the z part of the Laplacian:

$$\nabla^2 E_z = \nabla_\perp^2 E_z + \frac{\partial^2 E_z}{\partial z^2}$$

$$\nabla^2 E_z = \nabla_\perp^2 E_z - \beta^2 E_z \tag{58}$$

We may thus rewrite (57) as follows:

$$\nabla_\perp^2 E_z + \left[-(\beta^2 - k^2) + \frac{\omega_p^2}{v_0^2} \frac{\beta^2 - k^2}{(\beta_e - \beta)^2} \right] E_z = 0$$

where we have also factored out v_0^2 and made use of the wave numbers $k = \omega/c$ and $\beta_e = \omega/v_0$. Let the expression in the bracket be represented by T^2; that is, let

$$T^2 \equiv -(\beta^2 - k^2) + \frac{\omega_p^2}{v_0^2} \frac{\beta^2 - k^2}{(\beta_e - \beta)^2} = (\beta^2 - k^2) \left[\frac{\beta_p^2}{(\beta_e - \beta)^2} - 1 \right] \tag{59}$$

where we have further substituted the wave number $\beta_p = \omega_p/v_0$. Then the differential equation takes the simple form

$$\nabla_\perp^2 E_z + T^2 E_z = 0 \tag{60}$$

The following section is concerned with the solution to this equation for various boundary conditions.

---

[1] In cartesian coordinates, the two-dimensional Laplacian is given by

$$\nabla_\perp^2 E_z = \frac{\partial^2 E_z}{\partial x^2} + \frac{\partial^2 E_z}{\partial y^2}$$

In circular cylindrical coordinates,

$$\nabla_\perp^2 E_z = \frac{1}{r} \frac{\partial}{\partial r} \left(r \frac{\partial E_z}{\partial r} \right) + \frac{1}{r^2} \frac{\partial^2 E_z}{\partial \theta^2}$$

and since the field is independent of the azimuth in many problems involving circular cylindrical coordinates, the second term often vanishes.

4.3   Solutions of the Space-charge-wave Equation

The space-charge-wave equation (60) may be solved for arbitrary values of T.   We are interested in selecting values of T that also satisfy the prescribed boundary conditions (i.e., the eigenvalues).   As stated in the derivation of Eq. (60), we have limited ourselves to cases in which the electrons are constrained to move only in the z direction.   The more difficult problem of taking transverse motion into account will be considered in a later section.

a. Infinite cross section

In solving Eq. (60), we are really concerned with finding the values that the propagation constant β may assume for the various configurations. The case that leads to the simplest analysis is one in which no boundary conditions need be considered, i.e., a beam that extends infinitely in the transverse directions.   Then E_z cannot vary in the transverse plane, so that $\nabla_\perp^2 E_z = 0$, which means that $T^2 = 0$:

$$(\beta^2 - k^2)\left[\frac{\beta_p{}^2}{(\beta_e - \beta)^2} - 1\right] = 0 \qquad (61)$$

This equation has four roots.   Two are obtained by setting

$$\beta^2 - k^2 = 0$$

so that

$$\beta = \pm k = \pm\frac{\omega}{c} \qquad (62)$$

This pair of propagation constants represents plane waves with phase velocities equal to the velocity of light; i.e., the electric field corresponding to these propagation constants is given by a constant multiplied by $\exp j\omega[t \pm (z/c)]$.   (Actually, since we have assumed an electric field component E_z in the direction of propagation, these waves are not ordinary transverse plane waves.   They really represent the limiting case of TM waves such as would be obtained in a waveguide of very large cross section, not in free space.   In the case considered below, a finite beam within conducting boundaries, these solutions are more significant and reduce to the usual TM_{01} mode.)

The other pair of roots is obtained by setting the quantity inside the square bracket in (61) equal to zero, which results in

$$\beta = \beta_e \pm \beta_p \qquad (63)$$

These propagation constants correspond to the space-charge waves that serve to describe the phenomenon of bunching.   This is the same result as was obtained in Sec. 4.1, where the motion of the electrons was described (in a fixed frame of reference) by Eq. (27).

b. Confined beam

Taking finite boundaries into account does not result in undue complexity as long as it is assumed that electron motion remains restricted to the z direction. In practice, deviations from a path parallel to the z axis can be made negligibly small by the application of a strong magnetic field (Chap. 2).[1] If the beam is assumed to be confined in this way, a solution of (59) can again be obtained, but this time $T^2 \neq 0$. By analogy with the solution for the beam of infinite cross section, we might expect that the values of the propagation constant that we seek will differ from β_e by terms with magnitudes of the order of β_p. When the plasma frequency is much lower than the operating frequency, terms of the order of β_p are small compared with β_e:

$$\frac{\beta_p}{\beta_e} = \frac{\omega_p}{\omega} \ll 1 \tag{64}$$

There may be other circumstances when this condition does not apply. The equations for the propagation constants may still apply, but some of the approximations used below may then not be valid. The difference between each of the two roots of β corresponding to the space-charge waves and β_e may be designated by β_q, so that we have again

$$\beta = \beta_e \pm \beta_q \tag{65}$$

To see how the results of the above analysis can be applied to a specific example, consider the case of a strip beam of width $2a$ extending infinitely at right angles to the paper (i.e., the behavior of the beam is independent of the y coordinate) and traveling in the z direction between two parallel conducting plates a distance $2a$ apart (i.e., the beam fills the entire space between the walls). This special case will also serve to demonstrate certain aspects of space-charge-wave theory that do not appear in the infinite-beam analysis but do appear in most other applications of space-charge waves. Even though all *motion* normal to the z direction is assumed to be restricted by some means such as a very strong magnetic field in the z direction, it should be particularly noted

---

[1] To reduce the deviation to zero, an infinitely large magnetic field would be required in principle. In practice, a value of B such that ηB ($= \omega_c$, the cyclotron frequency) is several times the plasma frequency ω_p is sufficient to reduce the deviations to a negligible amount. Moreover, the analysis does not take into consideration that in such a model, the potential (and hence the velocity) is not uniform over the entire cross section because of the potential depression caused by the beam space charge.

that the various quantities involved can have a *variation* in the x direction; in fact, the x dependence is a very significant property of the solution we shall derive. In this case, Eq. (60) becomes

$$\frac{d^2 E_z}{dx^2} + T^2 E_z = 0 \tag{66}$$

where

$$T^2 = (\beta^2 - k^2) \left[\frac{\beta_p^2}{(\beta_e - \beta)^2} - 1 \right] \tag{67}$$

Again, it should be noted that β is still unknown; one of the objectives of the solution is to determine β. Equation (66) has well-known solutions of the form

$$E_z = A \cos Tx + B \sin Tx \tag{68}$$

To be sure, β (and therefore T) is still undetermined. However, the solutions of the equation must be such that $E_z = 0$ at $x = \pm a$. It is this condition, applied at the boundary, that determines the allowed values of T and, therefore, the allowed values of β. It is obvious that for the boundary condition to be satisfied, the solutions must be of the form

$$E_z = A \cos \frac{2n + 1}{2a} \pi x + B \sin \frac{m\pi x}{a} \tag{69}$$

where n and m are integers. The sine solution can be discarded, since it is odd with respect to reflections through the midplane and such solutions are usually not of interest. They are, however, perfectly good solutions to the problem and are being discarded here only because they are not necessary for most problems. If we write the cosine solutions as

$$E_z = A_n \cos T_n x \tag{70}$$

where

$$T_n = \frac{2n + 1}{2a} \pi \tag{71}$$

we see that these are the allowed values of T. For each such value of n, there are four corresponding values of β, which may be obtained from Eq. (67), which is a quartic in β. There are two pairs of allowed β values for each value of T, which we can label field waves and space-charge waves. For the field waves, which are less important for electron tubes, we can find approximate values of β by considering the fact that, for perturbed waveguide modes, $\beta < k(v_p > c)$ and therefore

$$\beta \ll \beta_e \tag{72}$$

Therefore, we can obtain approximate solutions for β in the form

$$\beta^2 \approx k^2 - \frac{T_n^2}{1 - (\beta_p/\beta_e)^2} \tag{73}$$

It is seen that these are slightly perturbed waveguide modes. (In the absence of space charge, $\beta_p = 0$ and we obtain ordinary waveguide modes.) We shall not consider them further.

For the other set of waves, the true space-charge waves, we can use the approximation that $\beta \approx \beta_e$ and $\beta \gg k$, that is, that the waves propagate with a velocity approximately equal to that of the beam. This approximation permits us to omit k^2 and set $\beta = \beta_e$ everywhere except in the term involving their difference. This term, of course, contains the crucial part of the solution. Using this approximation, we can solve for the appropriate values of β:

$$\beta_n = \beta_e \pm \frac{\beta_p}{[1 + (T_n/\beta_e)^2]^{\frac{1}{2}}} = \beta_e \pm \beta_{qn} \tag{74}$$

where β_{qn} is the reduced plasma propagation constant and the ratio

$$R_n \equiv \frac{\beta_{qn}}{\beta_p} = \frac{1}{[1 + (T_n/\beta_e)^2]^{\frac{1}{2}}} \tag{75}$$

is sometimes known as the *plasma frequency reduction factor*, since it represents a reduction in the plasma propagation constant β_p caused by the presence of the surrounding structure.

In terms of this solution we now have an infinite set of pairs of space-charge waves, one of each pair being known as the *fast wave* and the other as the *slow wave*, fast and slow being meant relative to the beam velocity. Each one of these propagation constants represents a possible solution to the differential equation consisting of the appropriate cosine term multiplied by $e^{-j\beta_n z}$, and this solution can have an arbitrary amplitude. Any one of these solutions (or a set of them) is a solution of the differential equation. To determine the appropriate amplitudes for any actual problem, we must use the *initial* conditions at $z = 0$. Since the initial conditions on a beam are usually given in terms of initial velocity and initial current, we must first obtain the current and velocity corresponding to each independent solution of the differential equation, i.e., for each different propagation constant. From Eqs. (53) and (46) we can get relations between v_z (and i_z) and E_z. For convenience we rewrite them here:

$$v_z = \frac{\eta E_z}{j(\omega - v_0\beta_n)} \equiv F_n E_z \tag{76}$$

$$i_z = \frac{\eta\omega\rho_0 E_z}{j(\omega - v_0\beta_n)^2} \equiv G_n E_z \tag{77}$$

where we have also defined the quantities F_n and G_n for convenience; β_n now denotes a particular value of β. The coefficients F_n and G_n, which are known, depend on the β_{qn}'s; for every term in a sum of terms representing E_z, there will be a corresponding term multiplied by the appropriate F_n or G_n in the related expression for either v_z or i_z, respectively. In terms of our infinite set of solutions we see that in general E_z can be written as a superposition of these various solutions with arbitrary coefficients:

$$E_z = \sum_n (A_n^- e^{-j\beta_{qn}z} + A_n^+ e^{j\beta_{qn}z}) \cos T_n x \, e^{-j\beta_e z} \tag{78}$$

The corresponding solutions for v_z and i_z are

$$v_z = \sum_n (F_n^- A_n^- e^{-j\beta_{qn}z} + F_n^+ A_n^+ e^{j\beta_{qn}z}) \cos T_n x \, e^{-j\beta_e z} \tag{79}$$

$$i_z = \sum_n (G_n^- A_n^- e^{-j\beta_{qn}z} + G_n^+ A_n^+ e^{j\beta_{qn}z}) \cos T_n x \, e^{-j\beta_e z} \tag{80}$$

In these equations, the summation is over the space-charge waves only; the field waves have been arbitrarily omitted. It usually turns out that if initial conditions on current and velocity have been specified, they are sufficient to determine the amplitudes of the space-charge waves. The value of E_z obtained by this summation is then that associated with the space-charge waves. This value does not exactly satisfy initial conditions on the fields at any modulating gap; to satisfy all initial conditions, some superposition of field waves (cutoff modes) would usually be required. Values of E, v, and i obtained by the use of both space-charge and field waves would be exact values that would differ somewhat from those obtained when field waves are ignored and conditions on current and velocity alone are used. However, the error proves to be small at even a small distance from the gap, and the principal effects are described quite accurately by the space-charge waves, provided that the field waves are cut off. If they are not, a propagating waveguide mode obviously exists and must be included if complete fields everywhere are to be obtained. But even then, the contribution to i, v, and what might be truly called the space-charge fields would be relatively small.

To determine the unknown amplitudes of Eqs. (78) to (80), we shall use the initial conditions that are usually stated in the form that at the input to the drift tube (at $z = 0$), i_z and v_z are given as some function of x, the transverse variable. Let us write that at $z = 0$,

$$i_z(x,0,t) = i'(x)e^{j\omega t} \tag{81}$$
$$v_z(x,0,t) = v'(x)e^{j\omega t} \tag{82}$$

Then the A_n's have to be so chosen that the series for i_z and v_z reduce to the Fourier expansions of these initial values at the initial plane $z = 0$:

$$v'(x) = \sum (F_n^- A_n^- + F_n^+ A_n^+) \cos \frac{(2n + 1)\pi x}{2a} \tag{83}$$

$$i'(x) = \sum (G_n^- A_n^- + G_n^+ A_n^+) \cos \frac{(2n + 1)\pi x}{2a} \tag{84}$$

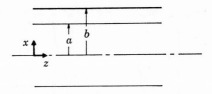

Fig. 4.2   Configuration for beam between parallel plates.

It appears that we can obtain an infinite set of pairs of algebraic equations, each pair sufficient to determine the amplitudes of a pair of space-charge waves.

We have gone through this somewhat formal approach in considerable detail to illustrate how one uses solutions after they have been obtained to fit a particular physical problem. It is always true that merely obtaining formal solutions of a differential equation does not constitute the complete answer; it is also necessary to determine the amplitudes of the various waves that may come out of the formal solution by fitting initial conditions. Actually, in the case that we are considering here (as well as in a closely related case, a cylindrical beam in a cylindrical drift tube), it is very often possible to replace the complete series of terms approximately by the wave of lowest order ($n = 0$) in order to describe the behavior with adequate accuracy. Using one pair of space-charge waves is hardly ever the exact solution to any problem, but it is very often the principal part of the exact solution and can give considerable information about the physical problem. In such an approximation, one would use the notation β_q and drop the additional subscripts. Note that $\beta_q/\beta_p < 1$. Since for a finite beam some of the field lines are not axial but radial, the axial field is thus reduced and the corresponding plasma frequency and propagation constant are also reduced. If a wall is present, this reduction in the axial field manifests itself as an effect of the r-f charge density in producing image charges of opposite polarity in the wall. The image charges then result in forces that tend to cancel the actual space-charge forces produced by the beam; in particular, the image charges cause $E_z \rightarrow 0$ at the wall. This is simply another way of defining what is meant by an image charge.

If the beam does not fill the entire space between the parallel conducting plates, a solution can still be found,[1] although one must now distinguish between values of T_n outside and inside the beam, say, T_o and T_i, with the solutions being matched at the beam boundary. If the beam extends to $x = \pm a$ and the conducting walls are located at $x = \pm b$ (Fig. 4.2), β is given by the solutions of the equation

$$T_i a \tan T_i a = T_o a \coth T_o (b - a) \tag{85}$$

[1] L. T. Zitelli, Space Charge Effects in Gridless Klystrons, *Stanford Univ. Microwave Lab., Rept.* 149, October, 1951.

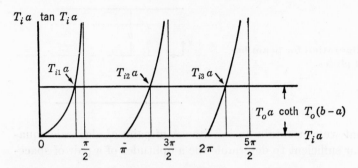

Fig. 4.3 Graphical solution of Eq. (85).

where T_i^2 is given by Eq. (67) and

$$T_o^2 \equiv \beta^2 - k^2 \qquad (67a)$$

This is a transcendental equation of a sort that can be solved graphically (Fig. 4.3).[1] The solutions, which correspond to intersections between the plots of the two sides of Eq. (85), are again infinite in number and yield an infinite number of values for T_i (and hence for the propagation constant β).

The procedure for the cylindrical case is quite similar.[2] As might be expected, the cosines and sines of the rectangular case are replaced by Bessel functions, and the Fourier series are replaced by Fourier Bessel series. The result for an axisymmetric beam of radius a contained inside a cylindrical conducting tube of radius b (Fig. 4.4) is stated below without derivation:

$$\frac{T_i a J_1(T_i a)}{J_0(T_i a)} = T_o a \frac{I_0(T_o b) K_1(T_o a) + I_1(T_o a) K_0(T_o b)}{I_0(T_o b) K_0(T_o a) - I_0(T_o a) K_0(T_o b)} \qquad (86)$$

where the J's, I's and K's are Bessel functions. A graphical solution of (86) may likewise be obtained, as shown in Fig. 4.5.[2]

The above analysis yields an infinite number of solutions, any one

---

[1] Figures 4.3 and 4.5 are plotted with the assumption that $\beta \approx \beta_e$ on the right-hand sides of Eqs. (85) and (86), respectively; this approximation is valid, as long as the term $(\beta - \beta_e)$ does not appear.

[2] Zitelli, *op. cit.*

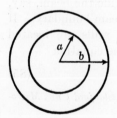

Fig. 4.4 Configuration for beam inside infinite cylinder.

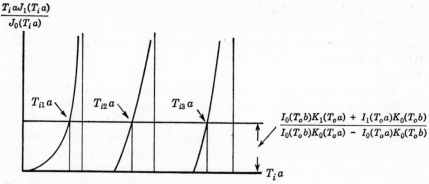

$$\frac{T_i a J_1(T_i a)}{J_0(T_i a)}$$

$$\frac{I_0(T_o b)K_1(T_o a) + I_1(T_o a)K_0(T_o b)}{I_0(T_o b)K_0(T_o a) - I_0(T_o a)K_0(T_o b)}$$

Fig. 4.5   Graphical solution of Eq. (86).

of which (or superposition of several) will satisfy the equations. The amplitudes A and B in Eq. (69) again depend on the initial conditions at the entrance to the beam region.

4.4   Double-beam Case

a. Qualitative treatment

Let us next consider the application of some of the above notions to a somewhat more complicated phenomenon, two beams involving space-charge waves which grow in amplitude as a function of distance. Tubes utilizing this phenomenon have been constructed and behaved as the theory predicts.[1] However, our primary interest lies in the *analysis* of this kind of device and in the introduction of certain notions that will not only be useful later in the study of traveling-wave tubes but also serve to illuminate the behavior of the space-charge waves themselves. Moreover, the analysis lends itself to the consideration of the behavior of a moving electron beam in the presence of a moving—or stationary—cloud of positive ions, a situation of interest in plasma devices.

As in the preceding section, consider a region of infinite cross section into which two electron beams (with different d-c velocities) are injected. Let the average velocity of the two beams be designated by

$$v_0 = \tfrac{1}{2}(v_{01} + v_{02}) \tag{87}$$

and the velocity difference by

$$2\delta = v_{02} - v_{01} \tag{88}$$

[1] L. S. Nergaard, Analysis of a Simple Model of a Two-beam Growing-wave Tube, *R C A Rev.*, **9**:585–601 (1948); J. R. Pierce and W. B. Hebenstreit, A New Type of High-frequency Amplifier, *Bell System Tech. J.*, **28**:33–51 (1949); A. V. Haeff, The Electron-wave Tube, *Proc. IRE*, **37**:4–10 (1949).

where v_{01} and v_{02} are the d-c velocities of the first and second beam, respectively. Again, as in the single-beam case, let us assume that a sufficient number of positive ions is present so that the d-c potential in the region is constant (in other words, that the average charge density is zero).

Before we undertake a detailed mathematical analysis of the so-called double-beam tube, we shall find it useful to consider, from purely qualitative considerations, what one might expect in the presence of two electron beams within the same region. We cannot expect to derive detailed quantitative answers from such a qualitative analysis; however, we shall be able to see why the presence of two beams leads to space-charge waves with an increasing amplitude. Moreover, we shall be able to derive a relationship that will establish the significant combination of parameters that determines whether or not such growing waves result. The general nature of the approach is to consider each beam by itself and (as a first approximation) consider its motion as if unaffected by the presence of the other beam, and then to add the effect of the other beam as a perturbation. If we pick the numerical values of velocities, plasma frequencies, etc., properly, we shall find that space-charge forces of one beam are so phased as to increase the bunching (on the average) in the other beam. Stated more exactly, for a single beam, the space-charge forces on an electron are always so directed that the electron tends to be restored to its equilibrium position; therefore, the space-charge forces alternate in direction depending on which side of the equilibrium position the electron happens to be. With two beams, on the other hand, we shall find that the second beam (under suitable conditions) always results in a force on the electrons in the first beam that is unidirectional, i.e., that always acts on an electron in the same direction, so as to move it away from the equilibrium position. This force actually fluctuates in amplitude; but since it is always in the same direction, the cumulative effect tends to compress the bunches in either beam as a function of time or distance along the drift tube. (In the mathematical analysis to follow later, this effect takes the form of space-charge waves with an exponentially increasing amplitude.)

This phenomenon is illustrated by Fig. 4.6. Figure 4.6a is a plot of the charge-density distribution of the two beams as a function of distance. The r-f charge density also varies as a function of time, and the distribution shown is a "snapshot" representation of the instant when the r-f charge density is at a maximum in each beam, as determined by its own plasma oscillation. Thus the electron in beam 1 labeled A is in a region of greater than average density of beam 1, whereas the electron in beam 2 labeled A' is in a region of greater than average density in beam 2. In this plot, it has been assumed that the velocity difference between the two beams is much smaller than their individual average (d-c)

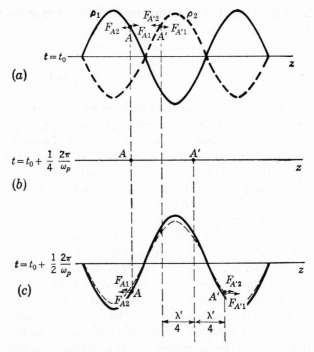

Fig. 4.6 Charge density in a double-beam tube.

velocities ($\delta \ll v_0$), so that one can define a beam wavelength that is approximately the same for both electrons:

$$\lambda' \equiv \lambda \frac{v_0}{c} = \frac{2\pi v_0}{\omega} \tag{89}$$

This quantity represents the distance that an electron travels in one cycle of the modulating frequency ω.

The arrows in the diagram indicate the direction of the force F_{A1} exerted on electron A by the space charge in its own beam and also by the space charge of the other beam, F_{A2}.

Let us now impose some conditions on the beams that would lead to the kind of interaction we desire. First of all, let us assume that the plasma frequency for each beam is approximately the same, so that

$$\omega_p{}^2 \approx \omega_{p1}{}^2 \approx \omega_{p2}{}^2 \tag{90}$$

where $\omega_{p1}{}^2 = \eta\rho_{01}/\epsilon_0$ is the plasma frequency of the first beam, and similarly for the second beam. Also, let us choose this common plasma frequency ω_p in such a way that in one cycle of the plasma frequency, beam 2 moves a distance of one beam wavelength relative to beam 1.

This is, in effect, a condition on the difference in the velocities:

$$\lambda' = 2\delta \frac{2\pi}{\omega_p} \tag{91}$$

or

$$\frac{2\delta}{\lambda'} \frac{2\pi}{\omega_p} = \frac{2\delta}{v_0} \frac{\omega}{\omega_p} = 1 \tag{92}$$

Figure 4.6a shows the two beams at the instant when the r-f charge density in each beam has reached a maximum value. The charge-density distribution of these same beams a quarter of a cycle of plasma frequency later, under the imposed conditions, is shown in Fig. 4.6b. The net charge density is now zero, since a quarter of a cycle of plasma frequency after a peak density the density is zero and all the electrons are passing through their respective equilibrium positions.

Another quarter cycle of plasma frequency later, the situation is as shown in Fig. 4.6c. Electron A, which was in a region of excess density in Fig. 4.6a, is now in a region of less than average density, and similarly for electron A'. The position of A' is as indicated because of the condition we have imposed on the relative velocity of the two beams and the plasma frequency (i.e., electron A' has moved $\lambda'/2$ relative to electron A during a half cycle of the plasma frequency). The arrows on electron A indicating the direction of the space-charge forces on it show that whereas the force owing to its own beam has reversed in direction (as would be indicated by single-beam theory), the force on electron A owing to the other beam is in the same direction as it was in Fig. 4.6a. In other words, the space-charge force of beam 1 on an electron in beam 1 fluctuates in direction, whereas the force of beam 2 on the same electron is always in the same direction (though it fluctuates in magnitude). This is entirely a consequence of the relation we have imposed between the relative velocity and the plasma frequency. By selecting values in accordance with Eq. (92), we have ensured that there is always a region of greater density in beam 2 to the right of electron A than to the left.

It is obvious that after another half cycle of the plasma frequency the beams again correspond to the situation illustrated by Fig. 4.6a. The net effect is the same as would result from the application of a unidirectional force to a pendulum, the magnitude of the force varying with time but being always in the same direction. Under these conditions the pendulum, in addition to oscillating back and forth (as it would normally), would gradually have its equilibrium position displaced in one direction. In the beam, this condition corresponds to forcing the charge density in each beam to become more and more tightly compressed as time goes on owing to the effects of the other beam. The r-f current in the beam thus increases with distance, rather than varying sinusoidally as it does for a single beam. The condition resulting in this sort of interaction is stated in Eq. (92), that is, a synchronism that permits one beam to "slip" behind the other beam by one modulating wavelength (λ') in one cycle of the plasma frequency. It is apparent from the way in which this condition has been applied that it is not a very precise condition and that the results described are obtained even if Eqs. (90) and (92) are satisfied only approximately; i.e., even though $(2\delta/v_0)(\omega/\omega_p)$ may depart slightly from unity, or if the plasma frequencies are not equal, some of the cumulative effects would still be obtained. That this is indeed the case will become evident from the following analysis.

b. Mathematical treatment

We shall again consider the case of infinite beams, where from symmetry, the r-f magnetic field is zero. Therefore, $\nabla \times \mathbf{E} = 0$ and we may introduce a potential V given by

$$\mathbf{E} = -\nabla V \tag{93}$$

Let us summarize our notation: ρ_{01} is the average charge density in beam 1; ρ_1 and v_1 are the r-f components of charge density and velocity, respectively; $\beta_{e1} = \omega/v_{01}$; $\beta_{p1} = \omega_{p1}/v_{01}$, where $\omega_{p1} = \sqrt{\eta\rho_{01}/\epsilon_0}$; and similarly for beam 2. We then have a system of equations that together determine the behavior of the two beams. First, we have Poisson's equation, which relates the potential to the charge density:

$$\nabla^2 V = -\frac{\rho_1 + \rho_2}{\epsilon_0} \tag{94}$$

We shall call this the *circuit equation*, in accordance with the explanation given in Chap. 2.[1] This is the equation in which the charge density (or space current) determines the potential on the circuit (in this case, empty space); we are assuming that somehow the charge density is known, and we use this equation to determine the potential. The counterpart to this equation, by which the motion of the electrons (and therefore their velocity and charge density) can be determined from the potential distribution, we shall call the *electronic equation*. The actual behavior of the beams must be such that both these equations are simultaneously satisfied. To obtain the electronic equation, we utilize the definition of r-f current density [Eq. (29)],

$$i_1 = \rho_1 v_1 + \rho_{01} v_1 + \rho_1 v_{01} \tag{95}$$

the equation of continuity [Eq. (28)],

$$\frac{\partial i_1}{\partial z} + \frac{\partial \rho_1}{\partial t} = 0 \tag{96}$$

---

[1] Equation (94) may be also shown to be a consequence of Eq. (37), which is the more general circuit equation. If the magnetic field is zero, the second terms on the two sides of (37) cancel one another. If one then defines E as in (93), Eq. (94) follows directly.

and the equation of motion [Eq. (40)],

$$\frac{dv_1}{dt} = \frac{\partial v_1}{\partial t} + (v_{01} + v_1)\frac{\partial v_1}{\partial z} = -\eta\frac{\partial V}{\partial z} \tag{97}$$

with similar equations for beam 2.   It should be noted that the equation of continuity applies *separately* to each beam, since the law of conservation of charge must be satisfied by each beam separately.   The equation of continuity has been written in a form which assumes one-dimensional motion, so that the only component of the r-f current (and, therefore, the only component of r-f velocity) is in the z direction.   As in the single-beam case, we can omit the quadratic terms in the r-f amplitudes from both the definition of current and the equation of motion, so that we are left with linear equations.   If we assume a time dependence of the form $e^{j\omega t}$, we obtain from Eqs. (96) and (97)

$$v_{01}\frac{\partial \rho_1}{\partial z} + \rho_{01}\frac{\partial v_1}{\partial z} = -j\omega\rho_1 \tag{98}$$

$$j\omega v_1 + v_{01}\frac{\partial v_1}{\partial z} = -\eta\frac{\partial V}{\partial z} \tag{99}$$

To solve these equations for ρ_1, let us first eliminate $\partial v_1/\partial z$.   Multiply (98) by v_{01} and (99) by ρ_{01} and subtract the second equation from the first:

$$v_{01}{}^2\frac{\partial \rho_1}{\partial z} - j\omega v_1\rho_{01} = -j\omega\rho_1 v_{01} + \rho_{01}\eta\frac{\partial V}{\partial z} \tag{100}$$

Next, differentiate Eq. (100) with respect to z, combine the result with (98), and make use of the definitions for β_{e1} and β_{p1}.   This procedure yields

$$\frac{\partial^2\rho_1}{\partial z^2} + 2j\beta_{e1}\frac{\partial \rho_1}{\partial z} - \beta_{e1}{}^2\rho_1 = \epsilon_0\beta_{p1}{}^2\frac{\partial^2 V}{\partial z^2} \tag{101a}$$

and similarly,

$$\frac{\partial^2\rho_2}{\partial z^2} + 2j\beta_{e2}\frac{\partial \rho_2}{\partial z} - \beta_{e2}{}^2\rho_2 = \epsilon_0\beta_{p2}{}^2\frac{\partial^2 V}{\partial z^2} \tag{101b}$$

These two equations for ρ_1 and ρ_2 together constitute what we have previously referred to as the electronic equation.   We are looking for the solution of the problem which satisfies both these equations and Poisson's equation.   The exact procedure from now on is somewhat arbitrary; it depends more on convenience than on anything else.   We can, for example, derive from these two electronic equations a single one simply by adding.   This result could also be called the electronic equation, and Poisson's equation would then be the circuit equation.

It is to be noticed that these are linear differential equations involving V, ρ_1, and ρ_2, and later we shall see how we can solve them.   Before

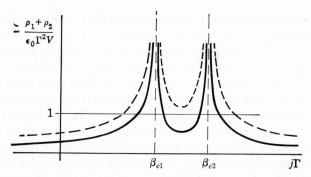

Fig. 4.7   Plot of $-(\rho_1 + \rho_2)/\epsilon_0\Gamma^2 V$ as a function of $j\Gamma$, Eqs. (102) and (103).

we do so, however, it is illuminating to examine these equations graphically.   Let us assume that the solutions for all quantities have a z dependence of the form $e^{\Gamma z}$.   If Eqs. (94) and (101) are rewritten in the light of this assumption, the following two relations are obtained for the ratio $(\rho_1 + \rho_2)/\epsilon_0\Gamma^2 V$:

$$-\frac{\rho_1 + \rho_2}{\epsilon_0\Gamma^2 V} = 1 \tag{102}$$

$$-\frac{\rho_1 + \rho_2}{\epsilon_0\Gamma^2 V} = \frac{\beta_{p1}{}^2}{(j\Gamma - \beta_{e1})^2} + \frac{\beta_{p2}{}^2}{(j\Gamma - \beta_{e2})^2} \tag{103}$$

The first of these equations was obtained from (94), and the second from the sum of (101a) and (101b).

We thus have two different ratios from the two equations.   (If we had chosen to work with currents instead of charge densities as the fundamental quantities, we could have obtained similar relations, which we could have labeled circuit and electronic admittance, depending on the equation from which the ratio had been derived.)[1]   Since there is no convenient nomenclature for the particular ratios that we did obtain, we shall not name them; the important fact for either set is that the solution of the problem is obtained for that value of Γ for which both ratios are numerically the same.   We shall presently attempt to find these values of Γ analytically for some special cases.   However, we can also examine the significance of these ratios graphically.

A plot of both these expressions for $-(\rho_1 + \rho_2)/\epsilon_0\Gamma^2 V$ as a function of $j\Gamma$, as shown in Fig. 4.7, yields some illuminating information.   The first plot, of course, is merely a straight line.   The second one is a curve with two cusps, each cusp corresponding to the poles at $j\Gamma = \beta_{e1}, \beta_{e2}$, or $\Gamma = -j\beta_{e1}, -j\beta_{e2}$.   The values of Γ that are the allowed propagation

---

[1] These relations can be obtained by setting $\rho_1 = j\Gamma i_1/\omega$ and $\rho_2 = j\Gamma i_2/\omega$ in the left-hand sides of Eqs. (102) and (103).

constants for this problem (and that result in both equations being simultaneously satisfied) are obtained by the intersection of the two curves. Two cases have been shown; they are represented by solid and dotted curves, respectively. The first yields four intersections; the velocity separation between the two beams and the charge density that determines the plasma wave number have been so chosen that the electronic curve drops down to a low value after passing the pole of β_{e1}, before it starts to come up again as it approaches the pole of β_{e2}. The four real intersections correspond to four real values of $j\Gamma$, and no growing waves are obtained. The dotted curve, on the other hand, is drawn for the case in which the combination of plasma wave numbers and separation of the velocities is such that before the electronic curve can come down to unity after passing the pole of β_{e1} it starts up again because it is approaching the pole of β_{e2}, and there are no intersections between the poles. In this case, only two imaginary roots are obtained. The two roots that have disappeared have become complex, and we obtain growing waves, since Γ now has a real component. This qualitative consideration thus enables us to see immediately under what circumstances we can get growing waves. The greater the separation of the velocities, the greater the charge density has to be to pull the electronic curve above unity between the two poles. On the other hand, as the poles approach each other, charge density can become much smaller and still result in imaginary roots. We can see that for a given separation of velocities there is some minimum value of charge density (or β_{p1} and β_{p2}) necessary to give us such growing waves. Conversely, for a given charge density, there is a maximum separation of velocities that will accomplish the same result. In terms of the discussion in the introductory part of the present section, we may say that δ must vary directly as ω_p. This is the sort of relation that we have previously indicated from a purely qualitative consideration.

One other result can be obtained from this graph. If one separates the velocities sufficiently, then in the neighborhood of either pole, the only significant term in the electronic equation is that of one of the beams alone, and the intersections that are obtained are determined entirely by the behavior of a single term. In this case, to a good approximation we may say simply that the four waves would be obtained by setting either one or the other term equal to unity, so that we obtain the four waves that are just what we should expect from each beam in the absence of the other beam.

All the results we have described can be derived analytically by determining the values of Γ algebraically from the equation

$$1 = \frac{\beta_{p1}{}^2}{(j\Gamma - \beta_{e1})^2} + \frac{\beta_{p2}{}^2}{(j\Gamma - \beta_{e2})^2} \tag{104}$$

To solve this equation for arbitrary values of the parameters requires a considerable amount of labor; we shall limit our treatment to a particular set of values that turns the equation into a biquadratic. We shall solve for the special case

$$\beta_{p1} = \beta_{p2} = \beta_p$$

We note that

$$\beta_{e1} = \frac{\omega}{v_{01}} = \frac{\omega}{v_0 - \delta} \approx \frac{\omega}{v_0}\left(1 + \frac{\delta}{v_0}\right) \tag{105}$$

$$\beta_{e2} = \frac{\omega}{v_{02}} = \frac{\omega}{v_0 + \delta} \approx \frac{\omega}{v_0}\left(1 - \frac{\delta}{v_0}\right) \tag{106}$$

Let us write β_e for ω/v_0; then if we assume that the unknown propagation constant Γ is close to β_e, that is, that $\Gamma = j(\beta_e + \epsilon)$, where $\epsilon \ll \beta_e$, the equation for Γ becomes

$$\frac{\beta_p{}^2}{(\epsilon + \beta_e\delta/v_0)^2} + \frac{\beta_p{}^2}{(\epsilon - \beta_e\delta/v_0)^2} = 1 \tag{107}$$

which has the solutions

$$\frac{\epsilon}{\beta_p} = \pm \sqrt{\left(\frac{\delta}{v_0}\frac{\beta_e}{\beta_p}\right)^2 + 1 \pm \sqrt{4\left(\frac{\delta}{v_0}\frac{\beta_e}{\beta_p}\right)^2 + 1}} \tag{108}$$

There are always at least two real roots for ϵ; they correspond to the choice of the plus sign under the first radical. This choice corresponds to Γ being pure imaginary, and the waves with these Γ's are of constant amplitude. (They correspond to the outermost intersections in Fig. 4.7; and as we just saw from the diagram, these roots always have Γ imaginary.)

For the choice of the negative sign under the radical, ϵ will be imaginary provided

$$\sqrt{4\left(\frac{\delta\beta_e}{v_0\beta_p}\right)^2 + 1} > 1 + \left(\frac{\delta}{v_0}\frac{\beta_e}{\beta_p}\right)^2$$

that is, if

$$0 < \left(\frac{\delta\beta_e}{v_0\beta_p}\right)^2 < 2$$

This condition then determines whether or not growing waves are obtained. If ϵ is imaginary, there will be two roots for Γ, one of which will represent a growing and the other an attenuating wave. It is to be noted that this criterion for gain involves the same parameters as originally derived by simple qualitative considerations of the interaction of two beams. In that approach the criterion obtained was that of Eq. (91), restated below in the form

$$\frac{\delta\beta_e}{v_0\beta_p} \approx 1 \tag{109}$$

which is similar to that obtained from the exact theory. It is also apparent that this inequality is compatible with the requirement obtained from the graphical approach; i.e., with large velocity separation δ, more current (larger β_p) is required to obtain gain. It can also be shown quite readily that for $\delta\beta_e/v_0\beta_p \gg \sqrt{2}$, which corresponds to little interaction between the beams, the four roots of Γ are very nearly the space-charge waves that would be obtained from each of both beams separately.

We have obtained four roots corresponding to four different waves. For each such wave there are corresponding values of the electric field, the charge density in each beam, the r-f velocity in each beam, etc. The ratios of these quantities for a given wave are determined by the various equations relating these quantities, such as Eqs. (50) to (53), applied to each beam. These ratios involve the particular value of Γ for that particular wave, and the ratios will therefore be different for different Γ's. Each wave, however, can have an arbitrary amplitude; the general solution is a super-position of all four waves, with the amplitudes so chosen that they satisfy some initial conditions at $z = 0$. A typical set, for example, would be that the currents at some initial plane are zero and the r-f velocities are not. This would give four initial conditions obtained from setting the two currents equal to zero and the two r-f velocities equal to their initial values. These four equations, then, are sufficient to determine the four amplitudes.

4.5   Space-charge Waves with Transverse Motion

Let us next consider the case of a beam of finite cross section (circular) with a uniform charge density moving under the action of a magnetic field B_z in such a way that the possibility of transverse motion is not excluded.[1] Under these circumstances, the d-c or unmodulated motion must be known; the expressions derived from Maxwell's equations (32) to (35) still hold, and the equation of motion in the axial direction takes the same form as (38):

$$\frac{dv_z}{dt} = \eta E_z \tag{110}$$

However, we must now also consider the motion in the radial direction, which is described by the equation[2]

$$\frac{dv_r}{dt} - r\dot{\theta}^2 = \eta(E_{rt} + r\dot{\theta}B_z) \tag{111}$$

---

[1] W. W. Rigrod and J. R. Pierce, Space-charge Wave Excitation in Solid-cylindrical Brillouin Beams, *Bell System Tech. J.*, **38**:99–118 (1959).

[2] Equations (110) and (111) are in Lagrangian variables, which will have to be later transformed to Eulerian variables. See also footnote at Eq. (40).

where E_{rt} describes the total electric field in the r direction, i.e.,

$$E_{rt} = E_r + \frac{\rho_0 r}{2\epsilon_0} \qquad (112)$$

where E_r is the radial r-f field and the term containing the d-c charge density ρ_0 per unit volume is the radial d-c field at a radius r; the magnetic field arising from the motion of the electrons themselves is again neglected. If we specialize the analysis further to the case of the Brillouin flow described in Chap. 2, we have for the d-c motion and a-c,

$$\dot{\theta} = -\omega_H = -\frac{\eta B_z}{2} \qquad (113)$$

In that case, we can write for acceleration at points *inside* the beam

$$\frac{dv_r}{dt} = \eta E_r + \frac{\eta \rho_0}{2\epsilon_0} r - \omega_H^2 r = \eta E_r \qquad r \leq a \qquad (114)$$

because of the Brillouin-flow condition $\omega_H^2 = \omega_p^2/2 = \eta \rho_0/2\epsilon_0$. It should be noted that the same result would be obtained in the absence of the magnetic field ($\omega_H = 0$) provided we could specify that the electronic space charge was completely neutralized by positive ions ($\rho_0 = 0$).

Outside a beam of radius a, Eq. (111) becomes

$$\frac{dv_r}{dt} = \eta E_r + \frac{\eta \rho_0 a^2}{2\epsilon_0 r} - \omega_H^2 r = \eta E_r + \omega_p^2 \frac{a^2}{2r} - \omega_H^2 r$$

$$\frac{dv_r}{dt} = \eta E_r + \frac{\omega_p^2}{2}\left(\frac{a^2}{r} - r\right) \qquad r \geq a \qquad (115)$$

In practice, we are interested in the case in which the beam radius does not deviate very much from a. Let the radius of the outermost electron be described by

$$r = a + \Delta r \qquad (116)$$

where $\Delta r \ll a$. Then for the outermost electron, Eq. (115) can be approximated by

$$\frac{dv_r}{dt} \approx \eta E_r + \frac{\omega_p^2 a}{2}\left[\left(1 - \frac{\Delta r}{a}\right) - \left(1 + \frac{\Delta r}{a}\right)\right] = \eta E_r - \omega_p^2 \Delta r$$

$$r \geq a \qquad (117)$$

This expression applies for electrons outside the original beam boundary in the case of Brillouin flow, but not for positive-ion focusing, in which case the second term would be zero. This term represents a restoring force on an electron outside the original beam boundary made up of the magnetic and d-c space-charge forces, which do not cancel in this region as they do inside the beam. For the positive-ion case, on the other hand, the d-c electrostatic field is everywhere zero.

The solutions to Eqs. (114) and (117) proceed in much the same fashion as indicated in Sec. 4.2. Once again we assume the solutions to have a time and space dependence given by $e^{j(\omega t - \beta z)}$; the total derivative, as defined in deriving Eq. (42), here becomes

$$\frac{dv_r}{dt} = \frac{\partial v_r}{\partial t} + v_0 \frac{\partial v_r}{\partial z} \tag{118}$$

so that the equation corresponding to Eq. (43) for the region *inside* the original beam boundary becomes (see also footnote at Eq. 40)

$$E_r = j(\omega - v_0\beta)v_r \tag{119}$$

or

$$v_r = \frac{\eta}{j(\omega - v_0\beta)} E_r \tag{120}$$

The position of an electron inside the beam can be described by $r_0 + \Delta r < a$, where r_0 is the radius of the electron's initial position. The radial velocity v_r is then

$$v_r = \frac{dr}{dt} = \frac{d}{dt}(\Delta r) = j(\omega - v_0\beta)\,\Delta r \tag{121}$$

since taking the particle derivative of a quantity varying as $e^{j(\omega t - \beta z)}$ evidently corresponds to multiplying that quantity by $j(\omega - v_0\beta)$. Therefore

$$\Delta r = -\frac{\eta}{(\omega - v_0\beta)^2} E_r \tag{122}$$

where Δr is now a Eulerian variable, the radial displacement at the point (r,z).

For an electron which (because of radial displacement) moves outside the original beam boundary, Eq. (115) leads to the following expressions for radial velocity and displacement:

$$v_r = \frac{j(\omega - v_0\beta)}{\omega_p{}^2 - (\omega - v_0\beta)^2} E_r \tag{123}$$

$$\Delta r = \frac{\eta}{\omega_p{}^2 - (\omega - v_0\beta)^2} E_r \tag{124}$$

So far we have used only the equations of motion to provide relations between velocities, displacements, and the fields. We shall presently derive (from Maxwell's equations) some relations for the fields that must hold both inside and outside the beam. The problem that immediately arises is how to apply the boundary conditions at the interface between the two regions. The difficulty is that the beam boundary is scalloped

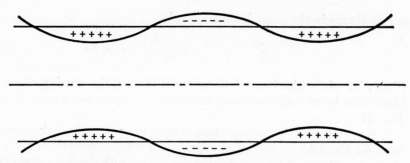

Fig. 4.8 "Scalloped" beam boundary is displaced by an equivalent surface charge distribution.

(since Δr varies with z and t), so that one cannot apply the usual continuity conditions for fields at a cylindrical boundary. Hahn[1] and others have proposed that this problem might be solved approximately, as follows. We replace the scalloped beam boundary by a boundary of constant radius, with the excess or dearth of charge (represented by the scallops) replaced by an equivalent surface charge distribution. This equivalent surface charge distribution contains the same amount of charge as was represented by the scallops that have been removed (Fig. 4.8). Thus, an outward scallop is replaced by a negative charge; an inward displacement represents a dearth of negative charge, and it is therefore replaced by a positive surface charge. The total excess charge in a region corresponding to an outward bulge is that contained in a region of the original beam outside a radius r_0, where r_0 is the initial radius of an electron that reaches the boundary radius a of the beam after it has been displaced. The problem, then, is to find the value of r_0 such that

$$r_0 + \Delta r(r_0) = a \tag{125}$$

The displacement of the electron originally at a is $\Delta r(a)$. Then for any electron which was originally close to this surface, say, at r_0, and which after displacement is at a, the displacement is given by

$$\Delta r(r_0) = \Delta r(a) + \left(\frac{\partial \Delta r}{\partial r}\right)_a (r_0 - a)$$

$$\Delta r(r_0) = \Delta r(a) - \left(\frac{\partial \Delta r}{\partial r}\right)_a \Delta r(r_0) \tag{126}$$

However, for small displacements, the second term is of second order and can be neglected, so that the displacement of the electron that started at r_0 is the same as that of the electron that started at a. This displacement is given by Eq. (122) evaluated at the radial position a. The total

---

[1] W. C. Hahn, Small Signal Theory of Velocity-modulated Electron Beams, *Gen. Elec. Rev.*, **42**:258–270 (1939).

excess charge in the bulge is then given by

$$\frac{\pi(a^2 - r_0^2)\rho_0}{2\pi a} = \frac{(a + r_0)(\Delta r)\rho_0}{2a} \approx \rho_0 \, \Delta r \qquad (127)$$

Similarly, where the beam has scalloped inward, the missing charge is also given by the displacement evaluated at the radius a according to Eq. (122).

We shall need the surface charges later to evaluate boundary conditions for the fields at the beam edge, but it was convenient to evaluate the surface charge at this juncture in connection with the discussion of the actual radial displacements. We can obtain the differential equations for the fields in the most simple fashion by rewriting Eq. (110) in Eulerian variables as

$$v_z = \frac{\eta E_z}{j(\omega - v_0\beta)} \qquad (128)$$

and combining it with Eq. (120) and with the equation of continuity

$$j\omega\rho = -\nabla \cdot (\rho \mathbf{v}_0 + \rho_0 \mathbf{v}) = -(\mathbf{v}_0 \cdot \nabla\rho + \rho_0 \nabla \cdot \mathbf{v})$$
$$j\omega\rho = -v_0 \frac{\partial \rho}{\partial z} - \rho_0 \nabla \cdot \mathbf{v} \qquad (129)$$

After performing the differentiation, we therefore obtain a relation for the charge density:

$$j \frac{\rho}{\rho_0} (\omega - v_0\beta) = -\nabla \cdot \mathbf{v} \qquad (130)$$

It is possible to rewrite $\nabla \cdot \mathbf{v}$ in terms of the electric fields by use of Eqs. (128) and (120), so that Eq. (130) becomes

$$\rho = \frac{-\rho_0 \nabla \cdot \mathbf{v}}{j(\omega - v_0\beta)} = \frac{\rho_0 \eta \nabla \cdot \mathbf{E}}{(\omega - v_0\beta)^2} \qquad (131)$$

However, since $\nabla \cdot \mathbf{E} = \rho/\epsilon_0$, we have

$$\rho = \frac{\rho_0 \eta}{(\omega - v_0\beta)^2} \frac{\rho}{\epsilon_0} \qquad (132)$$

This equation can be satisfied either (1) if $\rho = 0$ or (2) if

$$\frac{\rho_0 \eta}{\epsilon_0(\omega - v_0\beta)^2} \equiv \frac{\omega_p^2}{(\omega - v_0\beta)^2} = 1$$

In the second case we obtain

$$\beta = \frac{\omega}{v_0} \pm \frac{\omega_p}{v_0} \qquad (133)$$

These propagation constants correspond to the same space-charge waves as in the infinite-beam case, with no condition imposed upon the transverse dependence of the fields inside the beam. The axial dependence, of course, is determined by the propagation constants that we have just evaluated. Evidently any transverse dependence of the fields is permitted. The accompanying values of the velocities are determined by Eqs. (128) and (120), and the charge density is determined by Eq. (130). It should be pointed out that this volume charge density is also characterized by displacements at the boundary. To determine the fields outside the beam, one must use the notion of a fictitious surface charge, such as has been described previously, to match the fields on the inside and on the outside. Outside the beam boundary, Maxwell's equations for a region free from charge density or current apply. We shall not consider these waves further here, except to point out that they occur in a finite beam with Brillouin flow (or positive-ion neutralization) when modulation is by planar grids.

A more interesting case arises from the first alternative described in connection with Eq. (132), namely that $\rho = 0$. In this case, for zero r-f charge density inside the beam, the equations for the fields are simply obtained from $\nabla \cdot \mathbf{E} = 0$. In cylindrical coordinates, with no dependence on angle, this relation becomes

$$\frac{1}{r} \frac{\partial}{\partial r} (rE_r) + \frac{\partial E_z}{\partial z} = 0 \tag{134}$$

To convert this equation into one that involves a single component of the field, we can combine two components of the curl equations, namely, for $(\nabla \times \mathbf{E})_\phi$ and $(\nabla \times \mathbf{H})_r$, as follows:

$$\frac{\partial E_z}{\partial r} + j\beta E_r = j\omega\mu_0 H_\phi$$

$$j\beta H_\phi - j\omega\epsilon_0 E_r = J_r$$

By eliminating H_ϕ, we obtain a relation for E_r in terms of E_z and J_r:

$$E_r = \frac{j}{\beta} \frac{\partial E_z}{\partial r} - \frac{j\omega\mu_0}{\beta^2} J, \tag{135}$$

However, the r-f current can be expressed in terms of r-f velocity and, by virtue of Eq. (120), in terms of the electric field. Also, it can be shown that the second term on the right-hand side of Eq. (135) is negligible compared with the left-hand side and can therefore be dropped. Equation (134) can be thus written entirely in terms of E_z:

$$\frac{1}{r} \frac{\partial}{\partial r} \left(r \frac{\partial E_z}{\partial r} \right) + \beta^2 E_z = 0 \tag{136}$$

It might be pointed out that we would have obtained the same equation if we had started with Eq. (44) and used the fact that the charge density is zero and that the current density is related to the fields in the way we have indicated above.

It should be also pointed out that in using the curl equations above, as well as in writing the equations for the velocity components earlier, we have tacitly assumed that we are dealing with a TM space-charge mode. Thus we have not considered the possibility of any θ component of current or velocity in writing the velocity of components; we have assumed that H_z is also zero. Actually, one *can* define TE modes which have such components; moreover, in the case of Brillouin flow, these two types of modes are not uncoupled and not really independent. They are uncoupled for positive-ion focusing, and under that condition what we have written so far would be exactly correct. For Brillouin flow, as soon as v_r has a nonzero value, the focusing field starts to convert this velocity into a v_θ component, and one can no longer consider the modes to be uncoupled. However, it can be shown that for most cases of interest this coupling is small. Actually, the principal effect of the radial r-f velocity is not in producing a current J_r or J_θ, but in producing a displacement that produces the surface charge described previously. This surface charge, multiplied by the d-c velocity in the axial direction, is the important final result, since it provides the principal r-f current.

The equation we have just derived is merely Laplace's equation for E_z and also applies outside the beam.[1] However, the solutions are not continuous because of the presence of the surface charge. The solution of the equation inside the beam is

$$E_{zi} = A I_0(Tr) \tag{137}$$

where I_0 is the imaginary-argument Bessel function and $T^2 = -\beta^2$; and from Eq. (135),

$$E_{ri} = \frac{jA I_1(Tr)}{T(\omega - v_0\beta)} \left[j(\omega - v_0\beta) - \omega_p{}^2 \frac{v_0}{c} \right] \tag{138}$$

Outside the beam, between the beam radius a and the radius b of the surrounding cylinder,

$$E_{zo} = A'[I_0(T'r)K_0(T'b) - I_0(T'b)K_0(T'r)] \tag{139}$$

where $T' = -\beta^2 - k^2$, so that $E_z = 0$ at $r = b$, and

$$E_{ro} = \frac{\beta A'}{T'} [I_1(T'r)K_0(T'b) - I_0(T'b)K_1(T'r)]$$

---

[1] For the case in which $\rho = 0$, we have $\mathbf{E} = -\nabla V$ and $\nabla^2 V = 0$, but since $E_z = -j\beta V$, we may write $\nabla^2 E_z = 0$ for the z component of field as well.

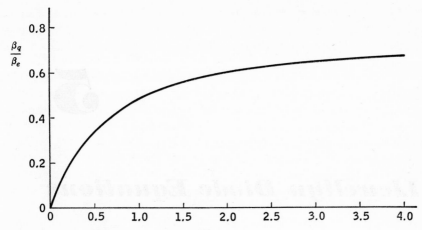

Fig. 4.9 Plot of plasma reduction factor β_q/β_e.

The boundary condition $E_{zo} - E_{zi} = 0$ at $r = a$ gives one relationship between A and A'. Another is obtained from

$$E_{ro} - E_{ri} = \frac{\rho_0}{\epsilon_0} \Delta r$$

where $\rho_0 \Delta r$ is the surface charge, which can be written in terms of E_{ri} from Eq. (122). Equating the two ratios A/A', we obtain an expression for β,

$$\frac{\beta_p}{(\beta_e - \beta)^2} - 1 = \frac{T}{T'} \frac{I_0(Ta)}{I_1(T'a)} \frac{I_0(T'b)K_1(T'a) + I_1(T'a)K_0(T'b)}{I_0(T'b)K_0(T'a) - I_0(T'a)K_0(T'b)} \quad (140)$$

Once again we may write

$$\beta = \beta_e \pm \beta_q \quad (141)$$

as in Eq. (65). β_q is of the same order as β_p, as can be seen from the fact that $\beta_e/\beta_p = \omega/\omega_p \gg 1$ in practice, so that $\beta \approx \beta_e$, $\beta_e \gg k$, and both T and T' are of the order of β_e. Actual values of the plasma reduction factor β_q/β_e are illustrated in Fig. 4.9.

The waves corresponding to zero r-f charge density arise when the modulating fields have transverse components, as in a gridless gap. The details of the kind of modulation produced by a gridless gap, and the mechanism for the excitation of these waves, are discussed in Chap. 8.

5

Llewellyn Diode Equations

5.1 Introduction

We now come to the consideration of electron motion, including
space-charge effects, from an entirely different viewpoint. The
analysis (usually associated with the name of Llewellyn) yields
equations that are valid under a variety of d-c conditions, including accelerated and decelerated motion of the sort mentioned in
Sec. 4.1 (and first discussed by Smullin[1]). The equations are valid
for a flow of electrons normal to conducting planes with no transverse variation in any of the relevant quantities, i.e., particularly
for approximately planar configurations including many diodes,
triodes, and tetrodes. The results have also been extensively
applied to the treatment of noise in the cathode-anode region of
microwave beam tubes on the assumption that this region is an
approximately planar configuration. The results were first

---

[1] L. D. Smullin, Propagation of Disturbances in One-dimensional Accelerated Electron Streams, *J. Appl. Phys.*, **22**:1496–1498, 1951.

derived in a form that would permit the calculation of all the relevant r-f quantities in passing from one planar region to another.

The method differs from that used in the space-charge-wave treatment of Chap. 4 in that the Lagrangian treatment of the electron dynamics is here carried further before one translates the problem into Eulerian variables for the final form of the equations. In the space-charge-wave approach, essentially one never calculates the detailed motion of an electron but immediately transforms to Eulerian variables and calculates velocities, densities, etc., as functions of the space-time coordinates. This transformation comes at a later stage in the Llewellyn analysis. The final answers are in Eulerian variables; but by actually calculating the equation of motion of individual electrons by a perturbation analysis, one can carry the calculations to higher-order perturbations and calculate nonlinear effects in a way that is less direct when one immediately goes to Eulerian variables.

The purpose of this analysis is to obtain small-signal linear relationships for a plane diode (or a parallel-plane gap) in which total current and potential difference and convection current and velocity at the *exit* plane are expressed in terms of the *entrance* quantities and the external impedance. The results are valid for all possible d-c conditions, with the exception of the case in which reflected electrons are present (e.g., in the reflex klystron). The treatment is largely that of F. B. Llewellyn, who summarized his work in the realm of uhf vacuum tubes prior to 1939

$A^*, B^* \cdots I^*$	electronic coefficients	r_c	slope of static characteristic
a, b (subscripts)	refer to entrance and exit plane	S	$= 2 - 2e^{-\beta} - \beta - \beta e^{-\beta}$
a	d-c acceleration	T	d-c transit time
a_T	total acceleration	T_0	zero-space-charge T
C	capacitance between unit area of parallel planes	t	time
		u	d-c velocity
C_c	$= 3C/5$	v	r-f velocity
C_s	$= C[1 - (\zeta/3)]/(1 - \zeta)$	X	diode reactance
E	electric field	X_c	reactance due to C
I	alternating current	x	position
I_D	direct current	Z	diode impedance
I_m	limiting current	α	r-f acceleration
I_T	total current	β	$= j\theta = j\omega T$
P	$= 1 - e^{-\beta} - \beta e^{-\beta}$	δ	$= t - t_a - T$
p	$= j\omega$	ϵ_0	8.85×10^{-12} farad/meter
Q	$= 1 - e^{-\beta}$	ζ	space-charge factor
q	alternating convection current	θ	$= \omega T$
q_D	direct convection current $(= I_D)$	ρ	charge density
q_T	total convection current	ρ_D	d-c charge density at entrance plane
R	diode resistance		
R_c	$= r_c \frac{2}{3}\zeta/[1 - (\zeta/3)]$	ω	frequency in radians

in a now-classic monograph,[1] and further enlarged his results and applied them to the development of equivalent circuits for high-frequency vacuum tubes in a joint paper with L. C. Peterson.[2] The nomenclature used throughout the present chapter is summarized on page 121. It is based on that used by Llewellyn, with the exception of $\eta = |e|/m$. The notation should be distinguished from that used in the other chapters.

5.2 Equation of Motion

Consider the electron flow between two planes of infinite extent, a and b (Fig. 5.1), in the direction indicated. The total current[3] is customarily assumed to flow in the opposite direction. It is important to recall that according to Maxwell's definition, the total current I_T consists of two components (cf. Sec. 3.6):

$$I_T = \rho u + \epsilon_0 \frac{\partial E}{\partial t} \tag{1}$$

The first term is the convection current, and the second term is the displacement current. The total current is the same at any point in the circuit. Thus, when a group of electrons is liberated at the cathode of a diode, it will take a finite time to reach the anode. The convection current at the anode (the number of electrons arriving there in unit time) will be zero until the electrons get there, but the *total* current will be the same as at the cathode. The difference is made up by the displacement current (the change in the electric field caused by electrons still under way). This concept of the two components of total current is extremely important whenever the transit time of the electrons is not negligible. (At low frequencies, the current is almost all convection current.)

Poisson's equation $\rho = \epsilon_0 \nabla \cdot E$ becomes, for the case under consideration,

$$\rho = \epsilon_0 \frac{\partial E}{\partial x} \tag{2}$$

so that (1) may be rewritten

$$I_T = \epsilon_0 \left(u \frac{\partial E}{\partial x} + \frac{\partial E}{\partial t} \right) = \epsilon_0 \frac{dE}{dt} \tag{3}$$

[1] F. B. Llewellyn, "Electron-inertia Effects," Cambridge University Press, Cambridge, 1941. (Distributed in the United States by The Macmillan Company, New York.)

[2] F. B. Llewellyn and L. C. Peterson, Vacuum-tube Networks, *Proc. IRE*, **32:**144–166 (1944).

[3] *Current* means, of course, *current per unit area* in this problem; the reader should keep in mind that we are actually considering current densities throughout this chapter.

since the expression in the parentheses is the total (particle) derivative, that is, the total change in E as "seen" by the moving electron.

The equation of motion of the electron may be written in terms of a_T, the total acceleration, as follows:

$$a_T = \ddot{x} = - \eta E \tag{4}$$

The combination of (3) and (4) yields

$$- \frac{\eta}{\epsilon_0} I_T = \frac{da_T}{dt} \tag{5}$$

which gives acceleration as a function of time. This is known as *Llewellyn's equation*. It is the starting point of the present analysis of electron flow in the presence of space charge. It should be noted that the effect of charge density ρ on the electric field E is contained in (5) through the divergence equation (2), which was used in the derivation of Llewellyn's equation. Before proceeding with the solution, some of the assumptions made in it should be pointed out. First, magnetic effects are disregarded in (4); they do not become important until the electron moves with "relativistic" velocities (i.e., approaching the velocity of light). Second, all electrons are assumed to enter the region with a single velocity (rather than the actual random distribution of velocities). Third, the velocity must remain a single-valued function of x and t: in other words, the electrons must not overtake one another.

In addition to total current, two conditions at the entrance are given: the convection current ρu, which we shall designate by q_T, and the electron velocity. We shall aim at three linear equations connecting the potential difference, exit convection current, and exit velocity, on the one hand, with the entrance convection current, entrance velocity, and total current on the other hand. Even then, the problem is not completely specified. Only two of these six variables, the entrance convection and velocity, are usually known. They are determined either from the exit values in the preceding region, or (if one of the electrodes is a cathode) from a detailed consideration of the emission process. We thus need still another equation. This relationship is provided by the ratio of total current to potential difference, as determined by the external impedance. The fourth equation is thus a circuit equation as distinct from the other three equations, which are electronic equations.

All quantities that enter into the analysis, such as current, potential, and velocity, are separable into d-c and r-f components. If we employ the subscript D for the d-c components and no subscript for the r-f components, we have for the current,

$$I_T = I_D + I e^{pt} \tag{6}$$

where $p = j\omega$. The factor η/ϵ_0 occurs so often in what follows that it is convenient to define

$$I'_T \equiv -\frac{\eta}{\epsilon_0} I_T$$

Similarly for I_D, I, and any other quantity, *the prime signifies multiplication by* $-\eta/\epsilon_0$. Then (5) becomes

$$\frac{da_T}{dt} = \ddot{x} = I'_D + I'e^{pt} \tag{7}$$

Integration gives the total acceleration

$$a_T = \ddot{x} = I'_D(t - t_a) + \frac{I'}{p}(e^{pt} - e^{pt_a}) + a_a + \alpha_a e^{pt_a} \tag{8}$$

The subscript a specifies that we have taken the value of the quantity at the entrance plane. The last two terms in (8) represent the *initial acceleration* (d-c and r-f, respectively).

Another integration yields the velocity:

$$\dot{x} = \tfrac{1}{2}I'_D(t - t_a)^2 + \frac{I'}{p^2}(e^{pt} - e^{pt_a}) + \left(-\frac{I'}{p}e^{pt_a} + a_a + \alpha_a e^{pt_a}\right)(t - t_a)$$
$$+ u_a + v_a e^{pt_a} \tag{9}$$

The last two terms in (9) represent the *initial velocity* (d-c and r-f, respectively).

A third integration gives the position:

$$x = \tfrac{1}{6}I'_D(t - t_a)^3 + \frac{I'}{p^3}(e^{pt} - e^{pt_a}) + \frac{1}{2}\left(-\frac{I'}{p}e^{pt_a} + a_a + \alpha_a e^{pt_a}\right)(t - t_a)^2$$
$$+ \left(u_a + v_a e^{pt_a} - \frac{I'}{p^2}e^{pt_a}\right)(t - t_a) \tag{10}$$

The constants of integration have been so chosen that $x = 0$ at $t = t_a$, which means that position is measured from the a plane.

We have thus obtained three equations that determine $\ddot{x}$, $\dot{x}$, and x in terms of t and t_a. If the initial conditions at the time t_a are specified, then the acceleration, velocity, and position at any time t may be found from (8), (9), and (10), respectively. Up to this point we have been using Lagrangian variables, so that we have equations that describe the motion of individual particles. The quantity t_a that appears in these equations is not usually specified and we are ultimately not interested in the motion of individual particles; rather, we shall state the problem in Eulerian variables: current density and r-f velocity at various planes. Equations (8) to (10), however, are the vehicles by which one can obtain these answers in Eulerian variables. They lend themselves to a method of successive approximations by which one can include the nonlinear effects of large signals in quite a straightforward manner. This analysis has been carried through by Llewellyn. We shall not repeat it here, except to point out that it is possible to use the equations in this fashion.

In using these equations, it is convenient to introduce a new variable, the *d-c transit time*, which is uniquely related to x and is independent of t or the r-f level. The d-c transit time T is the time that an electron requires to reach the plane x in the absence of all r-f fluctuations. Since T is uniquely defined by x, it is in effect an equivalent space variable, i.e., a way of specifying a particular plane, even though it is measured in terms of time. In Eq. (10), it is the value of $t - t_a$ when all the r-f quantities vanish.

5.3 D-C Solution

Before we proceed with the r-f problem with the help of the new variable, let us consider the d-c solution (when all the r-f quantities are zero) in terms of the new variable. For this case, Eqs. (8) to (10) become

$$\ddot{x}_D = I'_D T + a_a \tag{11}$$
$$\dot{x}_D = \tfrac{1}{2} I'_D T^2 + a_a T + u_a \tag{12}$$
$$x_D = \tfrac{1}{6} I'_D T^3 + \tfrac{1}{2} a_a T^2 + u_a T \tag{13}$$

These results may be used to obtain the potential difference between the two planes a and b, by means of the potential equation

$$V_b - V_a = - \int_a^b E \, dx \tag{14}$$

The sign is chosen to correspond to the assumed current direction, toward the cathode when $V_b > V_a$ (Fig. 5.1).

But from (4), $E = -\ddot{x}/\eta$, so that

$$V_b - V_a = \frac{1}{\eta} \int_a^b \ddot{x} \, dx \tag{15}$$

This is quite a general equation; it holds for the r-f case as well, and it will be used in the derivation of the final results of the next section.

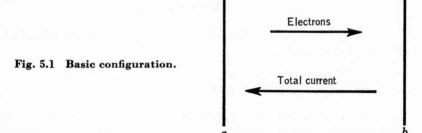

Fig. 5.1 Basic configuration.

Electrons

Total current

a b

For the d-c case, $\ddot{x}$ is given by (11) and dx is obtained from (12) or (13):

$$dx = (\tfrac{1}{2}I'_D T^2 + a_a T + u_a)\,dT$$

Therefore, the d-c component of potential difference is

$$(V_b - V_a)_D = \frac{1}{\eta}\int_0^T (I'_D T + a_a)(\tfrac{1}{2}I'_D T^2 + a_a T + u_a)\,dT$$

$$= \frac{1}{\eta}\,(\tfrac{1}{8}I'^2_D T^4 + \tfrac{1}{2}I'_D a_a T^3 + \tfrac{1}{2}I'_D u_a T^2 + \tfrac{1}{2}a_a{}^2 T^2 + a_a u_a T) \quad (16)$$

It should be noted that a formal solution of Eq. (15) may also be written down directly, in terms of the velocity:

$$(V_b - V_a)_D = \frac{1}{\eta}\frac{u_b{}^2 - u_a{}^2}{2} \quad (17)$$

This is an equally good representation, but it does not show the effect of the individual terms arising out of the initial conditions.

Two special cases of interest will be considered next.

a. Temperature-limited diode (low current)

If only a few electrons are emitted from plane a with very low initial velocity, then I'_D and u_a both approach zero, so that (12), (13), and (16) become

$$\dot{x}_D = a_a T = u_b \quad (18)$$
$$x_D = \tfrac{1}{2}a_a T^2 \quad (19)$$
$$(V_b - V_a)_D = \frac{1}{\eta}\frac{a_a{}^2}{2}\,T^2 = \frac{1}{\eta}\frac{u_b{}^2}{2} \quad (20)$$

Although the quantity u_b that appears in the above equations carries the subscript b, it should be understood to apply to the d-c velocity $\dot{x}_D$ in any plane x. (The subscript b may be taken to refer to any intermediate plane as well.) If a_a is eliminated between (19) and (20), an expression for the d-c transit time is obtained:

$$T = x\sqrt{\frac{2}{\eta(V_b - V_a)_D}} \quad (21)$$

Both (20) and (21) are the familiar equations of electron flow in the absence of space charge.

b. Space-charge-limited diode

Under the conditions of "complete" space charge, just enough electrons (with negligible initial velocity) are drawn from plane a to reduce the field there to zero. Then a_a as well as u_a approach zero, and (13) and (16) become

$$x_D = \tfrac{1}{6} I'_D T^3 \tag{22}$$

$$(V_b - V_a)_D = \frac{1}{\eta} \frac{I'^2_D}{8} T^4 \tag{23}$$

If I'_D is eliminated between (22) and (23), the following expression for the d-c transit time is obtained:

$$T = \frac{3}{2} x \sqrt{\frac{2}{\eta(V_b - V_a)_D}} \tag{24}$$

This interesting result shows the d-c transit time under complete space-charge conditions to be exactly $\tfrac{3}{2}$ times that given by (21) for zero space-charge conditions.

The above equations may also be used to solve for I'_D:

$$I'_D = \frac{4\sqrt{2}\,\eta^{\frac{1}{2}}}{9} \frac{(V_b - V_a)_D^{\frac{3}{2}}}{x^2} \tag{25}$$

By means of the equality $I'_D = -(\eta/\epsilon_0)I_D$, (25) may be written in terms of the actual current,

$$I_D = -\frac{4\sqrt{2\eta}}{9}\,\epsilon_0\,\frac{(V_b - V_a)_D^{\frac{3}{2}}}{x^2}$$

$$I_D = -2.331 \times 10^{-6}\,\frac{(V_b - V_a)_D^{\frac{3}{2}}}{x^2} \tag{26}$$

This is, of course, the familiar $\tfrac{3}{2}$-power equation (Child's law) for the space-charge-limited diode.

5.4 R-F Solution

In the presence of the fluctuating components, we may define

$$t - t_a \equiv T + \delta \tag{27}$$

where T is again the d-c transit time, and functions of $(t - t_a)$ may be expanded in terms of a power series in δ. We shall be concerned mostly with small values of δ, so that quadratic and higher-order terms in δ will become negligible; but the analysis may be carried out to any degree of accuracy, and Llewellyn has actually considered second-order effects by this method in his original treatment.[1]

For small δ, we have for instance

$$e^{j\omega t_a} = e^{j\omega t}e^{-j\omega T}e^{-j\omega\delta} = e^{pt}e^{-\beta}(1 - p\delta + \cdots) \tag{28}$$

[1] Llewellyn, *op. cit.*

where we have defined an imaginary transit angle

$$\beta \equiv pT \tag{29}$$

and $p = j\omega$, as before.

With the aid of the above definitions, (10) becomes

$$
\begin{aligned}
x = {} & \tfrac{1}{6}I'_D(T^3 + 3\delta T^2) + \frac{I'}{p^3} e^{pt}[1 - e^{-\beta}(1 - p\delta)] \\
& + \frac{1}{2}\left[-\frac{I'}{p} e^{pt}e^{-\beta}(1 - p\delta) + a_a + \alpha_a e^{pt}e^{-\beta}(1 - p\delta) \right](T^2 + 2\delta T) \\
& + \left[u_a + v_a e^{pt}e^{-\beta}(1 - p\delta) - \frac{I'}{p^2} e^{pt}e^{-\beta}(1 - p\delta) \right](T + \delta) \quad (30)
\end{aligned}
$$

where all terms in δ of order higher than linear have been left out. Next, the multiplications indicated in (30) are carried out, again with omission of quadratic and higher terms as well as all terms in which δ multiplies an r-f quantity such as I', v_a, or α_a. But the distance to a point x is also given in terms of the d-c transit time T to that point, as in Eq. (13). If we set this equation equal to (30), the d-c terms cancel out and we obtain for the first-order value of δ:

$$\delta = -\frac{(I'/p^3)(1 - e^{-\beta}) + \tfrac{1}{2}[\alpha_a - (I'/p)]T^2 e^{-\beta} + [v_a - (I'/p^2)]Te^{-\beta}}{\tfrac{1}{2}I'_D T^2 + a_a T + u_a} e^{pt} \tag{31}$$

It may be observed in passing that the denominator of (31) is the d-c velocity given by (12).

This is the first-order r-f modulation in transit time, and it may be seen to depend on r-f terms in the current, acceleration, and velocity. It should be noted that δ is here an Eulerian variable, since it describes the variation of transit time as a function of time t and position T and no longer refers to individual particles; it is, therefore, via Eq. (31) that we make the transition to Eulerian variables. By substituting into the appropriate equations of Sec. 5.2, using the relation that $t - t_a = T + \delta$, we could obtain the first-order r-f expressions for exit velocity and acceleration in terms of their entrance values stated as functions of time and coordinates (t and T). Actually, we are more usually interested in exit velocity and convection current. These quantities are continuous at the boundary between two adjacent regions (i.e., the exit values of one region are also the entrance values of the next, except for possible instantaneous jumps), whereas acceleration is not. To introduce this convection current, let us designate the term ρu that appears in (1) by q_T, so that

$$I_T = q_T + \epsilon_0 \frac{\partial E}{\partial t}$$

or, with the help of (4) and the usual definition $q_T' = -(\eta/\epsilon_0)q_T$,

$$I_T' = q_T' + \frac{\partial \ddot{x}}{\partial t} \tag{32}$$

Here $\partial \ddot{x}/\partial t$ is the *local derivative*, i.e., the rate of change in the acceleration of successive particles as they pass a fixed point; it depends only on the r-f terms of the equation and is zero for the d-c case. To find its value, we must first rewrite (8) in terms of δ and differentiate. Note that δ is a function of t:

$$\ddot{x} = I_D'(T + \delta) + \frac{I'}{p}(1 - e^{-\beta})e^{pt} + a_a + \alpha_a e^{-\beta}e^{pt} \tag{33}$$

$$\frac{\partial \ddot{x}}{\partial t} = I_D' p\delta + I'(1 - e^{-\beta})e^{pt} + \alpha_a p e^{-\beta}e^{pt} \tag{34}$$

Therefore

$$q_T' = I_T' - \frac{\partial \ddot{x}}{\partial t} = I_D' + I'e^{pt} - [I_D' p\delta + I'(1 - e^{-\beta})e^{pt} + \alpha_a p e^{-\beta}e^{pt}] \tag{35}$$

At the plane a, $\delta = 0$ and $\beta = 0$, and

$$q_T' = I_D' + I'e^{pt} - \alpha_a p e^{pt} \tag{36}$$

But the value of q_T' at this plane is also given, by definition, as

$$q_T' = q_D' + q_a'e^{pt} = I_D' + q_a'e^{pt} \tag{37}$$

since the d-c component of convection current comprises the total d-c current. A comparison of (36) and (37) therefore yields

$$\alpha_a = \frac{I' - q_a'}{p} \tag{38}$$

This equation provides the relation necessary to replace α_a by q_a' in the equations of motion.

We are now ready to compute the r-f voltage as defined by (15). The r-f acceleration is obtained from (33) by dropping the d-c terms,

$$\ddot{x} = I_D'\delta + \frac{I'}{p}(1 - e^{-\beta})e^{pt} + \alpha_a e^{-\beta}e^{pt}$$

and dx is related to dT by

$$dx = (\tfrac{1}{2}I_D'T^2 + a_a T + u_a)\,dT$$

Then from (15), the r-f voltage is given by

$$\eta(V_b - V_a) = \int_a^b \ddot{x}\,dx = e^{pt}\int_a^b \frac{I'}{p^3}\{[(1 - e^{-\beta})(-I_D') + I_D'pTe^{-\beta}]\,dT$$

$$+ p^2\,dx\} - q_a'\frac{e^{-\beta}}{p}(a_a T + u_a)\,dT - v_a I_D'e^{-\beta}T\,dT \tag{39}$$

Note that one of the integrands is advisedly expressed in terms of the spacing x; this term will be later shown to represent a capacitance.

The factor e^{pt} will henceforth be dropped because it occurs throughout. The result of the integration indicated in (39) is

$$\eta(V_b - V_a) = \frac{I'}{p^4}[p^3 x + I'_D(2 - 2e^{-\beta} - \beta - \beta e^{-\beta})]$$

$$+ \frac{q'_a}{p^3}[a_a(\beta e^{-\beta} + e^{-\beta} - 1) + u_a p(e^{-\beta} - 1)] + \frac{v_a}{p^2} I'_D(\beta e^{-\beta} + e^{-\beta} - 1) \quad (40)$$

where β now refers to the exit plane. This result may be written more simply with the aid of the following definitions:

$$P \equiv 1 - e^{-\beta} - \beta e^{-\beta} \quad (41)$$
$$Q \equiv 1 - e^{-\beta} \quad (42)$$
$$S \equiv 2 - 2e^{-\beta} - \beta - \beta e^{-\beta} \quad (43)$$

The substitutions $I' = -(\eta/\epsilon_0)I$ and $q' = -(\eta/\epsilon_0)q$ may also be made, to express the results in terms of the actual currents; so that the r-f voltage is finally

$$(V_b - V_a) = -\frac{I}{\epsilon_0 p^4}(p^3 x + I'_D S) + \frac{q_a}{\epsilon_0 p^3}(a_a P + u_a p Q) + v_a \frac{I_D}{\epsilon_0 p^2} P \quad (44)$$

The derivation of the voltage equation has been carried out in some detail; it is more difficult than the derivation of the other r-f equations (exit current and velocity) because it involves the integration indicated by (39). The r-f equations for q_b and v_b are obtained more simply from (32) and (9), respectively, in an analogous manner; i.e., by substituting $T + \delta$ for $t - t_a$, keeping only terms of order lower than quadratic in δ, and subtracting out the d-c terms. The final equations for the r-f exit current and velocity are

$$q_b = I\frac{I'_D P}{p^2 u_b} + q_a\left(1 - \frac{I'_D T^2}{2u_b}\right)e^{-\beta} + v_a \frac{I_D}{u_b}\beta e^{-\beta} \quad (45)$$

$$v_b = I\frac{\eta}{\epsilon_0}\frac{1}{p^2}\left(Q - \frac{a_b}{pu_b}P\right) + q_a\frac{\eta}{\epsilon_0}\frac{1}{p^2}\left(\frac{a_b T}{2u_b} - 1\right)\beta e^{-\beta} + v_a\left(1 - \frac{a_b T}{u_b}\right)e^{-\beta} \quad (46)$$

The subscript b may again be taken to refer to any intermediate plane x as well. Furthermore,

$$a_b = I'_D T + a_a \quad (47)$$
$$u_b = \tfrac{1}{2}I'_D T^2 + a_a T + u_a \quad (48)$$

where a_a is given in terms of x and u_a by

$$x = \tfrac{1}{6}I'_D T^3 + \frac{a_a}{2}T^2 + u_a T \quad (49)$$

The results of this section may now be summarized in a compact form, as follows:

$$V_b - V_a = A^*I + B^*q_a + C^*v_a$$
$$q_b = D^*I + E^*q_a + F^*v_a \tag{50}$$
$$v_b = G^*I + H^*q_a + I^*v_a$$

The coefficients are given by

$$A^* = -\frac{1}{\epsilon_0 p^4}(p^3 x + I'_D S) \qquad F^* = \frac{I_D}{u_b}\beta e^{-\beta}$$

$$B^* = \frac{1}{\epsilon_0 p^3}(a_a P + u_a p Q) \qquad G^* = \frac{\eta}{\epsilon_0}\frac{1}{p^2}\left(Q - \frac{a_b}{p u_b}P\right)$$

$$C^* = \frac{I_D}{\epsilon_0 p^2}P \qquad H^* = \frac{\eta}{\epsilon_0}\frac{1}{p^2}\left(\frac{a_b T}{2 u_b} - 1\right)\beta e^{-\beta}$$

$$D^* = \frac{I'_D P}{p^2 u_b} \qquad I^* = \left(1 - \frac{a_b T}{u_b}\right)e^{-\beta}$$

$$E^* = \left(1 - \frac{I'_D T^2}{2 u_b}\right)e^{-\beta}$$

where P, Q, and S are given by (41), (42), and (43), respectively.

It may be noted that the coefficient E^*, which relates the output and input current, may be written in terms of $\rho_D = -I_D/u_b$, the d-c charge density at the output plane, as follows:

$$E^* = \left(1 - \frac{\eta \rho_D}{\epsilon_0}\frac{T^2}{2}\right)e^{-\beta} = \left(1 - \frac{\omega_p^2 T^2}{2}\right)e^{-\beta}$$

where $\omega_p = \sqrt{\eta \rho_D/\epsilon_0}$ is the plasma frequency. The terms in the parentheses are the same as the first two terms of the expansion for $\cos \omega_p T$. It may be readily shown, from the results for a beam drifting in a field-free region (as treated in Chap. 4), that for a beam injected with current modulation the r-f current along the tube decreases as $\cos \omega_p T$. The similarity between the two results arises because both represent the same physical process: the effect of space-charge forces in *smoothing* any r-f density fluctuations. Similarly, H^* is the same as the first two terms of a sine expansion and represents the effects of the same space-charge density; the resulting forces tend to *increase* the r-f velocity.

It should be emphasized that the fact that the Llewellyn coefficients have the same form as the first two terms of a trigonometric expansion does not imply that Llewellyn's results are valid only for values of $\omega_p T$ for which such an expansion is valid. Llewellyn's results apply for any value of $\omega_p T$. They are not trigonometric; the case treated here is different from the constant-drift-velocity case of Chap. 4.

5.5   Space-charge Factor

If a single electron were introduced into the space between the two planes, its position at any time would be given by

$$x_0 = \frac{u_a + u_b}{2} T_0 \tag{51}$$

where the subscript 0 has been introduced to denote this case. The presence of other electrons (i.e., space charge) will affect the transit time, although u_a and u_b remain unchanged. The effect on transit time may be expressed by a suitable multiplying factor, so selected as to yield consistent equations. For instance, we may write

$$x = \frac{u_a + u_b}{2} T \left(1 - \frac{\zeta}{3} \right) \tag{52}$$

where

$$\zeta = 3 \left(1 - \frac{T_0}{T} \right) \tag{53}$$

is called the *space-charge factor*. The reader may readily verify that Eqs. (51) to (53) are consistent. The definition (53) has been picked out of several possible alternatives because it has a property that may be best seen from a comparison of (51) and (52): T assumes that value T_0 as ζ approaches zero. Thus $\zeta = 0$ specifies the condition of *zero space charge*, and $\zeta = 1$ specifies the condition of *complete space charge*, i.e., the condition when the maximum number of electrons that will move from a to b without turning back has been injected through the a plane. (If the a plane is the cathode, this condition corresponds to space-charge-limited emission.) This maximum current, which we shall call I_m, is in general given by

$$I_m = - \frac{2\epsilon_0}{9\eta} \frac{(u_a + u_b)^3}{x^2}$$

This expression reduces to the $\frac{3}{2}$-power equation for the case when $u_a = 0$. The actual current I_D may be shown to be related to the maximum current by the equation

$$\frac{I_D}{I_m} = \frac{9}{4} \zeta \left(1 - \frac{\zeta}{3} \right)^2 \tag{54}$$

and the current I_D may be expressed in terms of the space-charge factor by

$$I'_D = (u_a + u_b) \frac{2\zeta}{T^2} \tag{55}$$

where again $I'_D = - (\eta/\epsilon_0) I_D$.

Table 5.1   Coefficients for Eqs. (50)

	General case	$\zeta = 0$	$\zeta = 1$
A^*	$\dfrac{1}{\epsilon_0}(u_a + u_b)\dfrac{T^2}{2}\dfrac{1}{\beta}\left[1 - \dfrac{\zeta}{3}\left(1 - \dfrac{12S}{\beta^3}\right)\right]$	$\dfrac{1}{\epsilon_0}(u_a + u_b)\dfrac{T^2}{2}\dfrac{1}{\beta}$	$\dfrac{1}{\epsilon_0}(u_a + u_b)\dfrac{T^2}{3\beta}\left(1 + \dfrac{6S}{\beta^3}\right)$
B^*	$\dfrac{1}{\epsilon_0}\dfrac{T^2}{\beta^3}[u_a(P - \beta Q) - u_b P + \zeta(u_a + u_b)P]$	$\dfrac{1}{\epsilon_0}\dfrac{T^2}{\beta^3}[u_a(P - \beta Q) - u_b P]$	$\dfrac{1}{\epsilon_0}\dfrac{T^2}{\beta^3}u_a(2P - \beta Q)$
C^*	$-\dfrac{2\zeta}{\eta}(u_a + u_b)\dfrac{P}{\beta^2}$	0	$-\dfrac{2}{\eta}(u_a + u_b)\dfrac{P}{\beta^2}$
D^*	$2\zeta\left(\dfrac{u_a + u_b}{u_b}\right)\dfrac{P}{\beta^2}$	0	$2\left(\dfrac{u_a + u_b}{u_b}\right)\dfrac{P}{\beta^2}$
E^*	$\dfrac{1}{u_b}[u_b - \zeta(u_a + u_b)]e^{-\beta}$	$e^{-\beta}$	$-\dfrac{u_a}{u_b}e^{-\beta}$
F^*	$\dfrac{\epsilon_0}{\eta}\dfrac{2\zeta}{T^2}\left(\dfrac{u_a + u_b}{u_b}\right)\beta e^{-\beta}$	0	$\dfrac{\epsilon_0}{\eta}\dfrac{2}{T^2}\left(\dfrac{u_a + u_b}{u_b}\right)\beta e^{-\beta}$
G^*	$-\dfrac{\eta}{\epsilon_0}\dfrac{T^2}{\beta^3}\dfrac{1}{u_b}[u_b(P - \beta Q) - u_a P + \zeta(u_a + u_b)P]$	$-\dfrac{\eta}{\epsilon_0}\dfrac{T^2}{\beta^3}\dfrac{1}{u_b}[u_b(P - \beta Q) - u_a P]$	$-\dfrac{\eta}{\epsilon_0}\dfrac{T^2}{\beta^3}(2P - \beta Q)$
H^*	$-\dfrac{\eta}{\epsilon_0}\dfrac{T^2}{2}\left(\dfrac{u_a + u_b}{u_b}\right)(1 - \zeta)\dfrac{e^{-\beta}}{\beta}$	$-\dfrac{\eta}{\epsilon_0}\dfrac{T^2}{2}\left(\dfrac{u_a + u_b}{u_b}\right)\dfrac{e^{-\beta}}{\beta}$	0
I^*	$\dfrac{1}{u_b}[u_a - \zeta(u_a + u_b)]e^{-\beta}$	$\dfrac{u_a}{u_b}$	$-e^{-\beta}$

The concept of the space-charge factor ζ has been introduced mainly because the coefficients appearing in (50) may be expressed very conveniently in terms of ζ; then the two cases of considerable interest, that of zero space charge and complete space charge, may be obtained directly simply by setting $\zeta = 0$ and $\zeta = 1$, respectively. It is useful to eliminate a_a and a_b from these coefficients as well; so that in addition to (52) and (55), we shall need

$$a_a = \frac{1}{T}\left[u_b - u_a - (u_a + u_b)\right]$$
$$a_b = \frac{1}{T}\left[u_b - u_a + (u_a + u_b)\right]$$

$$(56)$$

We obtain Eqs. (56) from (49) and (47) by substituting for x and I'_D from (52) and (55), respectively. Moreover, by subtracting a_a from a_b and rearranging, we obtain

$$\zeta = \frac{T}{2}\frac{a_b - a_a}{u_a + u_b} \tag{57}$$

With the help of Eqs. (52), (55), and (56), the coefficients which appear in (50) may therefore be rewritten in terms of the space-charge factor. Table 5.1 gives the value of each coefficient in the general case, for zero space charge and for complete space charge.

It may also be noted that for small transit angles β, the abbreviations expressed by the symbols P, Q, and S, defined by (41), (42), and (43), respectively, may be written as follows

$$P = 1 - e^{-\beta} - \beta e^{-\beta} \approx \frac{\beta^2}{2} - \frac{\beta^3}{3} + \frac{\beta^4}{8} - \cdots \tag{58}$$

$$Q = 1 - e^{-\beta} \approx \beta - \frac{\beta^2}{2} + \frac{\beta^3}{6} - \frac{\beta^4}{24} + \cdots \tag{59}$$

$$S = 2 - 2e^{-\beta} - \beta - \beta e^{-\beta} \approx -\frac{\beta^3}{6} + \frac{\beta^4}{12} - \frac{\beta^5}{40} + \frac{\beta^6}{180} - \cdots \tag{60}$$

5.6 Diode Equations

The Llewellyn-Peterson equations will now be applied to some specific examples. Let us assume, for instance, that *no electrons* are present in the region between the parallel planes. In that case, $I_D = q_a = 0$, and (44) reduces to

$$V_b - V_a = \frac{Ix}{\epsilon_0 p} \tag{61}$$

The impedance between a unit area of parallel planes is therefore given by

$$\frac{V_b - V_a}{I} = \frac{x}{\epsilon_0 p} = \frac{1}{j\omega}\frac{x}{\epsilon_0} = \frac{1}{j\omega C} = jX_C \tag{62}$$

where

$$C = -\frac{1}{\omega X_C} = \frac{\epsilon_0}{x} \tag{63}$$

is the well-known expression for the capacitance per unit area between parallel planes, as was to be expected.

Next, consider the diode. The a plane is now a cathode which emits electrons, and the b plane is an anode operated at a more positive potential than the cathode. In general, two cases may arise:

1. The anode potential is so high that all electrons emitted from the cathode travel to the anode. Then the initial r-f current $q_a = 0$.
2. Only some of the electrons are drawn off, and the electric field at the cathode approaches zero. This is the condition of complete space charge ($\zeta = 1$); then for the initial d-c velocity $u_a = 0$, it follows that $B^* = 0$.

In either case, then, $B^*q_a = 0$. Also, since the initial velocity is a function of the cathode temperature alone, the signal r-f initial velocity $v_a = 0$. For any diode (or, for that matter, for any case in which a *constant* stream of electrons is injected through the a plane, so that $q_a = v_a = 0$),

$$V_b - V_a = A^*I \tag{64}$$

The coefficient A^* may thus be considered to be the series impedance of the diode:

$$A^* = R + jX = -\frac{1}{\epsilon_0 p^4}(p^3 x + I'_D S) \tag{65}$$

If we substitute for S (remembering that $\beta = j\theta = j\omega T$) and separate the real and imaginary parts, we obtain

$$R = \frac{I'_D}{\epsilon_0 \omega^4}[2(1 - \cos\theta) - \theta\sin\theta] \tag{66}$$

$$X = -\frac{x}{\epsilon_0 \omega} - \frac{I'_D}{\epsilon_0 \omega^4}[\theta(1 + \cos\theta) - 2\sin\theta] \tag{67}$$

The diode impedance thus turns out to be a resistance in series with a capacitive reactance. Comparison with (63) shows that the first term of (67) is associated with the vacuum capacitance between cathode and anode; the second term may therefore be considered as a correction representing the effect of the electron beam.

The current I'_D may also be expressed in terms of more convenient quantities. From (52) and (54), we may write

$$\frac{I'_D}{\epsilon_0\omega^4} = \frac{1}{[1 - (\zeta/3)]\epsilon_0\omega^4 T^3} \tag{68}$$

It is possible to relate x and the static characteristic (SC) through its slope r_c, defined by

$$r_c \equiv -\frac{\partial(V_b - V_a)_D}{\partial I_D} \tag{69}$$

which for the space-charge-limited diode becomes

$$r_{c(\text{SC})} = -\frac{2}{3}\frac{V}{I_D} \tag{70}$$

Then (23) and (24) yield for the space-charge-limited case

$$r_{c(\text{SC})} = \frac{xT_{\text{SC}}}{2\epsilon_0} \qquad \text{or} \qquad x = \frac{2\epsilon_0 r_{c(\text{SC})}}{T_{\text{SC}}} \tag{71}$$

The multiplier $I'_D/\epsilon_0\omega^4$ that occurs in Eqs. (66) and (67) may be therefore expressed in terms of the space-charge factor ζ, with the help of Eqs. (52) and (55), as follows:

$$\frac{I'_D}{\epsilon_0\omega^4} = \frac{\frac{2}{3}\zeta}{1 - \zeta/3}\frac{12r_{c(\text{SC})}}{\theta^3}\frac{1}{\theta_{\text{SC}}} \tag{72}$$

But from (53),

$$1 - \frac{\zeta}{3} = \frac{T_0}{T} = \frac{\frac{2}{3}T_{\text{SC}}}{T} \tag{73}$$

so that

$$\theta_{\text{SC}} = \omega T_{\text{SC}} = \frac{3}{2}\left(1 - \frac{\zeta}{3}\right)\theta \tag{74}$$

and (72) becomes

$$\frac{I'_D}{\epsilon_0} = \frac{\zeta}{1 - \zeta/3} = \frac{12r_{c(\text{SC})}}{\theta^4(1 - \zeta/3)} = \frac{12}{\theta^4}\frac{r_{c(\text{SC})}(\frac{4}{9}\zeta)}{(1 - \zeta/3)^2} = \frac{12R_c}{\theta^4} \tag{75}$$

where we have defined

$$R_c \equiv \frac{\frac{4}{9}r_{c(\text{SC})}}{(1 - \zeta/3)^2} \tag{76}$$

Similarly, the first term of (67) becomes, from (71), (74), and (76),

$$\frac{x}{\epsilon_0\omega} = \frac{2r_c}{\theta} = \frac{2R_c}{\theta}\frac{1 - \zeta/3}{\frac{2}{3}\zeta} \tag{77}$$

The expressions for the resistance and reactance of a diode therefore become

$$R = \frac{12R_c}{\theta^4}[2(1 - \cos\theta) - \theta\sin\theta] \tag{78}$$

$$X = -\frac{12R_c}{\theta^4}\left[\frac{\theta^3}{6} + \theta(1 + \cos\theta) - 2\sin\theta\right] - \frac{x}{\epsilon_0\omega}\frac{1 - \zeta}{1 - \zeta/3} \tag{79}$$

In the very important case of complete space charge, $\zeta = 1$ and $R_c = r_c$; so that for this case,

$$R_{\zeta=1} = \frac{12r_c}{\theta^4}\left[2(1 - \cos\theta) - \theta\sin\theta\right] \tag{80}$$

$$X_{\zeta=1} = -\frac{12r_c}{\theta^4}\left[\frac{\theta^3}{6} + \theta(1 + \cos\theta) - 2\sin\theta\right] \tag{81}$$

$$Z_{\zeta=1} = r_c\left[\frac{2}{\beta} + \frac{12S}{\beta^4}\right] \tag{82}$$

The quantities given by Eqs. (80) and (81) are plotted as a function of the transit angle θ in Fig. 5.2. We note that the resistive component becomes negative for certain values of θ. This property suggests that a diode could be made to oscillate at certain frequencies. Diode oscillators have been built on this principle at frequencies from 300 to 3000 Mc

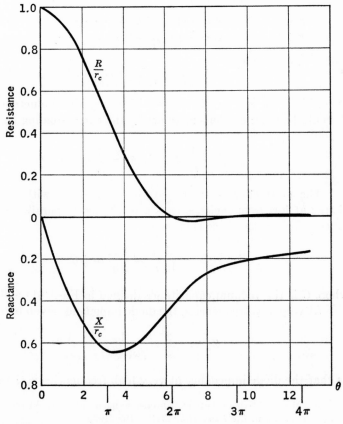

Fig. 5.2 **Diode impedance with complete space charge.** (After **Llewellyn and Peterson.**)

and are described in the literature.[1,2] It may be well to mention in this connection that the above analysis is based on the assumption that the *a* plane coincides with the cathode. Actually, the space-charge barrier causes the potential minimum to appear at a small distance from the cathode, and another impedance would have to be added between the potential minimum and the cathode to account for the displacement. If this additional impedance should turn out to have an appreciably large resistive component (and there is some evidence that this is the case at high frequencies and low currents), the small negative resistance may be partially or completely canceled. For diode oscillators, therefore, the cathode temperature should be so adjusted that the number of electrons emitted is only very slightly larger than that needed for the electron stream.

At very *low* frequencies, the complete-space-charge expressions (80) and (81) may be reduced by means of the series expansions for sin θ and cos θ to the following form:

$$R = r_c(1 - \tfrac{1}{15}\theta^2 + \cdot \cdot \cdot) \tag{83}$$
$$X = -r_c(\tfrac{3}{10}\theta - \tfrac{1}{84}\theta^3 + \cdot \cdot \cdot) \tag{84}$$

and for very small θ,

$$Z = r_c(1 - j\tfrac{3}{10}) \tag{85}$$

This is a resistance in series with a negative inductance; evidently it would be more convenient to derive the corresponding parallel circuit, as follows:

$$\frac{1}{Z} = \frac{1}{r_c}(1 + j\tfrac{3}{10}\theta) = \frac{1}{r_c} + j\omega C_c \tag{86}$$

The most effective representation of a diode with complete space charge at low frequencies is thus a resistance in parallel with a capacitance. The capacitance is given by

$$C_c = \frac{3}{10}\frac{T}{r_c} = \frac{3}{5}\frac{\epsilon_0}{x} = \tfrac{3}{5}C \tag{87}$$

where C is the vacuum capacitance defined in Eqs. (61) and (62).

At very *high* frequencies, the diode impedance given by (82) becomes

$$Z_\infty = r_c\frac{2}{\beta} = \frac{1}{j\omega(\epsilon_0/x)} = \frac{1}{j\omega C} \tag{88}$$

so that the diode impedance at very high frequencies is the same as that

[1] J. Müller, Experimentelle Untersuchungen über Elektronenschwingungen, *Hochfrequenztech. u. Elektroakustik*, **43**:195–199 (1934).

[2] F. B. Llewellyn and A. E. Bowen, The Production of Ultra-high Frequency Oscillations by Means of Diodes, *Bell System Tech. J.*, **18**:280–291 (1939).

due to the vacuum capacitance per unit area between parallel planes. It is unaffected by the electron beam.

In the more general case of partial space charge, the resistive component is given by (78). Its graph is exactly the same as that shown in Fig. 5.2 for the complete-space-charge case, except that r_c must be replaced by R_c. The reactive component is not so simply related to that of the complete-space-charge case. This component is given by (79), and it consists of two terms: the term obtained when r_c is replaced by R_c in the complete-space-charge expression (81) and a term which represents a capacitance

$$C_s = C \frac{1 - (\zeta/3)}{1 - \zeta} \tag{89}$$

where C is again the free-space capacitance ϵ_0/x.

The general diode impedance therefore consists of three series components: (1) the resistance given by the graph of Fig. 5.2, (2) the reactance given by the graph of Fig. 5.2 (both with R_c replacing r_c), and (3) a reactance due to the capacitance given by (89).

As the frequency is increased, this general diode impedance approaches the value

$$Z = -12 R_c \frac{\sin \theta}{\theta^3} - j \frac{x}{\omega \epsilon_0} \tag{90}$$

so that the vacuum capacitance (unaffected by the electron stream) again appears, this time in series with a small resistance.

5.7   Multielement Tubes; Other Applications

The results of the preceding analysis may be applied directly to multi-element tubes by considering the region between two successive electrodes to be a diode. The exit conditions of one region determine the entrance conditions of the next. Specifically, the convection current is always continuous at a boundary. The velocity is also continuous, unless there is an instantaneous jump in voltage; but even in that case, the velocities on either side of the boundary are simply related and their relationship may be obtained from the law of conservation of energy or, for a short gap, simply from I^*.

The above analysis has also been utilized in the development of equivalent circuits for triodes, tetrodes, and pentodes.[1] These circuits apply in the high-frequency range, where the conventional equivalent circuits fail because they were not designed to take transit-time effects into consideration. The terminals of these equivalent circuits do not

[1] F. B. Llewellyn and L. C. Peterson, Vacuum-tube Networks, *Proc. IRE*, **32**:144–166 (1944).

always coincide with the external terminals of the tube, and the circuits are generally based on the nodal (rather than the mesh) type of analysis; they have been selected in accordance with mathematical convenience rather than with regard to the tube configuration.

From the viewpoint of microwave electronics, the Llewellyn-Peterson equations are useful in describing the conditions of space-charge electron flow in velocity-modulated tubes, and they prove to be of great help in many problems relating to klystrons and traveling-wave tubes.

The Llewellyn-Peterson equations have also been applied to the study of noise.[1]

[1] L. C. Peterson, Space-charge and Transit-time Effects on Signal and Noise in Microwave Tetrodes, *Proc. IRE*, **35**:1264–1272 (1947).

6

Traveling Waves

A large class of microwave devices, such as linear accelerators, traveling-wave tubes, and backward-wave oscillators, comprises structures capable of propagating an electromagnetic wave and at the same time enclosing an electron beam, the operation of the device depending on the interaction between the beam and the traveling wave. The nature of this interaction in microwave tubes and the conditions that lead to their successful operation are described in the present chapter. The actual configurations ("circuits") used in such tubes are not discussed in detail, except as convenient practical examples of the theoretical concepts.

The operation of the traveling-wave tube (the first microwave tube successfully to utilize the traveling-wave principle[1]) was briefly described in Sec. 1.1*d*. The underlying principles will now be discussed in some detail.

[1] J. R. Pierce, "Traveling-wave Tubes," D. Van Nostrand Company, Inc., Princeton, N.J., 1950, contains a bibliography of early papers on this tube.

6.1   Interaction of Traveling Waves with the Electron Beam

Let us consider the interaction of an electron beam with a propagating structure, i.e., with a structure which in the absence of an electron beam will propagate electromagnetic energy with a fixed phase velocity in some given field configuration.   Any such structure (e.g., a helix or a loaded waveguide) is always capable of propagating energy in various field configurations, designated as *modes*.   In the present discussion, we shall refer to the modes that exist in the absence of an electron beam as the *cold modes* of the structure.   Conventional waveguide structures are not suited to the purpose of interacting with an electron beam in a simple manner, since the phase velocity of the electromagnetic waves is usually much greater than that of the electrons.   The structure must be modified in such a manner that it will have modes whose propagation velocities are close to possible electron-beam velocities.   Moreover, the field configurations must satisfy certain conditions before useful interaction between the electron beam and the circuit can be obtained.

Although the most common structure used for traveling-wave tubes is a helix, this is by no means the only one possible; the theory of interaction of an electromagnetic structure with an electron beam need not be confined to a helix.   In general, what is required is, first, an electron beam that travels with a velocity close to the velocity of the unperturbed wave on the circuit and, second, a field configuration of the propagating mode that can affect the electron beam, i.e., a propagating mode having field components which will affect the motion of the electrons.   If the velocity of the electrons and of the wave are approximately the same and power is injected into the circuit, there will be not only interaction but *cumulative* interaction, since the electrons and the cold-circuit wave travel along together.   If one examines such interaction in detail, one finds that the resulting behavior can be described in terms of a new set of waves which are very closely related to the wave that could be propagated on the circuit in the absence of the electron beam, except for certain modifications in the propagation constant. More particularly, one finds that whereas in the cold circuit only one wave for any given mode could propagate from left to right, the phenomena arising from the presence of a beam can be described in terms of three waves propagating in that direction; all have propagation constants close to the constant of the cold circuit but not exactly equal to it. Moreover, one of these waves can have a growing amplitude.   The result is that in the presence of such interaction between a beam and a circuit, this growing wave will exist, the amplitude of the wave will grow, and if one injects a small amount of r-f power at one end of the circuit, one will obtain larger r-f power at the output (i.e., a net gain) at the expense of the beam kinetic energy. The purpose of the theory, then, is to calculate the propagation constants of the waves that can exist on the structure in the presence of an electron beam and to calculate the gain of the device from these constants. There are several ways of arriving at this final result. We shall describe the more significant ones in some detail.

One approach, which in principle can give exact answers, is to consider the electron beam in the propagating structure as a separate problem in field theory which considers the structure and the electron beam together. Starting from Maxwell's equations and the equation of the motion of the electrons, we may obtain a system of equations the solutions of which will completely describe the behavior of the system without reference to any previous knowledge of the propagating properties of the circuit in the absence of the beam. This method, though in principle correct, does not lend itself to easy manipulation in practice, and while the problem has been formulated in this manner by various authors,[1] no very useful quantitative results have been obtained.

A second method, which is also rigorous and should in principle yield a complete answer, starts from a knowledge of the cold modes of the structure. The effect of introducing the electron beam is to excite all these cold modes, and the behavior of the total system may be considered as a superposition (in the circuit) of all the possible modes. This is a more feasible method than the theoretical-field approach, since in practice it turns out that only one (or possibly two) of the modes of the system is excited with appreciable amplitude and any others which make significant contributions can be treated by an approximate method or their contribution can be calculated in other ways. This is the so-called *normal-mode method*. If properly used, it can give quite accurate quantitative results.

A third method (which really should not be classed with the first two, since it is not actually an alternative approach to a complete solution of the problem) essentially uses transmission-line theory to provide relations between the electron motion and the field of the structure, and also the field on the structure that is produced by the current in the electron beam. In this case it is necessary to insert in the equations certain coupling constants (describing the interaction between the electron beam and the circuit) that have to be obtained from other considerations, namely, from some sort of a mode description of the circuit. If these coupling constants are inserted in the proper fashion, it is possible to arrive at all the significant results. The theory obtained in this fashion is actually the simplest and probably the most illuminating, since it omits

[1] L. J. Chu and J. D. Jackson, Field Theory of Traveling-wave Tubes, *Proc. IRE*, **36**:230–233 (1948).

certain purely mathematical details which may obscure the main physical significance of traveling-wave-tube interaction.

6.2   Transmission Line Theory Approach

Let us first consider this last approach, in which some approximate and nonrigorous concepts are used to derive the fundamental equations for traveling-wave-tube behavior.   In many cases, it will be necessary to use plausibility arguments rather than precise definitions to justify the use of certain concepts.   To determine the behavior of a propagating structure in the presence of an electron beam, one must consider the problem in two parts.   First, assuming that the electric field in the structure is known, one can calculate the motion of the electrons as produced by this field.   Using the equation of continuity, the definition of current, and the equation of motion, one can then find the current in the electron beam at any point along the structure as produced by this assumed field.   The resultant equation (which is in the form of an inhomogeneous differential equation for the current as produced by the field, with the field being essentially the driving term in the differential equation) will be called the electronic equation (see Sec. 2.2), since it arises from a solution of a dynamical problem for the motion of the electrons.   The second half of the problem starts by assuming that the current at various points in the structure is known.   It is then possible to calculate the field induced on the circuit by the existing current.   This procedure results in an inhomogeneous differential equation for the electric field in the circuit produced by the assumed distribution of current, the current being the driving term.   This latter equation we call the circuit equation, since it describes the manner in which a given distribution of current near the circuit produces fields on the circuit.   The solution of the pair of differential equations is in the form of waves; for a suitable choice of parameters one of the waves has a positive real exponential corresponding to an increase in amplitude as a function of distance along the beam.

To obtain the electronic equation, we proceed very much as we did in Chap. 4, starting with the equation of continuity, the definition of current density, and the equation of motion.   With the same assumptions (no transverse motion, small signals, r-f current uniform across the beam cross section, and a time dependence $e^{j\omega t}$), these equations again become[1]

$$\frac{\partial i}{\partial z} + j\omega\rho = 0 \tag{1}$$

$$i = \rho_0 v + \rho v_0 \tag{2}$$

$$-\frac{e}{m} E = j\omega v + v_0 \frac{\partial v}{\partial z} \tag{3}$$

[1] See Eqs. (28), (31), and (42) of Sec. 4.2.

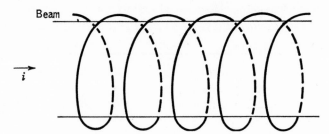

Fig. 6.1   Schematic representation of traveling-wave
circuit.

Solve (1) for ρ, substitute the result in (2) and solve for v, and again
substitute the result in (3) to obtain

$$\frac{\partial^2 i}{\partial z^2} + 2j\beta_e \frac{\partial i}{\partial z} - \beta_e{}^2 i = j\beta_e \frac{e\rho_0}{m v_0} E \tag{4}$$

where use was made of the definition $\beta_e \equiv \omega/v_0$. The right-hand
side of Eq. (4) can be rewritten by use of the equations for voltage,
$V_0 = -mv_0{}^2/2e$, and current, $I_0 = -\sigma\rho_0 v_0$ (where σ is the cross-sectional
area of the beam), to yield

$$\frac{\partial^2 i}{\partial z^2} + 2j\beta_e \frac{\partial i}{\partial z} - \beta_e{}^2 i = \frac{j\beta_e}{2\sigma V_0/I_0} E \tag{5}$$

It is to be noted that in this derivation we used the total field which
exists at the position of the electron.   Equation (5), the electronic equation, represents one of the equations that we require; the other equation
(which determines the field produced on the circuit by the current in the
beam) requires more consideration.

Let us consider an arbitrary propagating circuit which fits closely
around the beam, as shown in Fig. 6.1.   For our purposes, we need not
specify whether this circuit consists of a helix, a loaded waveguide, or any
other, similar propagating device; we merely need specify that the
circuit is close to the beam.   We wish to investigate how such a beam,
carrying current, can produce a field of a frequency ω on the circuit.

To visualize how this field is produced, we must return to the concept
of total current, as described previously.   The total current density
consists of convection current density i due to the motion of charges
and displacement current density $\epsilon_0\, \partial E/\partial t$.   The total current flowing
out of a volume, such as that enclosed by the surface S in Fig. 6.2, must
be zero; i.e.,

$$\int \mathbf{I} \cdot d\mathbf{S} = \int \left(\epsilon_0 \frac{\partial \mathbf{E}}{\partial t} + \mathbf{i}\right) \cdot d\mathbf{S} = 0 \tag{6}$$

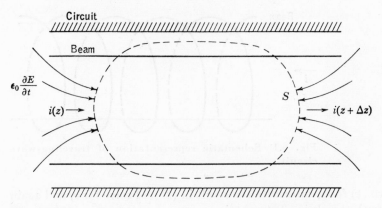

Fig. 6.2 Flow of total current into a volume element.

or in the differential form, with i having only a z component,

$$\nabla \cdot \mathbf{i}_D + \frac{\partial \mathbf{i}}{\partial z} = 0 \tag{7}$$

where $\mathbf{i}_D = \epsilon_0\, \partial E/\partial t$ is the displacement current density. The convection current density $\mathbf{i}$ is due to the charges in the beam and for r-f modulation varies with distance, so that $\partial i/\partial z \neq 0$ and therefore the displacement current flowing out through the surface is also not zero. The distribution of this displacement current density over the surface depends in great detail on the location of the beam, the size of the aperture in the circuit, and so forth. For example, if the circuit were located far from the beam and the beam itself were quite thick, most of this displacement current would flow out from one portion of the beam to another, with very little of it flowing into the circuit. On the other hand, if the beam is close to the circuit, some of this displacement current flows *into the circuit* in some way which is determined by the detailed distribution of r-f current and by the circuit configuration. Displacement current flowing into the circuit in this way must, of course, result in an equivalent conduction current flowing in the conductors comprising the propagating circuit. The reason is that, if we again enclose any part of the propagating circuit in a closed surface, the net flow of current through such a surface must be zero; and if there is a net flow of displacement current into it because of the presence of the beam, there must be a net flow of some other kind of current, namely, conduction current, in conductors out of the volume.

The circuit has, in general, a large number of propagating and non-propagating modes. We cannot say much about how the current will be distributed among these modes, since the distribution among the various modes in turn depends on how the displacement current is distributed along the boundaries of the circuit. Without going into any great mathematical detail at this point, one can see that the strength with which a particular mode is excited by some displacement current at a particular point in a propagating circuit depends on how well the geometrical distribution of the displacement current matches that of the mode. In a more formal development, one would want to expand the displacement current produced by the r-f beam as a superposition of the various normal modes; their relative amplitudes would then determine the magnitude of the excitation at the point in question. For the moment, however, it is obvious that for any mode excited by an r-f current in the beam, the amount of excitation at any point will be proportional to the r-f current in the beam at that point (assuming that geometrical factors, such as the radial distribution of current, are kept constant). The proportionality constant between the amount of current induced in a circuit at any given point and the current in the beam at the same point is then a problem in field theory. The mechanism should be apparent from what has just been said, and the fact that a proportionality exists is also apparent.

To formulate this problem more quantitatively, consider, for instance, an electron beam flowing past a helix (Fig. 6.3). If we assume that *all* of the displacement current flows out of the beam into the circuit (rather than into an adjacent part of the beam), we see that the net outward flow from a pillbox-shaped element (of length ds and cross-sectional area σ) is $\sigma(\partial i/\partial z)\,dz$. From Gauss's theorem,

$$\int (\mathbf{i}_D + \mathbf{i}) \cdot d\mathbf{s} = 0$$

so that

$$\int \mathbf{i}_D \cdot d\mathbf{s} = -\int \mathbf{i} \cdot d\mathbf{s} \tag{8}$$

$$P i_D \, dz = -\sigma \frac{\partial i}{\partial z} \, dz \tag{9}$$

$$P i_D = -\frac{\partial i}{\partial z} \sigma \tag{10}$$

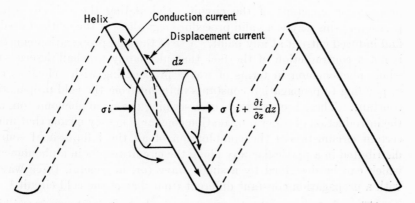

Fig. 6.3   Flow of displacement current into circuit of helix traveling-wave tube.

Here Pi_D is the total displacement current per unit length flowing into the circuit (i.e., out of the beam). This current flows into *all* the modes; to determine how it divides among them, we would have to perform a field calculation. For the present, suffice it to say that in each interval dz along the circuit the presence of an r-f current in the beam acts as a generator which feeds the circuit at that point with an infinitesimal current that is proportional to $\partial i/\partial z$ at that point. If we assume that we know the proportionality constant for any mode of interest, then we can say that the entire effect of the beam current at that point in a particular mode is contained in this equivalent current generator. Any such infinitesimal current contribution fed in at a point in the circuit results in two waves of equal amplitude spreading out from that point in opposite directions, one to the left and one to the right.

In other words, if we consider that the r-f current in the beam at that point acts as a current generator (for a given mode), it sees an impedance at the point consisting of the two halves of the transmission system in parallel, each terminated in its own characteristic impedance. The impedance seen by the generator is thus one-half of this characteristic impedance, and the (infinitesimal) voltage produced is determined by this impedance. The effect of the current distributed all along the beam is equivalent to a set of such generators, one at each point along the propagating circuit with a strength proportional to the current at that point. The total field in that mode at any point on the circuit then corresponds to a superposition of all the field components arriving at that point along the transmission line, propagating from the various generators (both to the left and to the right), with appropriate phase factors indicating the time delay from their origin to their arrival at the point under consideration. In this statement, we must keep in mind that all of these infinitesimal contributions from the various generators along the transmission system travel with a velocity corresponding to the cold propagation constant of the circuit. Calculating the field by superposition in this way is a valid procedure regardless of the method used to find induced current at any point. Use of the cold propagation constant is not a contradiction of the fact that ultimately we shall describe the whole phenomenon in terms of waves propagating with velocities corresponding to propagation constants different from the cold propagation constant. These are two ways of describing the same phenomenon, and the introduction of other propagation constants merely means that under certain circumstances the combination of all the infinitesimal sources distributed in a particular way along the circuit results in a phenomenon which can be described by a single wave (or, in general, three waves) with a propagation constant different from that of the cold circuit.[1]

[1] The use of superposition is even correct in the large-signal case, in which the simple linear theory used here in determining beam current does not apply. No

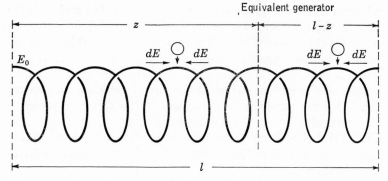

Fig. 6.4 Schematic representation of equivalent generators (shown outside the circuit for convenience) feeding the circuit.

For completeness, one should include the fields due to all the possible modes of the circuit, since each of them will be contributing to the total field and each of them will be produced, in some amount, by the beam. However, the simplest and a very useful approximation is to neglect all of the modes except the one that has a cold propagation constant near that of the electron beam, since this mode interacts most strongly with the electron beam and produces the important effects. We shall arbitrarily call this mode number 1 and designate the field in this mode as E_1. (We shall later consider the effect of omitting the other modes that exist in the circuit and whose effects may not be entirely negligible.)

With this preliminary statement regarding the effect of the current on the circuit in mind, we can immediately write down a relation for the field at any point along the circuit. It consists of three terms. One is due to the power injected at the input end of the circuit, traveling from left to right with the cold phase velocity of the circuit (Fig. 6.4). A second contribution is the effect of all the infinitesimal generators to the left of the point z; each makes its own infinitesimal contribution that is characterized by a suitable phase factor corresponding to the distance from the point z. The third contribution arises from a similar sum of effects from all the sources to the right of the point z. The relation is then[1]

$$E \approx E_1 = E_0 e^{-j\beta_1 z} + \tfrac{1}{2}\int_0^z A(x) e^{-j\beta_1(z-x)}\,dx + \tfrac{1}{2}\int_z^l A(x) e^{j\beta_1(z-x)}\,dx \quad (11)$$

matter how the current is determined (and in the large-signal case, numerical calculations might have to be used), the field can always be obtained from the current in the manner we have indicated, even though it might not be possible to employ the three-wave solution of linear theory. (Only the beam is nonlinear, i.e., the velocity may be multivalued; the circuit is always considered to be linear.)

[1] Equation (11) assumes a lossless circuit; if there is attenuation α, we must replace $j\beta_1$ by $j\beta_1 + \alpha$.

where β_1 is the cold propagation constant in mode 1 and E_0 is the magnitude of the injected field.   Here $\frac{1}{2}A(x)\,dx$ $(=dE)$ represents the increment of field produced at each point x by the current in the beam at that point.   We shall presently define it in terms of the current.   Since $A(x)$ depends on i, Eq. (11) thus yields a relation between the field E at any point and the current, which is the circuit equation that we are looking for.   It is not particularly convenient in this form; we prefer to replace this integral equation with a differential equation.   We must differentiate Eq. (11) twice, keeping in mind that the variable of differentiation appears in the limits of integration of the integral,[1] and we finally obtain the equation

$$\frac{d^2E_1}{dz^2} + \beta_1{}^2E_1 = -j\beta_1A(z) \tag{12}$$

One more step is necessary.   We have to define A in terms of the current i in some suitable way.   As mentioned previously, the qualitative argument shows that A is proportional to $\partial i/\partial z$ (or, as we shall see, to i); the proportionality constant must, of course, have the proper dimensions.   The actual evaluation requires some consideration of the field configurations; all we can say at the moment is that we shall write the proportionality constant in any way which seems convenient.   From dimensional and other considerations we may, for instance, write

$$\frac{A}{2} = \frac{dE_1}{dz} = -i\cdot\frac{\beta_1{}^2}{2}\,K\sigma \tag{13}$$

where K has the dimensions of ohms.   We shall return to a consideration of the significance of these constants in Sec. 6.4, after we have considered the equations.

If this definition of A is introduced, the circuit equation becomes

$$\frac{d^2E_1}{dz^2} + \beta_1{}^2E_1 = j\beta_1{}^3K i\sigma \tag{14}$$

This equation, together with the electronic equation (5), determines the behavior of the system of circuit plus electron beam.   Since these are two differential equations with constant coefficients, it is apparent that they can be solved in terms of exponentials.   It should perhaps again be stressed that this is not a contradiction of our original statement that the

---

[1] Differentiation under the integral sign, when the limits of integration are functions of a parameter appearing in the integrand, can be carried out according to the formula of Leibnitz:

$$\frac{d}{dz}\left[\int_a^b f(\alpha,z)\,d\alpha\right] = \int_a^b \frac{\partial f(\alpha,z)}{\partial z}\,d\alpha + f(b,z)\frac{\partial b}{\partial z} - f(a,z)\frac{\partial a}{\partial z}$$

where a and b are functions of z.

various infinitesimal contributions to the total field travel to the point under consideration at the cold propagation velocity.   When we solve these equations in exponentials, we are merely saying that the net result of beam plus circuit can be described in this form, nothing more.

Let us assume that the solutions of these two equations are given by

$$i = Ae^{-\Gamma z} \qquad E = Be^{-\Gamma z} \tag{15}$$

If we substitute these solutions into the differential equations, we obtain two algebraic equations for A and B, either one of which can be solved for the ratio A/B (which is the same as the ratio of the current to the field).   For an arbitrary choice of the propagation constant Γ, the two ratios would not be the same, of course; the condition that they should be the same is what actually gives us a relation from which we can determine the allowed propagation constant.   If we substitute Eqs. (15) into the electronic equation (5) and solve for the ratio of i to E, we obtain

$$\frac{i}{E_1} = \frac{A}{B} = \frac{-j\beta_e/2\sigma R_0}{(\beta_e + j\Gamma)^2} \tag{16a}$$

where we have also written R_0 for the V_0/I_0 ratio of Eq. (5).   The corresponding manipulation of the circuit equation (14) yields

$$\frac{i}{E_1} = \frac{A}{B} = \frac{\Gamma^2 + \beta_1^2}{j\beta_1^3 K\sigma} \tag{16b}$$

Setting these two expressions equal gives a quartic equation for the propagation constant for the waves.   In general, this equation has four roots, corresponding to four possible propagation constants; for each root, there is a corresponding ratio of the current to the field for that particular wave.   Before we consider the solutions and the significance of this equation, we may profitably examine a graphical representation, much as we did in the double-beam case of Sec. 4.4.   This examination will also serve to point out under what conditions we may obtain the growing waves which are necessary for amplification in the device.   The equation we wish to solve is

$$\frac{\Gamma^2 + \beta_1^2}{j\beta_1^3 K\sigma} = -\frac{j\beta_e/2\sigma R_0}{(\beta_e + j\Gamma)^2}$$

or
$$\frac{\beta_1^2 - (j\Gamma)^2}{\beta_1^3 K} = \frac{\beta_e}{2R_0(\beta_e + j\Gamma)^2} \tag{17}$$

Plots of both the left-hand and the right-hand sides (i.e., of circuit admittance and electronic admittance) as functions of $-j\Gamma$ are shown in Fig. 6.5.   Note that the electronic equation has a pole at $-j\Gamma = \beta_e$ and the circuit equation has zeros at $-j\Gamma = \pm\beta_1$.   As shown in Fig. 6.5, there are four intersections between the two curves; they correspond

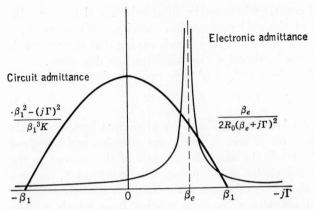

Electronic admittance

Circuit admittance

$$\frac{\cdot\beta_1^2-(j\Gamma)^2}{\beta_1^3 K}$$

$$\frac{\beta_e}{2R_0(\beta_e+j\Gamma)^2}$$

$-\beta_1$ 0 β_e β_1 $-j\Gamma$

Fig. 6.5 Graphical determination of propagation constants (all $j\Gamma$'s real).

to the four roots of the equation. At these four intersections the equation is exactly satisfied, since the left-hand side of Eq. (17) is equal to the right-hand side.[1] Figure 6.5 is a plot against $-j\Gamma$ real (that is, Γ pure imaginary), so that all four roots correspond to propagating waves without increase or attenuation; therefore, no gain would be obtained. However, the two curves can be shifted with respect to one another by one of several possible changes in the parameters in such a way that the two roots at the right disappear. For example, if the beam velocity is decreased (i.e., β_e is increased) so that it approaches the cold velocity of the circuit, then the entire electronic curve is moved to the right (Fig. 6.6a). Similarly, an increase in beam current (i.e., a decrease in R_0) or an increase in the impedance K results in the circuit curve being displaced vertically with respect to the electronic curve at the same β_e (Fig. 6.6b). In either case, only two roots are left on the diagram. The other two then are no longer pure real, but become complex; and any two such roots must be complex conjugates. Therefore, one root represents a growing wave and the other an attenuating wave.

There is not much more in the way of quantitative information that can be obtained from such diagrams. They do indicate the relation between the relative beam velocity and the circuit velocity, and they show what combinations of constants K/R_0 are required for waves with a complex propagation contant. These requirements can, of course, also be found by actually examining the equation analytically. We shall not

[1] Note that the two roots nearest the horizontal ($j\Gamma$) axis lie very near the value $j\Gamma = \pm\beta_1$ (the cold propagation constant), and the other two roots differ by only small corrections from the value $-j\Gamma = \beta_e$. Moreover, it will become apparent shortly that the higher the beam current, the further from synchronism we can be and still obtain gain. This statement also applies to the impedance of the circuit.

consider the general case here since it involves a solution of a fourth-degree algebraic equation which can be solved for general values of the parameters, but only by numerical computations. Instead of solving the general case, let us consider a special choice of the parameters which makes the equation relatively easy to solve and yields characteristics that indicate the general behavior of a traveling-wave structure. Equation (17) can be rewritten

$$(\beta_e + j\Gamma)^2[\beta_1{}^2 - (j\Gamma)^2] - \frac{\beta_1{}^3\beta_e K}{2R_0} = 0 \tag{18}$$

We can solve (18) approximately for a simple, though by no means trivial, case. This is the case of the so-called *synchronous velocity*, when the beam is moving at the same velocity as the cold velocity of the circuit (that is, $\beta_e = \beta_1$).

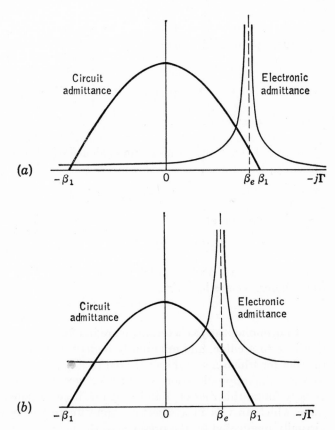

Fig. 6.6 **Conditions for growing waves (two complex**
$j\Gamma$**'s).** (*a*) **Effect of increase in** β_e; (*b*) **effect of increase in** K/R_0.

6.3 The Gain Parameter C

In order to introduce into the development presented above the well-known gain parameter C first suggested by Pierce,[1] let us write Eq. (18) for the case when $\beta_e = \beta_1$ in the form

$$(\beta_e + j\Gamma)^2[\beta_e{}^2 - (j\Gamma)^2] - 2\beta_e{}^4C^3 = 0 \tag{19a}$$

or

$$(\beta_e + j\Gamma)^3(\beta_e - j\Gamma) - 2\beta_e{}^4C^3 = 0 \tag{19b}$$

where we have defined

$$C^3 \equiv \frac{K}{4R_0} \tag{20}$$

It should be noted that the value of C for conventional traveling-wave tubes is well below unity, being in the range from 0.01 to 0.1, so that usually $10^{-6} < C^3 < 10^{-3}$. We have already seen from the graphical representations of Eq. (17) that three of the roots lie very near $j\Gamma = -\beta_1$ (or $-\beta_e$) and one near $j\Gamma = \beta_1$. For the latter root, we may rewrite Eq. (19b) approximately as

$$(2\beta_e)^3(\beta_e - j\Gamma) = 2\beta_e{}^4C^3 \tag{21a}$$

or

$$-j\Gamma = -\beta_e + \frac{\beta_e C^3}{4} \approx -\beta_e \tag{21b}$$

since C^3 is relatively small.

For the other three roots ($j\Gamma$ near $-\beta_e$), let us write $j\Gamma = -\beta_e(1 + \Delta)$, where $\Delta \ll 1$; and for reasons of convenience which will become apparent presently, let us define a complex number δ by $\Delta = jC\delta$, so that

$$j\Gamma = -\beta_e(1 + jC\delta) \tag{22}$$

Now Eq. (19b) becomes

$$(-j\beta_e C\delta)^3(2\beta_e + j\beta_e C\delta) - 2\beta_e{}^4C^3 = 0 \tag{23}$$

and since we can neglect $j\beta_e C\delta$ in comparison with $2\beta_e$ in the second parentheses, we are left with

$$\delta^3 = -j \tag{24}$$

In dropping the $j\beta_e C\delta$ term, we are in effect reducing a quartic equation in δ to a cubic, and apparently omitting one of the roots. This is the root for which $\Delta \ll 1$ does not hold (that is, $j\Gamma \approx -\beta_e$ does not hold), so that the approximation would not be valid. Actually, we have already found this root of $j\Gamma$ in Eq. (21b); it corresponds to a cold-circuit wave which travels in a direction opposite to the beam and which is virtually unaffected by the presence of the beam.

[1] J. R. Pierce, Theory of the Beam-type Traveling-wave Tube, *Proc. IRE*, **35**:111–123 (1947).

The other three roots correspond to solutions of (24); they are given by

$$\delta_1 = e^{-j\pi/6} = \frac{\sqrt{3}}{2} - \frac{j}{2}$$

$$\delta_2 = e^{-j5\pi/6} = -\frac{\sqrt{3}}{2} - \frac{j}{2} \tag{25}$$

$$\delta_3 = e^{j\pi/2} = j$$

so that the propagation constants become

$$\Gamma_1 = j\beta_e - C\beta_e \left(\frac{\sqrt{3}}{2} - \frac{j}{2} \right)$$

$$\Gamma_2 = +j\beta_e - C\beta_e \left(-\frac{\sqrt{3}}{2} - \frac{j}{2} \right) \tag{26}$$

$$\Gamma_3 = j\beta_e - jC\beta_e$$

We note that, of these three propagation constants, the first yields a wave which grows in the positive z direction, the second is attenuated in the z direction, and the third has a constant amplitude. Moreover, it is to be noted that the first two waves travel at the same speed, which is smaller than the beam velocity ω/β_e; whereas the third wave, the so-called fast wave, travels faster. (The growing wave always travels slower than the beam, as was confirmed for the general case by Brewer and Birdsall.[1]) Each of these solutions satisfies the differential equations. By means of the ratio i/E and the relations between the velocity, the charge density, and the current as given by Eqs. (1) to (3), one can get a set of values for all of these quantities for any one wave which satisfies all of the equations, i.e., continuity, definition of current, etc.

For an arbitrary excitation of the circuit or the beam, all three waves must be superposed with suitably chosen amplitudes to satisfy the given set of initial conditions. A possible set of such initial conditions might correspond to a beam injected into the circuit with no r-f current and no r-f velocity and with an r-f signal applied to the circuit, so that there is a nonzero initial value of the electric field. A complete solution of the problem is then given by a sum of the three waves with arbitrary amplitudes to express the field. From the appropriate ratios for i/E, v/E, etc. [using for example, Eqs. (16a) and (3)], which hold for each wave, one could obtain similar equations for i and v involving the same arbitrary amplitudes. The resulting three algebraic equations must satisfy the conditions that $i = 0$ and $v = 0$ at $z = 0$ and that E has some given initial value. These conditions are sufficient to determine entirely the behavior of the circuit and the beam. However, in most applications,

---

[1] G. R. Brewer and C. K. Birdsall, Traveling-wave-tube Characteristics for Finite Values of C, *IRE Trans. Electron Devices*, **ED-1**;1–11 (1954).

the tube is made sufficiently long that at the output end the growing wave proves to be much larger than the other two waves, and they can be ignored in calculating the output. As far as the growing wave is concerned, the gain is obtained simply by evaluating the ratio of its squared amplitude at $z = 0$ to that at a value of z corresponding to the output end of the tube. For the case we have just considered, this ratio can be written as

$$\text{Decibel gain} = 20 \log e^{CB_{ez}\sqrt{3}/2}$$
$$= 20 \log e^{2\pi NC\sqrt{3}/2}$$
$$\text{Decibel gain} = 47.3CN \tag{27}$$

where N is the length of the tube, in wavelengths. It is to be noted that the gain for that particular wave is not the power gain of the tube, since some of the total power injected into the tube at the beginning was required to launch the other two waves which were necessary to satisfy the initial conditions. In order to find the actual gain of the tube, then, one must find out what proportion of the total injected power actually went into the excitation of the growing wave.

The gain for the tube in general is usually written as

$$\text{Gain} = A + BCN \tag{28}$$

where B is a constant that depends on the rate of growth of the growing wave (which in general will be different from that obtained for the special case of $\beta_e = \beta_1$ considered here) and A denotes the initial loss arising from the circumstance that power is necessary to excite the nongrowing waves. For the initial conditions ($i = 0$, $v = 0$, and $E_1 = E_0$ at $z = 0$) and the special case treated here ($\beta_1 = \beta_e$), it turns out that all waves are initially excited with equal amplitude, i.e.,

$$E^{(1)}(0) = E^{(2)}(0) = E^{(3)}(0) = \frac{E_0}{3} \tag{29}$$

where E_0 is the amplitude of the total field and $E^{(1)}$, $E^{(2)}$, and $E^{(3)}$ are the amplitudes of the three waves; i.e., each wave has one-third the amplitude of the total injected field, and therefore only one-ninth of the power.[1] This corresponds to an initial loss of $A = -9.54$ db.

---

[1] The apparent anomaly in launching three waves of equal amplitude, but obtaining only one-ninth of the injected power (rather than one-third) in the wave in which we are interested, arises from the fact that the total power includes cross-product terms in the fields of the various waves. The waves are *not* orthogonal cold modes of the system carrying independent power. Thus, the total power carried by the field is proportional to $[E^{(1)} + E^{(2)} + E^{(3)}]^2$ and not merely to $[E^{(1)}]^2 + [E^{(2)}]^2 + [E^{(3)}]^2$. In other words, very near the input (before there is any r-f current or velocity in the beam), the field configuration looks just like that of the cold mode of the system with a superposition of the three waves yielding a field configuration very much like that of a cold mode, so that the power flow in the electromagnetic field is given by the first expression listed above rather than by the second.

6.4 Coupling Impedance

At this point, we must retrace our steps and justify the relation, postulated in Eq. (13), between the current in the beam and the induced field on the circuit, which was in turn used in deriving the circuit equation (14). Actually, the beam current produces a field on the circuit by inducing a circuit current; for the general case, it is necessary to perform some sort of a field calculation to find the displacement current and the corresponding current induced in the circuit. For a very thin beam, however, it is possible to derive the correct relation by energy considerations alone, just as was done in calculating the current induced in a circuit by an electron beam flowing across a capacitive gap in the circuit of Chap. 3.

Let us consider the cold transmission system. It is possible to write a relation between the electromagnetic power flowing along such a system and the amplitude of the axial field at any particular point in the cross section. We shall choose that position in the cross section of a transmission circuit at which we shall later introduce a thin electron beam. It is apparent that no matter where this point is, the power flow on the cold circuit will be proportional to the square of the field at the point. If the amplitude of the field moving to the right is designated by E_R, we may write for the power P_R flowing to the right

$$P_R = \frac{E_R{}^2}{2\beta_1{}^2 K} \tag{30}$$

and similarly for the power flow to the left. The proportionality constant has been chosen in a particular way which will turn out to be convenient and which involves the propagation constant β_1 of the cold circuit.

If the amplitude of the field flowing either to the left or to the right is increased at any point by an amount dE, then the increase in power flow can be obtained by differentiation:

$$dP_R = \frac{E_R\, dE_R}{\beta_1{}^2 K} \qquad dP_L = \frac{E_L\, dE_L}{\beta_1{}^2 K} \tag{31}$$

As has been previously pointed out, a beam current element at a particular point along the circuit produces an induced field at that point, with equal increments of field moving both to the left and to the right from the current element. In terms of the notation we have introduced here, $dE = dE_R = dE_L$. The total increase in power on the circuit will be the sum of the increase of power flowing to the left and to the right, or

$$dP = dP_R + dP_L = \frac{E_R\, dE_R}{\beta_1{}^2 K} + \frac{E_L\, dE_L}{\beta_1{}^2 K} = \frac{E_R + E_L}{\beta_1{}^2 K}\, dE \tag{32}$$

where dE is the increment of field produced at the point. We can also calculate the increase in power by calculating the loss in energy of the electrons due to the existing field at the point, i.e., a current element $i\sigma\,dz$ in the presence of the field $E_R + E_L$ will lose energy at a rate given by

$$dP = -(E_R + E_L)\frac{i\sigma}{2}\,dz \tag{33}$$

The minus sign arises from the fact that the energy loss from the beam is positive if the current and the field are directed oppositely. Equating the power lost by the beam to the power gained by the circuit yields

$$\frac{dE_1}{dz} = -i\,\frac{\beta_1{}^2}{2}\,K\sigma \tag{34}$$

Equation (34) is the relation between the current and the induced field at a point which we used in deriving the circuit equation. It is to be noted that in the derivation of (34), although we assumed a value of field existing at the beam and a corresponding power flow, both magnitudes have dropped out of the final result. (In Sec. 3.4, in the derivation of the induced current produced in a circuit by a beam moving across a gap, a similar result was obtained. There we introduced a voltage across the gap but the final equation contained only the ratio of this voltage to its gradient, which was a purely geometric factor; the result turned out to be independent of the amplitude of the voltage.)

6.5 Space-charge Effects

In deriving the equations and results which we have discussed up to now we have made several simplifications. The most trivial of these was that we solved (18) for a special case: we assumed that the circuit was lossless and that the velocity of the beam was equal to the cold-circuit velocity. Abandoning these two conditions merely complicates the algebraic equation (18); by doing a sufficient amount of additional numerical labor, it is possible to solve this equation for the more general case.

A more serious approximation was the implication, used in deriving Eq. (14), that all the field acting on the electrons was due to only a single circuit mode propagating along the circuit. This use of only a single circuit field in (5) omits the local interaction between the electrons (i.e., the space-charge forces) which also affects the motion of the electrons. These space-charge fields are not included in the field that propagates along the circuit. This latter field is propagated to the point under consideration from all the distant portions of the circuit, whereas the space-charge force is a much more localized one, similar to the field which would exist at the beam if we had a static-charge distribution like the charge distribution of the beam, with the circuit merely existing as a set of metal boundaries. Since we have omitted this field, the motion of the electrons as calculated is presumably not correct, the electronic equation as we have derived it is not complete, and the field that appears in this equation should include another term. In a way, the approximation we have made is analogous to that we made in Chap. 3 in considering the interaction of an electron with the gap, where we used for the forces on the electron only those fields produced by the voltage across the gap ($E = V/d$) and left out the space-charge effects. In that case, we also found that under certain circumstances this procedure was not accurate and that it was necessary to use some method such as the Llewellyn-Peterson equations which did include all the fields acting on the electron and not merely the field due to the charges on the electrodes.

The effect of space charge can be included in traveling-wave theory by several methods, some only approximate and others quite correct in principle but very difficult to use in practice. We shall indicate first a simple way of including space charge for the case we have considered here. Actually, this simple way gives results which are not too different from the correct ones; and since in more elaborate methods it is also necessary to make some approximations in calculating the final results, it is not at all certain that the method we shall use here is very much worse than the more elaborate methods. We shall have something to say about these more elaborate methods later.

To include the effect of space charge, let us simply write Eq. (5) as

$$\frac{\partial^2 i}{\partial z^2} + 2j\beta_e \frac{\partial i}{\partial z} - \beta_e{}^2 i = \frac{j\beta_e}{2\sigma R_0} (E_1 + E_s) \qquad (35)$$

where we have merely added a term E_s which represents the field due to a local space charge. By using a simplified model of the beam, we can evaluate this term quite easily. Since we are considering slow waves, we can represent the space-charge field as the gradient of a potential, i.e., we can write $E_s = -\partial V/\partial z$, where E_s really represents the z component of the total space-charge field, which in general will have both x and y components. The potential from which this field is derived satisfies Poisson's equation

$$\nabla^2 V = \nabla_\perp{}^2 V + \frac{\partial^2 V}{\partial z^2} = -\frac{\rho}{\epsilon_0}$$

which is written here in a conventional fashion as the sum of a transverse Laplacian and the z-derivative term and obviously can be rewritten as

$$\frac{\partial^2 V}{\partial z^2} = -\frac{\rho/\epsilon_0}{1 + \nabla_\perp{}^2 V/(\partial^2 V/\partial z^2)} \qquad (36)$$

The second derivative with respect to z as it appears in the denominator of the right-hand side involves the unknown propagation constant Γ (which is the main object of all the calculations), since V has the same z dependence as all the other variables, so that $\partial^2 V/\partial z^2 = \Gamma^2 V$. But Γ^2 appears alone and not as the difference between two almost equal terms, so that we can approximate to this derivative by replacing it by $-\beta_e^2 V$, since we know that the two propagation constants are approximately equal. The transverse Laplacian $\nabla_\perp^2 V$ is determined by boundary conditions at the walls or at the circuit; as in Eq. (4-60), the potential satisfies an equation of the form

$$\nabla_\perp^2 V + T^2 V = 0$$

where T depends on the boundary conditions (i.e., the configuration) but not on whether the roots are real or complex. We may thus write instead of Eq. (36)

$$\frac{\partial E_s}{\partial z} = -\frac{\partial^2 V}{\partial z^2} = \frac{\rho}{\epsilon_0}\left[\frac{1}{1 + (T^2/\beta_e^2)}\right] \tag{36a}$$

where the term in the brackets is the square of the conventional reduction factor β_q^2/β_p^2. This factor depends on the configuration and can in principle be evaluated.

We have already assumed that the r-f current has only a z component, and from the equation of continuity we can therefore write

$$\frac{\partial i}{\partial z} = -j\omega\rho \tag{37}$$

where we have assumed the usual time dependence for the charge density. If we equate these two relations for ρ, we obtain

$$\frac{\partial E_s}{\partial z} = -\frac{1}{j\omega\epsilon_0}\frac{\partial i}{\partial z}\left(\frac{\beta_q}{\beta_p}\right)^2 \tag{38}$$

where we have also utilized the plasma wave number β_p as previously defined in Eq. (2.59). After integration (with the initial condition that $E_s = 0$ when $i = 0$), Eq. (38) becomes

$$E_s = -\frac{i}{j\omega\epsilon_0}\left(\frac{\beta_q}{\beta_p}\right)^2 \tag{39}$$

Substitution of this result into (35) yields

$$\frac{\partial^2 i}{\partial z^2} + 2j\beta_e\frac{\partial i}{\partial z} - (\beta_e^2 - \beta_q^2)i = \frac{j\beta_e}{2\sigma R_0}E_1 \tag{40}$$

The equation has thus been altered from its original form, Eq. (5), merely by the addition of a correction in the third term on the left-hand side.

If we assume again that both the current and the circuit field vary as

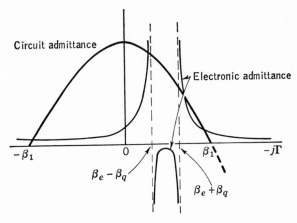

Fig. 6.7 Effect of space charge on admittance curves: low current.

$e^{-\Gamma z}$, we can see how the ratio i to E, as determined by the electronic equation, differs from that calculated previously without the space-charge term. The ratio now becomes

$$\frac{i}{E} = -\frac{j\beta_e}{2\sigma R_0}\frac{1}{(\beta_e + j\Gamma)^2 - \beta_q{}^2} \tag{41}$$

The ratio obtained from the circuit equation remains unchanged. If we again plot these two ratios on a common graph to examine the intersections graphically (Fig. 6.7), we find that the electronic equation has two poles at

$$-j\Gamma = \beta_e \pm \beta_q \tag{42}$$

Inspection of the electronic equation will indicate that the expression changes sign as $-j\Gamma$ passes through one pole and then again as it passes through the other. Once again, it is apparent that four waves will result. As shown in Fig. 6.7, these waves all correspond to $-j\Gamma$ pure real, i.e., no growing waves and no gain. Again, it is apparent that by increasing the current (which in this case will raise the level of the electronic curves and also push the poles farther apart by increasing β_q, as in Fig. 6.8), one can convert two of the real roots for $-j\Gamma$ into two complex roots, since two intersections on the diagram will disappear. It is to be noted that the growing waves, in a certain sense, can be said to arise from the slow space-charge wave, i.e., the branch of the electronic curve near the pole around $-j\Gamma = \beta_e + \beta_q$. It has been shown[1] that for very high current the phase velocity of the growing wave is actually that of the slow space-charge wave. That is about all one can say about the effect of space charge at this point.

[1] Brewer and Birdsall, *op. cit.*

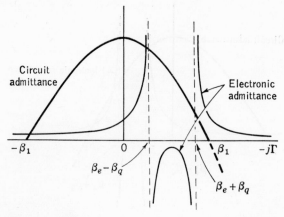

Fig. 6.8   Effect of space charge on admittance curves: high current.

One other interesting result arises from the introduction of space charge.   In the absence of space charge, the two real roots vanish below a certain beam velocity and one always has complex roots no matter how large the difference between the circuit velocity and the beam velocity, as long as the beam velocity is sufficiently low (Fig. 6.6a).   This result is somewhat unrealistic.   With the introduction of space charge, the lower portion of the electronic admittance curve shown in Fig. 6.7 will intersect the extension of the circuit admittance in the lower half plane if the beam velocity is decreased sufficiently for $\beta > \beta_1$ (Fig. 6.9), so that there is some lower limit on the beam velocity below which one can no

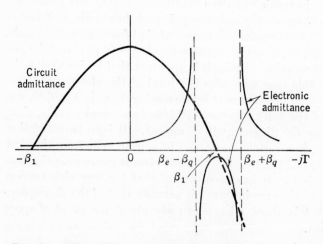

Fig. 6.9   Effect of decreasing beam velocity.

longer get complex roots. This result is more in accordance with reality.[1]

Assuming that β_q is not too far from the correct plasma propagation constant, one can use these equations to solve for the various values of Γ and put in the space-charge effects also. More elaborate techniques tend to result in the same equations that have been written here, although these methods attempt to calculate the true value of the constant $\beta_q{}^2$ that has been introduced here. We shall show that after one of these more elaborate approaches to traveling-wave-tube theory is carried out, the final equations reduce to exactly the same form as the equations which we have derived here.

6.6 Normal-mode Expansion

As mentioned in Sec. 6.1, it is possible to obtain more complete treatments of traveling-wave tubes by at least two methods. One method involves using the two sets of differential equations (i.e., the electronic equation and the circuit equation which is the inhomogeneous wave equation) and considering the problem purely as a field problem *ab initio*, concerned with obtaining solutions for fields and currents as functions of the coordinates. This procedure *can* be carried through, but it has the disadvantage that one cannot readily arrive at any general statements about the nature of the solutions for the general case of arbitrary circuit and beam parameters. It does, however, prove possible to obtain complete solutions for individual cases. (The equations that must be solved are the same as those stated in connection with the general space-charge-wave case of Sec. 4.2.)

Another approach, the *normal-mode expansion*, assumes complete knowledge of the normal modes of the "cold" propagating structure, including their completeness and orthogonality properties. It is then possible to write the solution of the wave-propagation problem in the presence of an electron beam as an expansion of the field in terms of the cold modes of the system. In the case of the system with the beam, one uses Maxwell's equation with nonzero current and charge; one then obtains, instead of the ordinary wave equation, an inhomogeneous wave equation which is essentially the circuit equation for the combination of beam and circuit. The electronic equation is the same as that derived previously [Eq. (4)] if the beam is constrained in such a way that current

---

[1] On the other hand, if under the conditions shown in Fig. 6.9 the lower portion of the electronic admittance curve is lowered (by a decrease of space charge and/or increase of C), the two roots again disappear from the real domain and growing waves again become possible. However, this is not ordinary traveling-wave-tube behavior; rather, it corresponds to the reactive-wall amplifier treated by C. K. Birdsall and J. R. Whinnery, Waves in Electron Stream with General Admittance Walls, *J. Appl. Phys.*, 24:314–323 (1953).

flows only in the z direction. If one writes the solution of the inhomogeneous wave equation as a superposition of the cold modes, one obtains a set of algebraic equations for the amplitude of each of the cold modes in terms of the expansion coefficients of the current distribution in the same modes. In principle, this set (together with the electronic equation) constitutes a complete solution of the problem. In practice it is not always possible to find the expansion coefficients exactly and one must resort to approximations. However, it is illuminating to go through this type of calculation to indicate what a complete solution should include even though it might not be possible to carry out the complete solution.

If one of the cold modes of the circuit has a velocity close to the beam velocity (as is usually the case), one actually can get an approximate solution from the normal-mode approach by considering only one term in the infinite expansion as the important one and making approximations as to the other terms. Because this condition (one normal mode with a velocity close to the beam velocity) is usually fulfilled in practice, the method is quite a useful one. We shall outline the method and show in particular that the final results can be so written as to yield the same equations we obtained previously by the much simpler approach. In the following treatment we impose certain conditions on the structure that make the equations we use somewhat simpler than would be required for a completely general structure. Let us assume that the circuit under consideration (1) propagates only TE and TM modes and (2) is cylindrical.[1] These assumptions permit a greatly simplified treatment. Actually, in practice, many common circuits do not satisfy both conditions. The helix, for example, has modes which are not purely TE nor purely TM; instead, it requires each mode to have both longitudinal components (E_z and H_z). In other circuits producing purely transverse modes, on the other hand, we may encounter the additional complication that they are not cylindrically smooth, but are instead periodic structures in which a unit cell repeats at a fixed interval, so that the cross section is not the same for all values of z. Actually, it has been shown[2] that a treatment similar to the one given below can be presented for such more general types of structures, leading to results very similar to the ones that we shall derive here; the results of the present treatment can be thus considered as quite representative. The main modification that must be made to extend the treatment to these more general structures involves the nature of the orthogonality conditions among the various modes,

---

[1] "Cylindrical" does not imply axial symmetry; the word is used here in its mathematical sense as meaning the surface generated by a straight line moving around an arbitrary curve (the cross section), not necessarily a circle.

[2] G. S. Kino, Normal Mode Theory in Perturbed Transmission Systems, *Stanford Univ. Electronics Research Lab., Tech. Rept.* 84 (Contract N6onr 25107), May 2, 1955.

which are somewhat more complicated than for the purely TM modes in a cylindrical circuit. However, it should be kept in mind that such differences in details, though in practice not trivial, do not alter the basic form of the final results; moreover, the meaning and physical interpretation are, of course, similar.

Assuming, then, that we are dealing with a cylindrical structure in which the modes can be classified as TM or TE modes, for the case where the beam is so constrained by a magnetic field that only motion in the z direction is possible, the current has only a z component and the only modes required in the expansion of the inhomogeneous problem are TM modes which have an E_z component. Let us briefly list some of the required properties of the cold modes we shall need for the treatment of the circuit-plus-beam problem. From Maxwell's equations it is possible to derive in a conventional manner a wave equation satisfied by all of the field components, as was done in Chap. 4. For zero charge density and current, Eq. (44), Chap. 4, becomes, for the z component of the electric field,

$$\nabla^2 E_z + k^2 E_z = 0 \tag{43}$$

yielding the homogeneous wave equation for the cold circuit. If one looks for solutions of this equation of the form

$$E_z = E_{zn}(x,y)e^{-\Gamma_n z} \tag{44}$$

then the resulting equation becomes

$$\nabla_\perp^2 E_{zn} + (k^2 + \Gamma_n^2)E_{zn} = 0 \tag{45}$$

with the two-dimensional Laplacian $\nabla_\perp^2 E_z$ defined in the same way as at the end of Sec. 4.2. The normal modes are defined by the solutions of this equation. There is an infinite number of solutions, of course, and Γ_n is as yet unspecified. The *normal modes* of the system are defined as those solutions of Eq. (45) with the appropriate values of Γ_n which satisfy the boundary conditions. It is only for particular selected values of Γ_n that these boundary conditions are satisfied. The normal modes are also called the eigenfunctions, and the corresponding Γ_n's are the propagation constants; Γ_n is called the eigenvalue of the equation. If purely TM modes in a smooth cylindrical circuit are assumed, the boundary condition is applied at some conducting boundary of the circuit at which E_z would have to be zero. In this case the solutions which meet this requirement are the normal modes.

For more complicated circuits with open boundaries the boundary conditions are somewhat more complicated, and they are usually subject to some sort of condition such as that the fields must decrease with distance from the circuit in a manner that leads to a finite amount of energy per unit length of the circuit. The essential property of the

TM mode that we shall need here is that all the other field components can then be derived from E_z. The x and y components of Maxwell's equation for $\nabla \times \mathbf{H}$ yield

$$(\nabla \times \mathbf{H})_x = \frac{\partial H_z}{\partial y} - \frac{\partial H_y}{\partial z} = j\omega\epsilon_0 E_x$$
$$(\nabla \times \mathbf{H})_y = -\frac{\partial H_z}{\partial x} + \frac{\partial H_x}{\partial z} = j\omega\epsilon_0 E_y \tag{46}$$

since by definition for the TM mode $H_z = 0$ and the z dependence of all components is $e^{-\Gamma_n z}$. Equations (46) can be written in the form

$$\Gamma_n H_y = j\omega\epsilon_0 E_x$$
$$-\Gamma_n H_x = j\omega\epsilon_0 E_y \tag{47}$$

Similarly, the x and y components of $\nabla \times \mathbf{E}$ yield

$$\frac{\partial E_z}{\partial y} - \frac{\partial E_y}{\partial z} = -j\omega\mu_0 H_x$$
$$-\frac{\partial E_z}{\partial x} + \frac{\partial E_x}{\partial z} = -j\omega\mu_0 H_y \tag{48}$$

We can now perform the differentiations with respect to z and substitute for the components of $\mathbf{H}$ from Eq. (47) to obtain

$$(\Gamma_n{}^2 + k^2)E_y = -\Gamma_n \frac{\partial E_z}{\partial y}$$
$$(\Gamma_n{}^2 + k^2)E_x = -\Gamma_n \frac{\partial E_z}{\partial x} \tag{49}$$

which can be combined to give

$$E_\perp = -\frac{\Gamma_n}{\Gamma_n{}^2 + k^2} \nabla_\perp E_z \tag{50}$$

where the gradient $\nabla_\perp E_z$ is again the two-dimensional gradient in x and y. One can see from these equations that once we have solved for E_z we can find all the other components by differentiation, so that the problem of determining the vector field reduces to that of determining a single scalar quantity, E_z, that satisfies Eq. (45) subject to boundary conditions. If one designates the solutions of this equation for different values of Γ_n by the notation E_{zn} [a function of only x and y, as introduced in Eq. (44)], then one can show[1] in general that these solutions satisfy the property that

$$\int E_{zn} E_{zm} \, da = \delta_{nm} \times \text{a constant} \tag{51}$$

where the integral is over the cross section of the guide. We can further define normalized solutions of Eq. (45) such that the integral in Eq. (51)

[1] See, for instance, J. C. Slater, "Microwave Electronics," Chap. 1, D. Van Nostrand Company, Inc., Princeton, N.J., 1950.

is equal to unity when n is equal to m. The functions so defined are the *normalized eigenfunctions*. In terms of these normalized modes one can find any arbitrary field propagating along the circuit as a superposition of all the various modes with suitably chosen amplitudes:

$$E_z = \sum_n (A_n e^{-\Gamma_n z} + B_n e^{\Gamma_n z}) E_{zn} \qquad (52)$$

where the A's and B's correspond to amplitudes of modes propagating in opposite directions. If any of the modes are cut off, i.e., for frequencies below the cutoff frequency, the corresponding Γ_n's will be pure real. Equation (52) gives E_z as an expansion in all the normal modes. Each normal mode propagates, of course, with its own propagation constant. Corresponding values for the transverse components of $\mathbf{E}$ and $\mathbf{H}$ would be obtained by applying Eq. (50) to each term in Eq. (52).

We shall need to evaluate the power flow for such a field in terms of the A's and B's and the normalized mode functions. The power flow is given in general by the integral of a Poynting vector over the cross section,

$$P = \tfrac{1}{2}\! \int \mathrm{Re}\,(\mathbf{E} \times \mathbf{H}^*) \cdot d\mathbf{s} = \tfrac{1}{2}\!\iint \mathrm{Re}\,(E_x H_y^* - E_y H_x^*)\, ds \qquad (53)$$

If one substitutes the proper values of E_x, H_y, etc., from Eqs. (47) and (50), then it is apparent that one will get a number of cross-product terms involving the derivatives of the various E_{zn}'s and E_{zm}'s and products of the A's and B's. If one uses Green's theorem for the two-dimensional case,[1] then in consequence of the boundary conditions of the differential equations satisfied by the E_{zn}'s all the cross-product terms vanish and the total power flow reduces to

$$P = \frac{1}{2}\,\mathrm{Re} \sum A_n A_n^* \frac{\Gamma_n^2}{\Gamma_n^2 + k^2}\left(-\frac{j\omega\epsilon_0}{\Gamma_n}\right) \int E_{zn}^2 \, ds \qquad (54)$$

and corresponding terms for the B_n's, with Γ_n of the opposite sign. That is, the total power flow is a sum of separate terms corresponding to each of the modes separately. If the mode in question is a propagating mode, one for which $-j\Gamma_n$ is real, then for that mode the power flow

---

[1] Green's theorem states that

$$\int_{\text{cross section}} \nabla \cdot (\psi \nabla \phi)\, da = \int_{\text{boundary}} \psi \nabla \phi \cdot ds$$

The right-hand integral is zero for $\psi = E_{zm}$ and $\phi = E_{zn}$ as a result of the boundary conditions, so that here

$$\int_{\text{cross section}} (\nabla \psi \cdot \nabla \phi + \psi \nabla^2 \phi)\, da = 0$$

But here $\nabla^2 \phi = \nabla_\perp^2 E_{zn} = -(k^2 + \Gamma_n^2) E_{zn}$, so that

$$\int \nabla \psi \cdot \nabla \phi\, da = \int \nabla_\perp E_{zn} \cdot \nabla_\perp E_{zm}\, da = \int (k^2 + \Gamma_n^2) E_{zn} E_{zm}\, da$$

in one direction is

$$P = \frac{1}{2} A_n A_n^* \frac{-j\Gamma_n \omega \epsilon_0}{\Gamma_n{}^2 + k^2} \tag{55}$$

Equation (55) concludes the derivation of the properties of the cold modes that we shall need. If we consider the case of an electron beam introduced into a circuit which has a set of such cold modes, then if the current has only a z component, the electronic equation which was derived previously is still valid. For the circuit equation we must now use Eq. (4.44), which is the inhomogeneous wave equation with driving terms that depend on the charge density and the current. If we assume that we are looking for a solution of the inhomogeneous equation in which the z dependence is as $e^{-\Gamma z}$, the resulting equation, in the beam region, becomes

$$\nabla_{\perp}{}^2 E_z + (k^2 + \Gamma^2)E_z = \mu_0 j \omega i + \frac{\partial}{\partial z}\left(\frac{\rho}{\epsilon_0}\right) \tag{56}$$

For the case where i has only a z component the continuity equation can be written as

$$j\omega\rho - \Gamma i = 0 \tag{57}$$

If we substitute Eq. (57) into Eq. (56) and perform the differentiations with respect to z and t, the resulting equation is

$$\nabla_{\perp}{}^2 E_z + (k^2 + \Gamma^2)E_z = -\frac{\Gamma^2 + k^2}{j\omega\epsilon_0} i \tag{58}$$

This is the generalized circuit equation that gives us the required relation between the field and the current. To solve it, using the normal modes of the cold circuit, we assume that we can write the current density i as an expansion in terms of the cold normal modes:

$$i = \sum_n i_n E_{zn} \tag{59}$$

where the expansion coefficients i_n are given by

$$i_n = \frac{\int_\sigma i E_{zn}\, ds}{\int E_{zn}{}^2\, ds} \tag{60}$$

It is assumed, of course, that we know the current density, so that this expansion can be evaluated. It is also assumed that the field can be expanded in terms of the normal modes as

$$E_z = \sum_n F_n E_{zn} \tag{61}$$

Then substitution of both of these expansions into Eq. (58) obviously yields an equation involving two infinite series in E_{zn} containing both the F_n's and the i_n's from the two expansions (59) and (61). Since the E_{zn}'s are all orthogonal, this equation can hold only if corresponding terms on opposite sides of the equation are equal. We thus obtain an infinite set of relations between the F_n's and i_n's:

$$\frac{F_n}{i_n} = \frac{j(\Gamma^2 + k^2)}{(\Gamma^2 - \Gamma_n^2)\omega\epsilon_0} \qquad (62)$$

To be sure, this set of relations between the F_n's and i_n's does not permit us to determine either separately; to do that, we must utilize another set, the one obtained from the electronic equation (5). This procedure (by which one obtains not only the F_n's and i_n's but the propagation constants as well) is carried out, in slightly modified form, in the next section. For the moment, let us apply the results obtained so far to a simple special case: an electron beam that has a very small cross section and moves with a velocity that is very nearly the same as the velocity of *one* of the modes (i.e., for one *particular* value, say, $n = 1$). Under these circumstances, Eq. (62) yields a larger amplitude for that particular mode than for any other, since Γ and Γ_1 are nearly the same if the beam velocity is approximately equal to the velocity of the cold mode. We are therefore justified in considering the contributions of all the modes except the synchronous one to be negligible. For a thin beam and a single mode $F_1 E_{z1}$, the ratio i/E_1 obtained from the electronic equation is simply that derived previously and given in Eq. (16a). To evaluate the magnitude of the field at the position of the thin electron beam (located at the point x_0, y_0 in the cross section) we find that the axial component of the field at this position is given by

$$E_z = F_1 E_{z1} = j i_1 E_{z1} \frac{\Gamma^2 + k^2}{(\Gamma^2 - \Gamma_1^2)\omega\epsilon_0} \qquad (63)$$

If the current is taken to be a thin filament at the position x_0, y_0, then we can evaluate the integral in Eq. (60) very easily. We can assume that the filament is small enough that, over its cross section, E_{z1} is essentially constant and equal to the value at x_0, y_0 and that the current has constant density I/σ, where σ is the beam cross-sectional area. In this case the integral merely becomes

$$i_1 = \int_\sigma \frac{I}{\sigma} E_{z1}\, ds = I E_{z1}(x_0, y_0) \qquad (64)$$

and Eq. (63) can be rewritten as

$$E_z(x_0, y_0) = I E_{z1}^2(x_0, y_0) \frac{j(\Gamma^2 + k^2)}{(\Gamma^2 - \Gamma_1^2)\omega\epsilon_0} \qquad (65)$$

We wish to modify this equation to introduce the coupling impedance that we used in our previous treatment of the traveling-wave tube. This impedance was defined in Eq. (30) as a relation between the power flow and the field at some point in the cross section. We can redefine it in terms of a *normalized amplitude* of the field at x_0, y_0 by taking into account that if the field in a cold mode is given by $E_z = A_1 E_{z1}$, then the amplitude A_1 as used in Eq. (55) can be written as

$$A_1 = \frac{E_z}{E_{z1}} \tag{66}$$

and from Eq. (55) the equation for the coupling impedance can be written (with the obvious change in notation, $\Gamma_1 \rightarrow j\beta_1$) as

$$\frac{1}{K} = -\frac{2P_1\Gamma_1^2}{E_z^2(x_0, y_0)} = \frac{j\omega\epsilon_0\Gamma_1^3}{E_{z1}^2(x_0, y_0)(\Gamma_1^2 + k^2)} \tag{67}$$

We can now replace the normalized amplitude at x_0, y_0 in Eq. (65) in terms of impedance as given in Eq. (67) and finally obtain

$$E_z(x_0, y_0) = \frac{I(\Gamma^2 + k^2)\Gamma_1^3 K}{(\Gamma_1^2 + k^2)(\Gamma_1^2 - \Gamma^2)} \tag{68}$$

for the relation between the field at the position x_0, y_0 and the r-f current at the same position. For all cases of interest all velocities are usually much smaller than the velocity of light, so that $\Gamma_1, \Gamma \gg k$, and Eq. (68) can be rewritten as

$$\frac{E_z(x_0, y_0)}{I} = \frac{K\Gamma^2\Gamma_1}{\Gamma_1^2 - \Gamma^2} \tag{69}$$

This is the same relation between the field and the current as previously derived [Eq. (16b)] by a much more elementary approach. The only difference is that $\Gamma^2\Gamma_1$ appears here rather than Γ_1^3; for many cases of practical interest, the difference between these two quantities is small. However, for large C the difference can be significant; in that case, Eq. (69) is the correct one rather than the ones given earlier.

In deriving the circuit equation, it should be noted that the circuit properties actually appear in the evaluation of i_1, as in Eq. (64), which depends upon the location of the current in the field. This integral is large only if the current exists in a region of large E_{z1} so that the coupling to a circuit depends upon the location of the beam. This is a result that we might expect intuitively; the integral of Eq. (64) puts it on a quantitative basis. Introducing the impedance in the above manner also states this same property, i.e., if the point at which the beam is located is such that the normalized field is large, this impedance is also large and the beam and the circuit are tightly coupled. On the other hand, if the normalized field is small, then the corresponding impedance is also small. It is apparent that one can extend this type of treatment even to a thick beam if one is concerned only with one cold mode, since the integral in that case is essentially an average of i over the cross section of the beam. (One might still define an impedance in terms of a particular point in the cross section; and such a definition could be made by writing the resulting integral in terms of the value of E_{z1} at that point, with the other terms that occur in the integral, i and σ, rewritten in such a way that the total integral had the correct value but still referred to the point under consideration.)

In using the normal-mode expansion we assumed that only one cold mode was important. This is, of course, an approximation which is usually not too bad, since the contribution of any other single mode is usually small. However, the total contribution of all the other modes is not necessarily negligible. Nevertheless, for a thin beam one could still evaluate the integrals (60) for all the other modes and in each case the value of the integral would presumably be proportional to the amplitude of the current in the filament, that is, i, multiplied by the cross section of the beam and the value of the normalized mode at that point. The result for the i_n for each mode would thus be similar to Eq. (64). Instead of Eq. (65), one would have a summation over all the modes with similar coefficients with a suitable Γ_n appearing in their denominators. Even though we cannot perhaps neglect all these other terms, it is true that if $\Gamma^2 - \Gamma_n{}^2$ is large, as it usually is for these other terms, the terms do not vary much as one changes any of the other parameters (such as beam velocity) slightly; but this would not be true for the one important term. If one is interested, then, in investigating the behavior of the circuit, and the beam including all of the field and not only that due to the one important mode, it is possible to write all the other terms of the series, except the one near synchronism, as a constant term of some kind. (By "constant" here is meant that the numerical value of the term will not be affected appreciably by changes in the velocity of the beam or frequency of the signal.) We can then write the relation between the *total* field and the current as

$$E = -i\sigma \left(\frac{K\Gamma^2\Gamma_1}{\Gamma^2 - \Gamma_1{}^2} + \frac{2jQ\Gamma^2K}{\beta_e} \right) \tag{70}$$

In this case the total field consists of two terms. The first term is the same one we have previously written. We call it the circuit field, because it includes effects of contributions to the field that have propagated to the point in question from remote points in the circuit, having been generated at those remote points by the current there. The second term is often designated the *space-charge field*. Perhaps the term *local field* would be preferable, since it is not obvious that one can separate the total field into a circuit field and a space-charge field with meaningful definitions for both. One could say that this space-charge field, for example, consists of the field which would exist at the point if we had the existing charge distribution of the beam and the circuit would consist of merely a conducting boundary. Such a field could presumably be computed from purely static considerations, but it is not at all certain that the second term in Eq. (70) consists only of this static field; it may also have contributions which one could call (strictly speaking) circuit fields, namely, fields that were induced on the circuit by current as remote points and which travel to this point just as for the first term. The only distinction would be that whereas for the first term all the contributions would arrive at the point in question more or less in phase because of the approximate synchronism between the beam and this particular cold mode, for the other cold modes this condition would not exist. It would be more plausible to assume that this local field would be large only in the neighborhood of the current, proportional to the amplitude of the local current, and would not contain appreciable contributions from distant points on the circuit. In any case, if we can assume that all the expansions in this normal-mode method are convergent, this extra term would be the one which could be considered constant and which would contain in it all the contributions of all the other modes except that of the one synchronous cold mode.

The terminology used in describing the second term in (70) involves the factor Q, which is the commonly used notation for this extra field term as first introduced by Pierce.[1] To evaluate this extra term is not simple, and it has usually been done by using certain properties of the field solution to obtain an approximate value. If we consider that this term is due to the space charge only and not to local excitation of other modes, we can find the relation of Q to other ways of defining the space charge, the description given in Sec. 6.5 in terms of β_q, for example. To do so, we recall that in the normal-mode expansion described above, the contributions of all the field components except the synchronous one are lumped together into one term, which is assumed to be a slowly varying function of the tube parameters. All these contributions are supposed to describe that portion of the field acting on the electrons which is not due to the one cold mode in approximate synchronism with the electron beam. This "additional" term should thus certainly include the local space-charge effects. In Sec. 6.5, however, we have already presented a different way of including space-charge effects merely by breaking up the field acting on the electrons into a so-called circuit field due to the synchronous mode and another term which was called the space-charge field. This term was evaluated in a very simple fashion with the help of certain approximations and resulted in a quite simple change: the electronic equation (5) is replaced by Eq. (40), involving only the

---

[1] J. R. Pierce, "Traveling-wave Tubes," Chap. 7, D. Van Nostrand Company, Inc., Princeton, N.J., 1950.

reduced plasma wave number β_q. By comparing the equations obtained using β_q and Eq. (70) involving Q, one obtains a relation between β_q and Pierce's QC (space-charge) parameter[1] and may clarify the way in which QC should appear in the theory. This point is particularly important because many of the published curves for the propagation constants[2] are plotted in terms of QC.

The way in which these two methods of describing space charge can be related is as follows. Equation (70) is an expression derived from a circuit equation for the *total field* acting on the electrons in terms of the current. The ratio $E/i\sigma$ can be set equal to the ratio of the total field to the current as given by the electronic equation (16a), so that

$$\frac{E_{\text{total}}}{i\sigma} = -\left(\frac{K\Gamma^2\Gamma_1}{\Gamma^2 - \Gamma_1{}^2} + j\frac{2\Gamma^2QK}{\beta_e}\right) = \frac{2R_0(\beta_e + j\Gamma)^2}{j\beta_e} \tag{71}$$

from which one can derive the propagation constants.

Another equally valid equation would be obtained by finding the ratio of the *circuit field* to the current. (In this context, circuit field means the field due to the synchronous cold mode.) This is the ratio given by Eq. (16b); it can be equated to the ratio of circuit $i\sigma/E$ as obtained from the electronic equation (41), which includes space-charge effects in the form of a β_q term. This procedure also yields an equation for the propagation constants. The two equations, one written in terms of β_q and the other in terms of Q, are as follows:

$$[\beta_1{}^2 - (j\Gamma)^2](\beta_e - j\Gamma)^2 - \frac{\beta_1{}^3K\beta_e}{2R_0} = \frac{Q(j\Gamma)^2}{R_0}[\beta_1{}^2 - (j\Gamma)^2] \tag{72}$$

$$[\beta_1{}^2 - (j\Gamma)^2][(\beta_e - j\Gamma)^2 - \beta_q{}^2] - \frac{\beta_1{}^3K\beta_e}{2R_0} = 0 \tag{73}$$

A comparison of Eqs. (72) and (73) shows that they are equivalent provided

$$\left(\frac{\beta_q}{\beta_1}\right)^2 \approx \left(\frac{\beta_q}{\beta_e}\right)^2 = 4QC^3 \tag{74}$$

6.7 Generalization of the Normal-mode Expansion

In the preceding section we described a method of expanding both the field and the current in terms of the normal modes of the circuit and then getting a relation between them from the inhomogeneous wave equation for the electric field, in which the current and the charge density appear as driving terms. The relation so derived was applied to the very simple

---

[1] *Ibid.*

[2] G. R. Brewer and C. K. Birdsall, Traveling-wave-tube Characteristics for Finite Values of C, *IRE Trans. Electron Device*, **ED-1**:1–11 (1954).

case of a filamentary beam with all except one of the modes being neglected, and a result that agreed with the simple theory could be obtained. However, if the normal-mode expansion is to be at all useful, it should be capable of being extended, at least in principle, to more general cases. In order to make such a generalization, one must also treat the electronic equation in terms of all the normal modes. Formally, it is possible to do so and to obtain an infinite set of homogeneous algebraic equations to determine amplitudes of the various normal modes, i.e., the F_n's as defined above. From such an infinite set of equations one derives a determinantal equation as a condition for the existence of a solution; this determinantal equation determines the propagation constants for the waves.

In principle, this procedure would constitute a complete solution of the problem. In practice, of course, the procedure cannot be readily carried through completely and one can solve the problem in some approximate way. A "zeroth" approximation leads to the normal solution as outlined at the beginning of the chapter. In principle, one could obtain higher approximations. It is difficult to determine how accurate they are without a great deal of additional work, since the detailed evaluation of higher approximations may be very laborious. The details of the formal solution are outlined below.

If we combine Eqs. (60) to (62), we obtain[1]

$$E_z = \sum_n F_n E_{zn} = \sum_n \frac{\Gamma^2 + k^2}{(\Gamma^2 - \Gamma_n{}^2)\omega\epsilon_0} j i_n E_{zn} = \sum_n \frac{j(\Gamma^2 + k^2)}{(\Gamma^2 - \Gamma_n{}^2)\omega\epsilon_0} \frac{\int_\sigma i E_{zn}\, ds}{E_{zn}{}^2\, ds} E_{zn}$$

$$(75)$$

The electronic equation (5) yields a relation between current density and field that applies everywhere within the beam. (Outside the beam, of course, the current vanishes.) For the usual z dependence $e^{-\Gamma z}$ of the solution, this relation is

$$i = \frac{-j\beta_e E_z}{2\sigma R_0(\beta_e + j\Gamma)^2} \qquad (76)$$

[1] Although the cited equations were derived for the case in which the orthogonality condition (51) applies, it can be shown that an expansion of the form

$$E_z = \sum_n \frac{j(\Gamma^2 + k^2)}{(\Gamma^2 - \Gamma_n{}^2)\omega\epsilon_0} \frac{\int_\sigma i E_{zn}\, ds}{P_n} E_{zn}$$

can be made even in cases in which (51) does not apply (e.g., in a helix). The derivations that follow can be also applied to such cases, since the orthogonality condition will not be used. In the above expression, P_n represents the nth normal mode and E_{zn} is the z component of the electric field in mode n. See Kino, *op. cit.*

Substitution of Eq. (76) into Eq. (75) gives

$$E_z = \sum_n \frac{\kappa^2 \int_\sigma E_z E_{zn}\, ds}{(\Gamma^2 - \Gamma_n{}^2) \int E_{zn}{}^2\, ds} E_{zn} \tag{77}$$

where we have also introduced the abbreviated notation

$$\kappa^2 \equiv \frac{\beta_e(\Gamma^2 + k^2)}{2\sigma R_0(\beta_e + j\Gamma)^2 \omega \epsilon_0} \tag{78}$$

It should be kept in mind that the integral in the numerator of Eq. (77) is taken over the cross section of the beam only, whereas the integral in the denominator is over the entire cross section.

As before, we may normalize the integral of Eq. (77) for convenience, putting $\int E_{zn}{}^2\, ds = 1$. The resulting equation is multiplied by any E_{zm} and integrated over the beam cross section. In writing down the result, we separate out the mth term by putting it on the left-hand side:

$$\int_\sigma E_z E_{zm} \left(1 - \frac{\kappa^2 I_{mm}}{\Gamma^2 - \Gamma_m{}^2}\right) ds = \sum_{n \neq m} \frac{\kappa^2 I_{mn}}{\Gamma^2 - \Gamma_n{}^2} \int_\sigma E_z E_{zn}\, ds \tag{79}$$

where
$$I_{mn} = \int_\sigma E_{zm} E_{zn}\, ds \tag{80}$$

If we perform these operations for all the normal modes (all values of m), we obtain an infinite set of algebraic equations for the amplitudes $G_n = \int_\sigma E_z E_{zn}\, ds$ given by

$$\sum_n G_n \left[\frac{\kappa^2 I_{mn}}{\Gamma^2 - \Gamma_n{}^2} - \delta_{mn}\right] = 0 \tag{81}$$

with the G_n's proportional to the i_n's as a result of the relation (76) between i and E_z inside the beam. The roots are determined by making the determinant of the coefficients vanish:

$$\begin{vmatrix} \dfrac{\kappa^2 I_{11}}{\Gamma^2 - \Gamma_1{}^2} - 1 & \dfrac{\kappa^2 I_{12}}{\Gamma^2 - \Gamma_2{}^2} & \dfrac{\kappa^2 I_{13}}{\Gamma^2 - \Gamma_3{}^2} & \cdots \\[3mm] \dfrac{\kappa^2 I_{21}}{\Gamma^2 - \Gamma_1{}^2} & \dfrac{\kappa^2 I_{22}}{\Gamma^2 - \Gamma_2{}^2} - 1 & & \\[3mm] & \cdot & & \\ & \cdot & & \cdot \\ & \cdot & & \end{vmatrix} = 0 \tag{82}$$

These equations are very similar to those which commonly occur in perturbation theory in quantum mechanics, and the procedures outlined below can be found in any standard text on quantum mechanics.[1] In the present case, the presence of the beam produces coupling between the various modes so that the new resulting waves are no longer merely individual cold modes of the unperturbed system, but are a superposition of them. As in the quantum-mechanical case, if one assumes that the perturbation is small, so that the propagation constant is nearly the same as for one of the normal modes (say, Γ_1), one can approximate by substituting $\Gamma_1{}^2$ for Γ^2 in all diagonal elements except the first. Since the difference between $\Gamma_1{}^2$ and $\Gamma_n{}^2$ is large compared with $\kappa^2 I_{mn}$, the $\kappa^2 I_{mm}/(\Gamma^2 - \Gamma_m{}^2)$ term may be omitted in all diagonal elements except the first.[2]

We also omit all nondiagonal elements except those in the first row and in the first column, since these elements represent coupling between pairs of nonsynchronous modes and are negligible. When these approximations are made, Eq. (82) becomes

$$\begin{vmatrix} \dfrac{\kappa^2 I_{11}}{\Gamma^2 - \Gamma_1{}^2} - 1 & \dfrac{\kappa^2 I_{12}}{\Gamma^2 - \Gamma_2{}^2} & \dfrac{\kappa^2 I_{13}}{\Gamma^2 - \Gamma_3{}^2} & \cdots \\[3mm] \dfrac{\kappa^2 I_{21}}{\Gamma^2 - \Gamma_1{}^2} & -1 & 0 & \\[3mm] \cdot & \cdot & & \\ \cdot & & \cdot & \\ \cdot & & & \cdot \end{vmatrix} = 0 \qquad (83)$$

which can be solved[3] to give

$$1 = \frac{\kappa^2 I_{11}}{\Gamma^2 - \Gamma_1{}^2} - \sum_{n \neq 1} \frac{\kappa^4 I_{1n}{}^2}{(\Gamma_n{}^2 - \Gamma_1{}^2)(\Gamma^2 - \Gamma_1{}^2)} \qquad (84)$$

[1] See, for instance, L. I. Schiff, "Quantum Mechanics," McGraw-Hill Book Company, Inc., New York, 1956.

[2] Using the fact that $\Gamma \approx \Gamma_1$ and introducing the interaction impedance for mode 1 at (x_0, y_0), $K = [E_{z1}{}^2(x_0, y_0)]/2P\beta_0{}^2$ [see Eq. (67)], we see that κ^2 reduces to

$$\frac{2C^3\beta_1{}^3\beta_e}{\sigma E_{z1}{}^2(x_0,y_0)(\beta_e + j\Gamma)^2}$$

so that $\kappa^2 I_{nm}$ is of the order of

$$\frac{C\beta_1{}^2 \displaystyle\int_\sigma E_{zn}{}^2 \, dA}{\sigma E_{z1}{}^2(x_0,y_0)}$$

since $(\beta_e + j\Gamma)^2$ is of the order of $C^2\beta_e{}^2$, as can be seen from Eqs. (21) to (24). Thus, $\kappa^2 I_{nm}$ is much smaller than $\Gamma_1{}^2 - \Gamma_n{}^2$.

[3] Schiff, *op. cit.*

We have, finally,

$$\Gamma^2 - \Gamma_1{}^2 = \kappa^2 I_{11} - \sum_n \frac{\kappa^4 I_{1n}{}^2}{\Gamma_n{}^2 - \Gamma_1{}^2} \tag{85}$$

Similarly, we can backtrack and solve for the amplitudes, which are given by

$$F_n = F_1 \frac{\kappa^2 I_{1n}}{\Gamma_1{}^2 - \Gamma_n{}^2} \tag{86}$$

As a first approximation, one can solve Eq. (84) for Γ by omitting the summation. This procedure results in the same equation as previously derived [Eq. (18)] except for a factor

$$\frac{\int_\sigma E_{z1}{}^2 \, dA}{\sigma E_{z1}{}^2(x_0, y_0)}$$

that multiplies K, the interaction impedance. This is a plausible correction, since it amounts to weighting K, as defined at (x_0, y_0), by a suitable average of the field over σ, the cross section of the beam. To obtain a more precise equation for Γ would require an evaluation of the summation, which might be difficult in practice, so that usually some subterfuge is necessary.

Backward-wave Interactions

7.1 Qualitative Description

Another important type of traveling-wave application in which a propagating circuit interacts with an electron beam is the backward-wave interaction, which can be employed for oscillation or amplification. Although a device utilizing backward-wave interaction often physically resembles a forward-wave traveling-wave tube, the principle of operation is different; this difference will become apparent in the course of the mathematical analysis. Backward-wave devices usually comprise a traveling-wave structure in which a particular component (*spatial harmonic*) of the wave has a phase velocity ω/β directed opposite to the group (energy) velocity $d\omega/d\beta$.[1] If the phase velocity of this component does not greatly differ from the velocity of the electron

---

[1] In certain media with special properties, such as plasmas and ferrites, there are frequency ranges in which ϵ or μ is negative, and backward waves can propagate even in a smooth structure.

beam, then the electrons can interact with such a wave in a cumulative fashion, since any electron is continually in a field of the same phase; and energy delivered by the electrons to the circuit at points along the circuit is also properly phased to add in a cumulative fashion, just as in the case of forward-wave devices. Unlike that case, in backward-wave-tube interaction the power delivered by the beam to the circuit is phased to provide a coherently phased wave along the circuit for energy traveling in the direction opposite to the beam; the power so produced comes out at the *cathode end* of the circuit.

Such a device can be used as an amplifier if a small amount of power is fed in at the *collector end*. As this power travels toward the cathode, the field acts on the electrons in the usual way. The electrons are bunched and deliver power to the circuit with the correct phase at various points along the circuit for energy traveling toward the cathode end. If one compares this description with the description accompanying the derivation of Eq. (6.11), for forward-traveling-wave tubes, one can see that for the backward-wave case the useful energy produced by an electron at any position travels toward the region where the electrons enter, whereas in the forward-wave case the energy travels in the same direction as the electrons, away from their entrance point. In the former case there is thus a feedback mechanism by which energy is transferred from the electrons near the collector end back to the electrons near the cathode end. It is quite obvious that under such circumstances oscillation might occur, and in fact it does occur under certain conditions. (To be sure, forward-wave traveling-wave tubes may also oscillate, owing to reflections, but backward-wave oscillators depend on regeneration along the entire length of the circuit, and not on the presence of growing waves.)

The concept of a backward group velocity with a forward phase velocity can perhaps be clarified by describing a simple circuit that has such velocity characteristics and that could thus be used for a backward-wave oscillator. If we consider a folded line such as shown in Fig. 7.1,

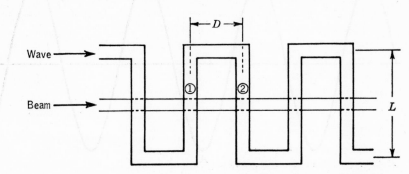

Fig. 7.1 Folded-line configuration for backward-wave interaction.

we can see that, for cumulative interaction of the electrons with the field, it is necessary for the electrons to travel from the center of one gap to the center of the next gap (a distance D) in the same time that the wave travels a distance along the circuit such that when the electron arrives at the next gap it encounters a field of the same phase as at the preceding gap. This requirement may be simply stated if one imagines the folded line stretched out so that the total wave pattern all along it can be viewed (Fig. 7.2). If the electron sees a field at point A on the wave when it is at gap 1, then the relationship between the distance from gap 1 to gap 2 and the beam velocity must be such that any of the points labeled B on the wave arrive at gap 2 at the same time as the electron. In Fig. 7.2, B actually has the opposite polarity to A, since for the folded line the field direction reverses in going around the bend, so that another half cycle must be added to provide the right polarity at the second gap. One can easily see that the condition for synchronization is given by

$$\frac{D}{v} = \frac{L + D + \lambda(2n + 1)/2}{c} \tag{1}$$

where v is the beam velocity, λ and c are respectively free-space wavelength and velocity, $L + D$ is the distance along the folded line from gap 1 to 2, and n is an integer. It is assumed that the wave travels along the folded line with velocity c. Equation (1) merely states the condition that in the time that electrons traveling with a velocity v cover a distance D, the wave should travel a distance $L + D$ plus an odd number of half wavelengths (B_0, $n = 0$; B_1, $n = 1$; etc.). However, it is evident that the points labeled B' on the wave would also provide the right field at gap 2 and could arrive there at the appropriate time if the wave were traveling in a direction opposite to the electrons with a suitable

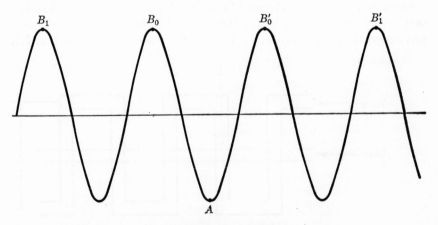

Fig. 7.2   Wave pattern on "developed" folded line.

velocity. In this case the condition would be

$$\frac{D}{v} = \frac{[\lambda(2n + 1)/2] - (L + D)}{c} \tag{2}$$

From this example, without even introducing the concept of spatial harmonics necessary for the mathematical analysis, we can see that the electron could be modulated in a cumulative way with the wave going either forward or backward; and similarly, if the beam would deliver energy to the wave, electrons at various points along the wave could deliver energy in a cumulative way to the wave even for the case in which it is traveling in the direction opposite to the beam.

It is possible to describe the above processes in terms of spatial harmonics. In such an analysis, the line and the wave are not unfolded, as indicated above; rather, the analysis is carried out entirely in terms of the field in the region through which the beam passes. In this approach, one can show from the well-known Floquet's theorem that the total field can be written as a superposition of various components written in the form

$$E_z = \sum_n A_n F_n(r) e^{-j\beta_n z} \tag{3}$$

where $\beta_n = \beta_0 + 2\pi n/D$, whether the energy is propagated to the right or to the left. In either case the wave has various components whose phase velocity is directed opposite to the energy propagation or group velocity; to obtain cumulative interaction it is merely necessary that the electrons synchronize with one of these components. Such a statement is completely equivalent to the previous description in terms of the wave traveling along the folded line; and it is more useful from an analytical viewpoint, though the former might be perhaps more illuminating.

7.2 Oscillation Conditions

It is now possible to derive the equation for the interaction of an electron beam with such a backward wave. (It should be understood that the term "backward" actually means that the group velocity is directed opposite to the beam velocity.) The derivation of the electronic equation is exactly the same as for the forward-wave traveling-wave tube, and therefore Eq. (6.5) applies. For the circuit equation one can use an integral similar to that which occurs in Eq. (6.11), with some important changes. As in that derivation, the electron beam acts as a generator at each point along the circuit and delivers power at each such point. This power divides into two waves which proceed respectively to the left and to the right, and the field at any selected point can be written as an accumulation of contributions from all other points along the circuit,

both to the left and to the right of the point of interest.   However, since
we are considering a backward-wave circuit, we must take into account
that the energy coming from the right of the selected point has a propagation constant corresponding to a phase velocity to the left and, conversely, the energy coming from the left has a propagation constant
corresponding to a phase velocity to the right.   We may thus use the
same integrals as in Eq. (6.11), and with the same limits, but with all
the phase constants reversed.   For the same reason any injected field
must be injected at the collector end and must have a phase velocity
that can synchronize with an electron.   Its contribution at any point
exhibits the phase shift that describes this backward-wave property.
The resulting equation that satisfies these requirements is

$$E_z = E_s e^{-j\beta_0(z-l)} + \tfrac{1}{2} \int_z^l A(x) e^{-j\beta_0(z-x)} \, dx + \tfrac{1}{2} \int_0^z A(x) e^{+j\beta_0(z-x)} \, dx \quad (4)$$

where β_0 can be the propagation constant for whatever spatial harmonic
is approximately in synchronism with the beam.   We now go through
the same process of differentiating the equation twice and combining
the results of these differentiations with the original equation to obtain
a differential equation

$$\frac{d^2E}{dz^2} + \beta_0{}^2 E = j\beta_0 A(z) \quad (5)$$

The only difference between this equation and the one derived for the
forward-wave traveling-wave-tube case of Chap. 6 is the sign of the term
on the right.   We shall see the consequence of this change later.   As in
the forward-wave case, one can assume solutions of the form

$$i = A e^{-\Gamma z} \qquad E = B e^{-\Gamma z} \quad (6)$$

Substitution into the differential equations yields values of the ratio
A/B from both the electronic equation and the circuit equation, just
as for the forward-wave traveling-wave-tube case.   Equating these two
values for the ratio leads to a quartic equation from which the unknown
propagation constants can be determined for any given set of conditions,
e.g., current, impedance, the velocity of the beam, and velocity of the
circuit at the frequency of interest.   Given the roots, one can proceed,
as in the forward-wave case, to impose boundary conditions in order
to find the amplitudes of the various waves.   Typical conditions, for
example, are that the injected current and velocity in the beam are zero
at the cathode ($z = 0$) and that there is an injected field at the collector
end ($z = L$).   One can then calculate the ratio of the field at the output
$z = 0$ to the injected field at $z = L$, that is, the voltage gain.

The above procedure may be thus used to describe the performance
of the device for whatever combination of parameters (electron velocity,

circuit velocity, etc.) is chosen. This performance may or may not represent a net gain. Because of the dispersion characteristic of a propagating structure with oppositely directed group and phase velocities, no gain at all results unless the beam velocity and frequency are chosen precisely. A backward-wave circuit changes its velocity rapidly with frequency, and, for a given beam velocity, it is only over a relatively narrow range of frequencies that approximate synchronism can exist and that amplification can result.[1]

However, backward-wave circuits have another interesting and important property which arises from the fact that internal feedback is present, as described above. This feature results in the possibility of oscillations, since any energy delivered by the beam at points along the circuit is transferred toward the cathode end, where it can act on the part of the beam that is just entering. This process does not take place in a forward-wave traveling-wave tube, in which oscillation can be generated only if actual mismatches exist owing to improper termination. To find the oscillation conditions for the backward-wave tube, one has to go beyond merely finding the roots of the determinantal equation.

The procedure is to consider, for a given beam velocity, some particular frequency and the corresponding circuit velocity and put these quantities into the equation for the propagation constants. Having found the roots, one can impose the usual boundary condition on the waves: zero current and velocity at the cathode end and a finite value of the injected field at the collector end. From these three boundary conditions one can calculate the field anywhere along the circuit and, in particular, at the output (cathode) end. The ratio of this field to the injected field then gives the gain (which may be actually less than unity). This ratio is, of course, a function of the length of the tube, of the beam current, and of the velocity of the beam and the propagation velocity of the circuit at the chosen frequency. Given such a functional dependence of the gain for the given beam and circuit velocities, one seeks a current and a length of the circuit such that the gain is infinite. This is the *start-oscillation condition* corresponding to a finite output with no input (i.e., implying start from noise).

In the early investigations of the backward-wave oscillator, the determination of these conditions proceeded by means of the exploration of a large range of circuit velocities in the neighborhood of the beam velocity; and for each of these velocities, the effects of the length of the

---

[1] From the definitions of phase and group velocities, $v_p = \omega/\beta$ and $v_g = d\omega/d\beta$, one can derive the expression

$$\frac{dv_p}{d\omega} = \frac{v_p}{\omega}\left(1 - \frac{v_p}{v_g}\right)$$

For any given magnitude $|v_g|$, this relationship always yields $dv_p/d\omega > v_p/\omega$ for negative v_p/v_g, whereas for positive v_p/v_g we obtain small (or zero) $dv_p/d\omega$.

tube and the amount of current had to be investigated. As a result of much exploration it was found that these results could be systematized, particularly for the case in which there was a considerable amount of space charge in the beam, i.e., where $4QC$ was unity or greater. We shall consider this case below.

It is important to point out here that marked difference exists between the behavior of the waves in the backward-wave oscillator and in the forward-wave traveling-wave tube. Specifically, no growing wave is needed in a backward-wave oscillator. With parameters for which oscillation would occur, a reduction in tube length or current would bring the conditions below the oscillation requirement. No oscillation would take place, but one could, in principle, obtain gain that could be made arbitrarily large depending on how close one approached the start-oscillation conditions of current and length. But it is found, for both amplifiers and oscillators, that a growing wave is not necessary for the process to occur and that, even if it is present, a growing wave does not enter into the process of producing the gain in the same way as in the traveling-wave tube.

Instead of the gain produced by a single growing wave that becomes dominant at the output end of the tube, in a backward-wave oscillator (or amplifier) the gain results from the interference between two (and sometimes three) of the waves of such form that at the input (collector end of the tube) these waves cancel out to zero field (or small input), and at the output end (cathode) the waves reinforce each other to produce a finite field (or amplified output). Corresponding statements can be made about the current and the velocity in the beam, except that the ends must be reversed. The gain mechanism, therefore, is the result of an interference effect. Typical plots (for several conditions of loss and space charge) of the relative magnitudes and phases of the three waves at the two ends of the tube are shown in Fig. 7.3. In case 1, for example, there is a growing wave E_1 and an attenuating wave E_2, but their relative amplitudes at the beginning and the end of the tube are such that they do not contribute to the gain mechanism. In case 3 no growing wave exists: there are only two waves with large amplitudes and one with almost negligible amplitude; it is the interference due to phase relations between the two large-amplitude waves that causes the difference in the behavior at the input and output end of the tube.

It was mentioned above that after a detailed exploration for the various possible conditions for backward-wave oscillation it was found that a simple condition for oscillation existed for the case in which space charge was appreciable, say, for $4QC > 1$. For typical circuits and typical currents used in backward-wave oscillators, this condition is quite common, so that the case is not a trivial one. For this case it was found empirically (and later verified analytically) that oscillation

Circuit field at gun   Circuit field at collector

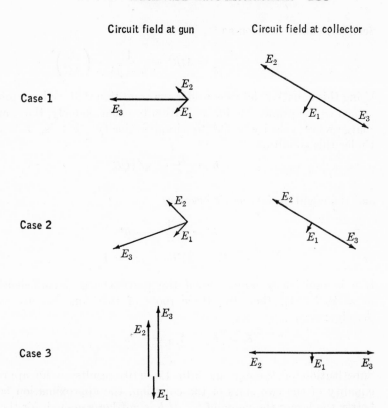

Fig. 7.3   Relative magnitudes and phases of the three waves at two ends of the tube.   Case 1: $QC = 0$, $d = 0$.   Case 2: $QC = 0$, $d = 0.5$.   Case 3: $QC = 1, d = 0$.   (After W. A. Harman, Backward-wave Interaction in Helix-type Tubes, Stanford Univ. Electron. Res. Lab. Tech. Rep. 13, April 26, 1954.)

would occur when the *circuit wave* was synchronous with the *slow* space-charge wave.   To discuss this case further, it is of value to introduce a common notation that can be used both in forward-wave traveling-wave tubes and backward-wave oscillators.   We define the following quantities:

$$b \equiv \frac{\beta_0 - \beta_e}{C\beta_e} \qquad C^3 \equiv \frac{K}{4R_0} \qquad K \equiv \frac{E^2}{2\beta_0^2 P} \qquad 4QC \equiv \left(\frac{\beta_q}{\beta_e C}\right)^2 \quad (7)$$

where β_0 = circuit phase constant

$\beta_e = \omega/v_0$, a beam phase constant

β_q = reduced plasma phase constant

In terms of these quantities, assuming no loss in the circuit and assuming that the roots can be written as $\Gamma = j\beta_e - \beta_e C\delta$, the equation for δ (see

Sec. 6.3) can be written as

$$\delta^2 = \frac{1}{b - j\delta} - 4QC = \frac{1}{b - j\delta} - \left(\frac{\beta_q}{\beta_e C}\right)^2 \tag{8}$$

Using this equation, let us consider the condition that we have previously named as the proper one for oscillation to occur, namely, the slow space-charge-wave velocity equal to circuit velocity, that is, $\beta_0 = \beta_e + \beta_q$. Under this condition

$$b = \frac{\beta_q}{\beta_e C} = \sqrt{4QC} \tag{9}$$

and the equation for the δ's becomes

$$\delta^2 = \frac{1}{b - j\delta} - b^2$$

or $$(b - j\delta)^2(b + j\delta) = 1 \tag{10}$$

If b is sufficiently large, i.e., if the space charge is sufficiently large ($b^2 = 4QC \geq 1$), then the three roots of this equation are (approximately):

$$\delta_1 = jb \qquad \delta_{2,3} = -jb \pm \frac{j}{\sqrt{2b}} \tag{11}$$

Substitution of these roots into Eq. (10) results in an approximate equality of the two sides of the equation, the approximation being the better the larger the value of b. If b is not large enough for these roots to be very accurate, it is also possible, by successive approximations, to obtain better values for them. It must be stressed at this point that so far we have not said much about the significance of this choice of conditions ($\beta_0 = \beta_e + \beta_q$) except to say that it is an interesting case. However, we can now take these roots and impose the following conditions on the three waves, zero current and velocity at the cathode end of the tube and finite initial value of the field at the collector end, and look for any consequence. If one goes through the algebra of fitting these boundary conditions for these waves, one can derive the ratio of the field at $z = 0$ (the output) to the field at $z = L$ (the input):

$$\frac{E(0)}{E(L)} = \frac{\dfrac{\delta_3 - \delta_2}{b - j\delta_1} + \dfrac{\delta_1 - \delta_3}{b - j\delta_2} + \dfrac{\delta_2 - \delta_1}{b - j\delta_3}}{\dfrac{\delta_3 - \delta_2}{b - j\delta_1} e^{-\Gamma_1 L} + \dfrac{\delta_1 - \delta_3}{b - j\delta_2} e^{-\Gamma_2 L} + \dfrac{\delta_2 - \delta_1}{b - j\delta_3} e^{-\Gamma_3 L}} \tag{12}$$

This is the voltage gain for the tube under the stated conditions of beam and circuit velocity and length. Oscillation occurs when this quantity becomes infinite or the denominator becomes zero. Given the roots derived above, we can see by inspection that the amplitude of the first term of the denominator is very small compared with the amplitude of the other two, and in the limit of large b this term approaches zero.   Moreover, the amplitudes of the second and third terms become approximately equal.   Therefore, the condition for the denominator to be zero is for the phases of the two waves in the second and the third term to differ by π at the end of the tube, so that one term is the negative of the other and the entire combination becomes zero (again subject to the approximation of large b).   The condition that the arguments of the two waves differ by π can be stated as

$$2\pi C N \delta_2 - 2\pi C N \delta_3 = (2n + 1)\pi j \tag{13}$$

and after substitution of the δ's this condition results in the following equation as the condition for oscillation:

$$2\pi C N \frac{2}{\sqrt{2b}} = (2n + 1)\pi$$

or, since $b = \beta_q / \beta_e C$,

$$C N = \frac{(2n + 1)^{\frac{2}{3}}}{2} \left(\frac{\beta_q L}{2\pi} \right)^{\frac{1}{3}} \tag{14}$$

One can see that an infinite set of such conditions exists, corresponding to different values of n.   It must be remembered that we have already imposed a condition for all of them previously, namely, that the circuit wave should be synchronous with the slow space-charge wave $(\beta_0 - \beta_e = \beta_q)$; and this represents another condition required for start oscillation.   The form of this second condition, for the phase difference between the two waves, serves to demonstrate the statement made earlier, that oscillation (and gain) for the backward-wave tube results from interference.   The reason why the denominator goes to zero is that the two terms have a phase difference of π at the appropriate location, and not that either of the waves is growing.   It can also be seen that the conditions for $n > 0$ which require greater current than for $n = 0$ are also conditions that correspond to a current at which the tube could be made to oscillate at a shorter length.   Thus the current corresponding to $n = 0$ is the smallest current for which the tube can oscillate; a higher value of n requires considerably more current, as $I_n = I_0(2n + 1)^4$, so that $I_n = 81I_0$ even for $n = 1$.   Since it has been found that backward-wave tubes run efficiently at about 4 times the starting current, higher-order modes need not be excited.   It is also true that the higher value of n then corresponds to a case in which the tube could have oscillated at the same current but with a shorter length. For example, if $n = 1$, then obviously with the same current and one-third of the length the conditions of a phase shift of π would have been satisfied between the two waves.   The denominator would have been zero and we would have again had oscillation.   In this sense one can say that the higher modes can be considered as resulting in a redundant-length oscillator.   Oscillators with excess length are merely cases for which one could have got exactly the same behavior at a shorter length, the two relevant waves merely having picked up an extra phase-shift difference of 2π.

Electron Motion in

Two-dimensional Systems

With the exception of the discussion of Sec. 4.5 regarding space-charge waves with transverse motion, all descriptions of modulation effects in the preceding chapters have been concerned with the case in which electron motion is restricted to the z direction. The beam was either assumed to extend infinitely in the transverse direction, in which case not only is the motion restricted to the z direction but in addition none of the associated quantities is allowed to vary with the transverse coordinates; or the beam was assumed to be confined by a very strong magnetic field B_z, in which case transverse variations are possible but the motion still remains restricted to the z direction. Such a restriction considerably simplifies the analysis, and indeed corresponds to reality in many practical cases. However, there are useful devices in which some transverse motion occurs and cannot be ignored. If the beam is focused (or rather, *balanced*) by positive-ion neutralization of the space charge or by one of the space-charge-balanced flow schemes described in Chap. 2 and the balance (or the entrance condition) is imperfect, we have seen that transverse motion is indeed possible and the beam has a scalloped envelope. Similarly, if r-f fields capable of producing radial motion are present on a circuit that surrounds a tubular beam, or if the space-charge forces produced by r-f currents in the beam have radial components, radial electron motion is possible and the analysis is substantially different from that for the case in which such motion is inhibited. However, since the operation of many devices depends on the total charge or current and not on the density, the overall physical behavior is much the same in confined and focused flow.

8.1 Motion Through a Nonplanar Gap

One example of a circuit that can produce such transverse fields is the modulating gap of a gridless klystron (Fig. 8.1a), in which there *is* an E_r component and in which E_z and E_r are not uniform across the gap. Another is the typical traveling-wave-tube circuit (Fig. 8.1b), in which there are E_r fields in addition to the E_z fields.

Figure 8.1a can be taken to represent a gridless gap of either circular or planar symmetry. The circular gap is more common in practice, with the gap driven by an external cavity and representing the space between two sections of a hollow cylindrical drift tube and with the beam usually not filling the drift tube. In the planar case the center line represents a plane of symmetry and the analysis of electron motion through the gap is quite similar, with obvious changes in the coordinate system. Both in the cylindrical-gap case and in the field configuration illustrated in Fig. 8.1b, which is a schematic representation of the field

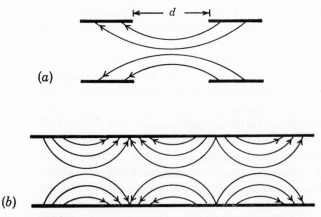

Fig. 8.1 **Modulating configurations giving rise to transverse motion:** (*a*) gridless klystron gap; (*b*) traveling-wave-tube circuit.

distribution at a given instant in a traveling-wave-tube circuit, transverse motion of the electrons results if the electrons are free to move transversely. The following discussion refers principally to the klystron case, although the extensions necessary to make the treatment applicable to a traveling-wave tube will be mentioned at appropriate points.

We shall consider the effects upon both the axial and the radial motion of the electrons; the discussion will serve as a preliminary to the calculation of the space-charge effects beyond the gap. The problem, therefore, is to calculate first v_r and then v_z. It is obvious that we are no longer dealing with a uniform field in the z direction in a gap such as shown in Fig. 8.1a, but it is possible to state the theory in such a form that the field need not be specified until the very end of the calculation. Then, under small-amplitude modulation conditions similar to those assumed in the planar case, it is possible to obtain some generally useful formulas for a variety of fields. A particular feature to be noted is that E_z (and hence E_r) is a function of both z and r, so that the motion of the electron depends strongly on its radial position in the beam. If, as is desirable, we wish to define a voltage across the gap, it proves to be most convenient to define it as the voltage between the edges of the gap, i.e., at $r = a$. Strictly speaking, if we define the voltage as the integral $\int_{-\infty}^{\infty} E_z(r,z)\, dz$ along any line at a fixed value of r inside the gap, the result will not be independent of r since, in general, some r-f magnetic field is present inside the gap and the potential is not truly a static one. However, for the dimensions usually involved no great error is introduced in assuming that the integral expression for voltage *is* independent of r; the resulting quasi-static approximation is quite good and may be usefully employed.

Let us introduce the following normalized notation:

$$\theta \equiv \omega t \qquad Z \equiv \frac{\omega}{u_0} z = \beta_e z$$

$$\dot{Z} \equiv \frac{u}{u_0} = \frac{dZ}{d\theta} = \frac{dz}{u_0\, dt}$$

$$G_z \equiv \frac{E_z(r,z)}{\beta_e \int_{-\infty}^{\infty} E_z\, dz}$$

$$V = - \int_{-\infty}^{\infty} E_z\, dz$$

In this notation, the equation of motion for the z coordinate,

$$\ddot{z} = \eta E_z \sin \omega t \tag{1}$$

becomes $\qquad\qquad \ddot{Z} = \frac{\alpha}{2} G_z \sin \theta \tag{1a}$

where $\alpha = V/V_0$ and $u_0{}^2/2 = - \eta V_0$. It should be noted that in this equation, the right-hand side depends not only on the radial and axial positions of the electrons but also on time, since the normalized electric field G_z is a function of both r and z and, of course, θ represents the normalized time variable. It would be difficult to solve this equation exactly. To do so, we would have to know the exact trajectory in advance in order to transform the right-hand side into a function of t only; i.e., we would have to know r and z as functions of time so that they could be substituted in G_z for integration. But the trajectory is precisely what we are trying to find. This impasse can be quite successfully avoided and adequate answers can be obtained if the small-amplitude approximation is used.

8.2   Calculation of Velocity Modulation

Let us assume that velocity modulation is sufficiently small that the trajectory is only slightly perturbed from the d-c trajectory. In this case, we are justified in using the relations between distance and time in the equation of motion (particularly with regard to the field and to the time dependence) that would correspond to the d-c trajectory. In such an analysis the radial position of the unperturbed trajectory remains constant and the axial position is given simply by the d-c velocity $z = u_0(t - t_0)$ or $Z = \theta - \theta_0$, where $t_0(\theta_0)$ is the time at which the electron crosses the center of the gap. With this relation between the axial position and time, one can convert Eq. (1a) into

$$\ddot{Z} = \frac{\alpha}{2} G_z \sin (Z + \theta_0) \tag{1b}$$

Now the right-hand side is simply a function of distance, and one integration can be performed, at least formally,

$$\dot{Z} = 1 + \frac{\alpha}{2} \int_{-\infty}^{Z} G_W \sin (W + \theta_0)\, dW \tag{2}$$

where W has been introduced as a dummy variable instead of Z. The constant of integration is unity because at $Z = -\infty$ the velocity is u_0, which corresponds to $\dot{Z} = 1$ in normalized variables. To obtain the exit velocity from the interaction region, the upper limit is taken at $+\infty$:

$$\dot{Z} = 1 + \frac{\alpha}{2} \int_{-\infty}^{\infty} G_W \sin (W + \theta_0)\, dW$$

Even though the integral is taken between two infinite limits, it is obvious that all the effective modulation takes place in a region whose width is of the order of the gap width d; the limits are used merely to facilitate the evaluation of the integral, as we shall see later. If we rewrite the equation for exit velocity as

$$\dot{Z} = 1 + \frac{\alpha}{2} \int_{-\infty}^{\infty} G_W(\sin W \cos \theta_0 + \cos W \sin \theta_0)\, dW \qquad (2a)$$

and if we note that G_W is even, corresponding to a symmetrical gap, the sine term vanishes and the integral becomes

$$\dot{Z} = 1 + \frac{\alpha}{2} \int_{-\infty}^{\infty} G_W \cos W \sin \theta_0\, dW = 1 + \frac{\alpha}{2} M \sin \theta_0 \qquad (2b)$$

where

$$M \equiv \int_{-\infty}^{\infty} G_W \cos W\, dW$$

is a generalized beam-coupling coefficient simply representing the Fourier cosine transform of the normalized field.   (In an asymmetrical gap the sine term would have to be retained, but the theory would be only slightly complicated by this generalization.)   Equation $(2b)$ for the exit velocity is all that is required to calculate the velocity modulation that yields the initial conditions for space-charge waves beyond the gap. On the other hand, if we are interested in determining, say, beam loading *in* a gridless gap of this kind, we must perform another integration to find Z to first order in α.   This value, when inserted into Eq. $(1b)$, yields the first-order r-f relation between z and t; integration of Eq. $(1b)$ with that correction inserted would then yield an expression for $\dot{Z}$ correct to quadratic terms in α, and so on.

To illustrate the use of the generalized beam-coupling coefficient, let us apply the formula to a case we have calculated previously, a uniform axial field in the gridded gap of width d.   For this case

$$G_z = -\frac{E}{\beta_e V} = \frac{1}{\beta_e V}\frac{V}{d} = \frac{1}{D} \qquad \text{for } -\frac{d}{2} < z < \frac{d}{2}$$

$$= 0 \qquad \text{for } |z| > \frac{d}{2}$$

where $D \equiv \beta_e d$ and $E = -V/d$.   Then

$$M = \int_{-\infty}^{\infty} \frac{1}{D} \cos W\, dW = \int_{-D/2}^{D/2} \frac{\cos W}{D}\, dW = \frac{\sin (D/2)}{D/2}$$

as before.

Let us calculate the case of the cylindrical gap without grids.   Subsequently we shall also need the modulation in the radial motion produced by such a gap, but that calculation will follow quite readily once we have obtained the effect on axial motion.

What is the nature of the modulating field?   In cylindrical coordinates, an independent solution of Maxwell's equations for the component of electric field E_z is

$$e^{jn\theta} J_n(r \sqrt{k^2 - p^2}) e^{jpz} \qquad (3)$$

where $k = \omega/c$. In the important case of axial symmetry (no θ variation around the gap) the solution is restricted to the case of $n = 0$, $J_0(r \sqrt{k^2 - p^2})e^{jpz}$. This solution is one possible solution of Maxwell's equation; the general solution for such a gap, with axial symmetry, is a superposition of all such possible solutions that is written in the form of a Fourier integral

$$-\frac{E_z}{\beta_e V} = G_z = \int_{-\infty}^{\infty} A(p)J_0(r \sqrt{k^2 - p^2})e^{jpz}\, dp \qquad (4)$$

with $A(p)$ chosen to satisfy the boundary conditions, at $r = a$, for instance. One can evaluate the beam-coupling coefficient M as given in Eq. (2b) in terms of this general form for the normalized field. For a symmetrical gap,

$$M(r) = \int_{-\infty}^{\infty} G_z \cos \beta_e z\, d(\beta_e z)$$

$$= \int_{-\infty}^{\infty} \int_{-\infty}^{\infty} A(p)J_0(r \sqrt{k^2 - p^2})e^{jpz} \cos \beta_e z\, d(\beta_e z)\, dp$$

$$M(r) = \frac{A(\beta_e)}{2\pi} J_0(r \sqrt{k^2 - \beta_e^2}) \qquad (5)$$

with G_z again even, so that $A(p) = A(-p)$. (We have momentarily reverted to unnormalized variables in order to indicate how the answer comes about.) In most cases of interest the beam velocity is much lower than the velocity of light, so that $\beta_e \gg k$ and

$$M(r) = \frac{A(\beta_e)}{2\pi} I_0(\beta_e r) \qquad (6)$$

The physical meaning of this result is that with the approximation that the electron's velocity is changed only slightly by the modulating field, the electron interacts only with that component of the total Fourier integral that has the same phase velocity as the electron beam. In other words, the electron performs a Fourier analysis of the field and is acted upon only by that component which is synchronous with the electron velocity. All the other waves are either traveling faster or slower and produce a zero net effect over the integration range from $-\infty$ to $+\infty$.[1]

Some doubt may attach to the validity of this procedure, even granting the small-signal approximation. The manner in which this particular value of M was derived involved integration from $-\infty$ to $+\infty$;

[1] Another practical application of Eq. (2a) that has been made is in obtaining the field produced in a resonator consisting of a resonant section of a slow-wave circuit of length d, as in the tube described by M. Chodorow and T. Wessel-Berg, A High-efficiency Klystron with Distributed Interaction, *IRE Trans. Electron Devices*, **ED-8**:44-55 (1961). In this case, the field is that of a standing wave having a sinusoidal variation along the axis of the resonator. Depending on whether one has an odd or an even number of half wavelengths of this standing wave, either the first or

under these circumstances, we can expect to get only a single Fourier component. Yet we are interested in the effect of a *finite* gap on the electron, since we propose to apply this to conditions beyond the gap, so that the appropriateness of an integration between infinite limits may be questioned. The plausibility of this procedure can perhaps be justified as follows. Let us concede that in reality the gap field extends over a distance of the order of the gap width; i.e., a field that penetrates into the cylinders perhaps a distance comparable with their diameters. Accordingly, modulation effects extend only over a finite length of the order of twice the gap spacing. The field is still given correctly by the Fourier integral of Eq. (4), but the integration that yields the coupling coefficient for a finite interaction length would have to be carried out between some finite limits on z. Such an integration might be difficult, but presumably the result would yield a form that would involve contributions from all Fourier components, so that there would be interaction terms even from waves that are not in exact synchronism with the electron beam. However, such interaction would be appreciable only for a range of Fourier components with propagation constants close to the constant of the beam. The result could be formulated in some kind of an average over a group of waves with propagation constants clustered about the beam propagation constant, for all of which the amplitudes $A(p)$ would be approximately the same. The final answer, except for a slight numerical difference, would then be quite similar to that obtained by using infinite limits.

The calculation has been carried out in detail for cylindrical configurations, but for planar slots the treatment is entirely analogous; instead of modified Bessel functions, hyperbolic functions enter into the computation, and the beam-coupling coefficient can be written as

$$M(y) = \frac{A(\beta_e)}{2\pi} \cosh \beta_e y$$

Note that in either case the beam-coupling coefficient is still a function of the transverse coordinate (r or y) as is to be expected. Electrons are modulated by an amount that depends upon their transverse position, and the beam-coupling coefficient is significantly larger for electrons

---

second terms of Eq. (2a) vanish and one obtains for the generalized beam-coupling coefficient

$$\frac{\sin\left[(\beta_0 - \beta_e)(d/2)\right]}{(\beta_0 - \beta_e)(d/2)}$$

where β_0 and β_e are the phase constants of the circuit and the beam, respectively. This represents a maximum coupling when the beam is synchronous with the traveling-wave constituent (of a standing wave) traveling in the same direction as the electron beam. The coupling coefficient decreases as there is a departure from synchronism.

close to the gap edge than for electrons near the center of the gap. This result is obviously what may be expected from a physical consideration of the configuration.

To obtain specific numerical values, the coefficient A must be evaluated. This can be done by a calculation of M at the gap edge (at $r = a$), assuming a field distribution at the edge for this purpose. Such an assumption corresponds to inserting boundary conditions on the original Fourier integral for G_z. The assumption of such a field is once again not quite rigorous, but proves to give quite accurate results in practice. To make the calculation exact, one would have to solve the field problem in the gap and in the cavity surrounding the gap, with suitable continuity conditions on the fields across the boundary (at the gap edge). It proves to be much easier to make a reasonable assumption about the nature of the field at the gap edge, from an electrostatic approximation, for example, and to proceed from it to an evaluation of the appropriate amplitudes of the A's. One reasonable assumption, commonly used for gridless klystron gaps, is to assume that at the edge of the gap the field is uniform as it would be in a gridded gap, so that for an electron passing close to the gap edge the coupling coefficient is the same as in a planar gap; i.e., that at $r = a$,

$$M(a) = \frac{\sin{(\beta_e d/2)}}{\beta_e d/2} = \frac{\sin{(D/2)}}{D/2}$$

Comparison with the value from Eq. (6) for the beam-coupling coefficient at $r = a$ yields

$$M(a) = \frac{A(\beta_e)}{2\pi} I_0(\beta_e a) = \frac{\sin{(D/2)}}{D/2} \tag{7}$$

Equation (7) determines A, so that the general beam-coupling coefficient at any value of r is given by

$$M(r) = \frac{\sin{(D/2)}}{D/2} \frac{I_0(\beta_e r)}{I_0(\beta_e a)} \tag{8}$$

Another and perhaps better choice for the field at the gap edge is to use the electrostatic field between two thin planes, the so-called *knife-edge field*. In this case the beam-coupling coefficient at the edge is given by $M(a) = J_0(D/2)$ and

$$M(r) = J_0(D/2) \frac{I_0(\beta_e r)}{I_0(\beta_e a)}$$

The value of $J_0(D/2)$ is not greatly different from $[\sin{(D/2)}]/(D/2)$, but experimental measurements of the fields have shown that for sharp edges the knife-edge assumption proves to be somewhat better, especially for relatively large values of gap spacing.

--- --- --- ---

Fig.   8.2   Multiple-gap
traveling-wave circuit.

--- --- --- ---

The above development also applies quite generally to traveling-wave tubes.   In that case the structure is periodic and the general theory of the fields in such structures indicates that the field must be written in the form

$$E_z = e^{-j\beta_0 z} U_p(z,r,\theta) \tag{9}$$

where the function U_p has the periodicity of the traveling-wave-tube circuit.   This property of the field of a periodic structure is a statement of Floquet's theorem for periodic structures.   In this case the periodic function can be expanded in Fourier series rather than a Fourier integral.   The Fourier series will have the same form as the integral used previously, except that the summation is over a discrete set of phase constants rather than a continuous set.   For the case of no θ dependence,

$$E_z = e^{-j\beta_0 z} \sum_n A_n F_n(r) e^{-j2\pi nz/L} \tag{10}$$

where L is the period of the structure.   If the term multiplying the periodic function is incorporated inside the summation, the series becomes $\sum_n A_n J_0(r\sqrt{k^2 - \beta_n{}^2}) e^{-j\beta_n z}$, where $\beta_n = \beta_0 + (2\pi n/L)$.[1]

In computing the amplitudes of the coefficients we can make the same assumptions about the field at the circuit boundaries as we do for the case of a single gap.   For example, if the boundary consists of a series of gaps alternating with metallic cylinders (Fig. 8.2), one assumes that at each gap the field is uniform, and then by going through a Fourier analysis[2] one arrives at the amplitudes of the coefficients as

$$A_n = \frac{V}{L} \frac{\sin(\beta_n d/2)}{\beta_n d/2} \frac{1}{I_0(\gamma_n a)} \qquad \gamma_n = \sqrt{\beta_n{}^2 - k^2}$$

The electrons interact strongly only with that component of the field for which β_n is approximately equal to β_e.   However, if there is no exact synchronism between the beam and this component, the coefficients just

---

[1] It should be noted that the above applies to a cylindrical periodic structure with no angular variations in the fields.   This case is, of course, similar to that of the klystron gap.   If field components with angular variations are present, as, for example, in the case of a helix, these expressions are modified to the extent that certain terms of the series are multiplied by functions of the form $e^{-jn\theta}$ and the zero-order Bessel functions are replaced by functions of the order n.

[2] J. R. Pierce, "Traveling-wave Tubes," chap. 4, D. Van Nostrand Company, Inc., Princeton, N.J., 1950.

derived must be multiplied by a beam-coupling coefficient of the form

$$\frac{\sin\left[(\beta_n - \beta_e)(d'/2)\right]}{(\beta_n - \beta_e)(d'/2)}$$

where d' is now the total distance over which the electrons interact with the circuit. This expression is analogous to that given in the footnote on pages 194 and 195.

Returning to the klystron case with a single gap, we find that we also need an expression for the transverse velocity of the electron after it leaves the gap. It is obvious that the fields in the gap have radial components that result in radial modulation, which is important in determining the relative amplitudes of the various space-charge waves excited beyond the gap. The radial equation of motion is

$$\ddot{r} = \eta E_r(r,z) \sin \omega t \tag{11}$$

Once again we are faced with the difficulty of integrating an equation whose right-hand side is a function of time as well as of the coordinates. The same approximation as used before proves to be permissible: we assume that the trajectory is only slightly modified by passage through the gap. To calculate the modulation approximately, we utilize the unperturbed trajectory on the right-hand side of the equation, as follows. First, we substitute for t its value in terms of z and the d-c velocity:

$$t = \frac{z}{u_0} + t_0 \qquad dt = \frac{dz}{u_0}$$

Second, we assume that there is no radial displacement within the gap, so that Eq. (11) becomes

$$\ddot{r} = \eta E_r \sin \left(\beta_e z + \theta_0\right) \tag{11a}$$

which integrates at once into

$$v_r = \dot{r} = \int_{-\infty}^{z} \frac{\eta E_r}{u_0} \sin \left(\beta_e z + \theta_0\right) dz \tag{11b}$$

with the initial condition that $v_r = 0$ at $z = -\infty$. This expression could be integrated once again to obtain the displacement r produced by the gap, but we are more interested in the radial velocity of the electron on its exit from the gap. (We could also use such a second integration to determine the component of beam loading that arises from this displacement and the radial velocity. Such a procedure would yield a radial displacement that is correct to linear terms and is then used to obtain the next approximation.)

To determine the value of radial velocity at exit we need an explicit expression for E_r. Consistent with our original assumption as to the nature of the axial fields, we obtain E_r from E_z [Eq. (3)] through Maxwell's equations (for $n = 0$):

$$- \frac{jp}{\sqrt{k^2 - p^2}} J_1(r \sqrt{k^2 - p^2}) e^{jpz} \tag{12}$$

and the equivalent of Eq. (4)

$$\frac{E_r}{\beta_e V} = \int_{-\infty}^{\infty} \frac{jp A(p)}{\sqrt{k^2 - p^2}} J_1(r \sqrt{k^2 - p^2}) e^{jpz} \tag{13}$$

Equation (11b) for the exit velocity can be written in complex notation as

$$\dot{r} = \frac{\eta}{u_0} \int_{-\infty}^{\infty} jE_r e^{j(\beta_e z + \theta_0)} \, dz = \frac{\eta V}{u_0} \int_{-\infty}^{\infty} \frac{jE_r}{\beta_e V} e^{j(\beta_e z + \theta_0)} \, d(\beta_e z) \tag{11c}$$

Substitution of expressions for the fields given by Eq. (13) yields

$$\dot{r} = \frac{j\eta V}{u_0} \left[\frac{j\beta_e}{\sqrt{k^2 - \beta_e^2}} \frac{A(\beta_e)}{2\pi} J_1(r \sqrt{k^2 - \beta_e^2}) \cos \theta_0 \right]$$

$$= - \frac{1}{\sqrt{k^2 - \beta_e^2}} \frac{\beta_e \eta V}{u_0} \frac{J_1(r \sqrt{k^2 - \beta_e^2})}{I_0(\beta_e a)} \frac{\sin (D/2)}{D/2} \cos \theta_0$$

$$\dot{r} \approx - \frac{\eta V}{u_0} \frac{I_1(\beta_e r)}{I_0(\beta_e a)} \frac{\sin (D/2)}{D/2} \cos \theta_0 \tag{14}$$

This is an expression for the radial exit velocity for an electron that passed through a gap center at $z = 0$ at the phase θ_0; so that the equations for the radial and axial velocities are finally

$$\frac{\dot{r}}{u_0} = \frac{\alpha}{2} \frac{I_1(\beta_e r)}{I_0(\beta_e a)} \frac{\sin (D/2)}{D/2} \cos \theta_0$$

$$\frac{\dot{z}}{u_0} = 1 + \frac{\alpha}{2} \frac{I_0(\beta_e r)}{I_0(\beta_e a)} \frac{\sin (D/2)}{D/2} \sin \theta_0 \tag{15}$$

In these equations the phase factors are particularly important: θ_0 is the phase at which an electron traveling with the velocity u_0 crosses the gap center. A consideration of this phase factor tells us a great deal about the relationship between axial and radial velocity for any electron. The maximum axial velocity is evidently associated with zero radial velocity, and vice versa. This relationship can be made more obvious if we consider a typical case. For example, consider the special case in which the transit time across the significant part of the field (i.e., the gap width) is approximately equal to π. Because of the sinusoidal time dependence, an electron acquires the maximum z component of velocity if it crosses the gap center at a phase such that the field is then passing through its maximum axial value. This phase implies that the electron must enter the region of significant field amplitude at the time when the field is changing from decelerating to accelerating, and it must leave the gap when the field is changing from accelerating to decelerating. That is, during the entire interval of electron passage through the gap, the field pattern is approximately as shown in Fig. 8.1 (with the amplitude of the field varying during the passage).

With regard to the radial velocity of this same electron, it will evidently be acted upon by an outward force as it enters and an inward force as it leaves, with the result that the net effect is approximately zero and the radial exit velocity is approximately zero.

Conversely, an electron *entering* the field at a time when acceleration is at a maximum sees an inward force as it enters; the field changes from accelerating to decelerating as it passes the center of the gap; and through the second portion of the gap the electron is subject to a decelerating field and *also* an inward radial field. The net effect is that the change in axial motion to first order is zero, since the field is accelerating for half of the transit and decelerating for the other half, but the radial field is inward during both halves of the transit and the resulting radial velocity is maximum.

It follows from this qualitative argument, as it does from the equations, that the maximum radial and maximum axial velocities are 90° out of phase. However, the equations for electron motion yield additional information as follows. If $\theta_0 = \omega t_0$ is the time the electron crosses the center of the gap, the position of that electron at any other time (if there were no space-charge forces beyond the gap) could be derived by means of the relationships

$$t - t_0 = \frac{z}{u_0}$$

or

$$\theta_0 = \omega t - \frac{\omega z}{u_0} = \omega t - \beta_e z$$

Then Eqs. (15) can be rewritten

$$\frac{\dot{r}}{u_0} = j \frac{\alpha}{2} \frac{I_1(\beta_e r)}{I_0(\beta_e a)} \frac{\sin (D/2)}{D/2} e^{j\omega t} e^{-j\beta_e z}$$

$$\frac{\dot{z}}{u_0} = 1 + \frac{\alpha}{2} \frac{I_0(\beta_e r)}{I_0(\beta_e a)} \frac{\sin (D/2)}{D/2} e^{j\omega t} e^{-j\beta_e z}$$

(16)

where the velocities are now defined in terms of the position of the electron at any time rather than in terms of the time t_0 at the gap center. Equations of this sort apply to each electron but, as just stated, only if there are no space-charge forces. We can then take Eqs. (16), consider them at a fixed time, letting z and r vary, and obtain the values of the instantaneous velocities of all the electrons in the drift tube just beyond the gap at this fixed time. (By "just beyond the gap" we mean a distance such that the space-charge forces have changed these velocities by a negligible amount.) The vector $(\dot{r}, \dot{z})$ defined by these two equations for a fixed time essentially represents the local velocity of the particle located at each point in space. It can be seen from these equations that the two r-f components of velocity at each point in space are proportional to corresponding Fourier terms in the expressions for electric field, i.e., the Fourier terms with a propagation constant β_e. In mathematical terms,

$$\mathbf{v} = \frac{\alpha}{4\pi} \, \mathbf{E}(\beta_e) \tag{17}$$

where $\mathbf{E}(\beta_e)$ represents the vector $[E_r(\beta_e), E_z(\beta_e)]$, which are the corresponding Fourier terms from Eqs. (4) and (13) with propagation constant β_e and which together satisfy Maxwell's equations (though not the boundary conditions). In particular, they satisfy the equation

$$\nabla \cdot \mathbf{E} = 0$$

Therefore, the velocity as defined by Eq. (16) also satisfies the relation

$$\nabla \cdot \mathbf{v} = 0 \tag{18}$$

If we now introduce the equation of continuity,

$$\frac{\partial \rho}{\partial t} + \nabla \cdot \rho \mathbf{v} = 0$$

or

$$\frac{\partial \rho}{\partial t} + \rho \nabla \cdot \mathbf{v} + (\mathbf{u}_0 + \mathbf{v}) \cdot \nabla \rho = 0$$

We obtain, by substitution from Eq. (18),

$$\frac{\partial \rho}{\partial t} + (\mathbf{u}_0 + \mathbf{v}) \cdot \nabla \rho = 0$$

or

$$\frac{d\rho}{dt} = 0 \tag{19}$$

where $d\rho/dt$ is the *particle derivative*, i.e., the rate of change as one travels with a particular particle. We find that the velocity distribution in the beam just beyond the gap produced by this type of gap results in a motion of the electrons such that the charge density in the beam remains constant at its unmodulated value. This is a plausible result and represents a more quantitative statement of the nature of the modulation which was discussed above in terms of the phase relations between maximum radial and maximum axial velocities. The modulation pattern produced by a gap field is that shown in Fig. 8.3. In regions where axial velocity is maximum, the beam is compressed axially but the radial velocities tend to decompress it, and vice versa. The over all effect is that there is no net change in charge density in the volume, but, of course, the fact that the radial velocities are alternately inward and outward along the boundaries of the beam causes a rippled surface.

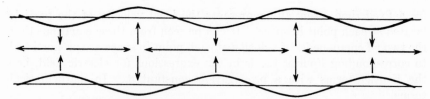

Fig. 8.3   Relative velocity distribution in modulated beams.

It is the rippling of the surface that is responsible for the r-f current in this kind of beam.

It was shown in Sec. 4.5 that space-charge waves can exist either in a Brillouin beam or in an ion-focused beam, for which the r-f charge density within the beam is zero but in which radial motion and rippling of the surface is possible.   The detailed analysis of the amplitudes of the waves launched by gap modulation shows[1] that the initial modulation that we have just described provides precisely the correct initial conditions for this pair of space-charge waves, and it is therefore just these space-charge waves that will exist.   Since the r-f charge density within the beam associated with these space-charge waves is zero, any fields produced by them correspond to changes in the surface ripple.   Inside the beam, with zero r-f charge density, the divergence of the electric field must be zero and any additional velocity changes produced in the beam must also have zero divergence.   The conditions launched by the gap are thus precisely those maintained by the space-charge-wave solutions.

The analysis of the current in a beam characterized by these space-charge waves also shows that most of the r-f current is, under normal circumstances, carried by the surface ripples.   There is some volume current: even though volume charge density is zero, the r-f velocity is not zero and contributes a nonzero term to the volume current.   However, the detailed analysis shows that the ratio of volume current to the surface current carried by the ripples is of the order ω_q/ω.

We can demonstrate these properties by considering the effects of a gridless gap in launching the various space-charge waves that can exist in a drift tube under conditions that permit transverse motion, i.e., with positive-ion neutralization or Brillouin focusing.   The relations governing these space-charge waves were given in Sec. 4.5.   In particular, Eqs. (4.137) and (4.138) determine the fields inside the electron beam for such waves, Eq. (4.140) the propagation constants, and Eqs. (4.120), (4.122), and (4.128) the relations of the radial and axial velocities and radial displacement, respectively, to the fields.   To relate the values

[1] W. W. Rigrod and J. R. Pierce, Space-charge Wave Excitation in Solid-Cylindrical Brillouin Beams, *Bell System Tech. J.*, **38**:99–118 (1959); M. Chodorow and L. Zitelli, The Radio-frequency Current Distribution in Brillouin Flow, *IRE Trans. Electron Devices*, **ED-6**:352–357 (1959).

of gap modulation obtained in the present chapter to the amplitudes of the space-charge waves described in Chap. 4, we need only satisfy initial conditions: we must show that we can combine space-charge waves in suitable linear combinations (and with proper amplitudes) so that they do reduce to the proper conditions at the beginning of the drift tube, i.e., at the modulating gap.

We pointed out in Chap. 4 that there are two pairs of space-charge waves. In one pair, the r-f charge density inside the beam is zero; in the other pair, it is not. With the values of velocity, charge density, and radial displacement as determined by the gap as initial conditions, it can be shown that if one attempts to satisfy these initial conditions by a superposition of all four waves, the result will be formally satisfied, at least to terms of the order $(\beta_q/\beta_e)^2$, if there are nonzero amplitudes for only the two space-charge waves with zero charge density, for which relations are given by the above-mentioned equations. It proves to be actually simpler to show that the $\rho = 0$ waves are sufficient to satisfy the initial conditions than to include the $\rho \neq 0$ waves. It is certainly plausible that the latter should not be required, since they involve a volume charge density, whereas the initial velocities derived in Eq. (16) lead to zero charge density.

If we thus assume that the $\rho = 0$ space-charge waves are the only ones that are important, we may write for v_z and v_r

$$\frac{v_z(r,z)}{v_0} = (V_1 e^{-j\beta_q z} + V_2 e^{j\beta_q z}) I_0(\beta_e r) e^{-j\beta_e z}$$
$$\frac{v_r(r,z)}{v_0} = j(V_1 e^{-j\beta_q z} + V_2 e^{j\beta_q z}) I_1(\beta_e r) e^{-j\beta_e z} \tag{20}$$

where I_0 and I_1 are modified zero- and first-order Bessel functions of the first kind and β_q is the modified plasma propagation constant [cf. Eq. (4.141) and Fig. 4.9]. We have also used the relations between fields and velocities given in Sec. 4.5 and the fact that for the pair of space-charge waves under consideration the values of β ($= \beta_e \pm \beta_q$) are so similar that both can be set equal to β_e in the argument of the Bessel functions. If we set $z = 0$ in Eqs. (20) and equate them to the values of the initial velocities, as given by Eqs. (16), at $z = 0$, we obtain from each of Eqs. (20)

$$V_1 + V_2 = \frac{\alpha}{2} \frac{\sin (D/2)}{D/2} \frac{1}{I_0(\beta_e a)} \tag{21}$$

Since both of Eqs. (20) result in the same equation, the two conditions are not sufficient to determine the amplitudes of the two space-charge waves. It becomes necessary to impose an additional initial condition consistent with the approximations made previously. The condition is that the displacement of the beam boundary is zero at the entrance plane. This is consistent with the approximations made in deriving, for example,

Eqs. (15); moreover, it is physically plausible, since in transit through the gap the first-order effects of the fields are to produce velocities but not first-order displacements. Equations (4.122) and (4.138) yield, for any position along the drift tube, a displacement of an electron originally at a boundary (at $r = b$) given in terms of the two relevant space-charge waves by

$$\Delta b(b,z) = -(V_1 e^{-j\beta_q z} - V_2 e^{j\beta_q z}) \frac{I_1(\beta_e b)}{\beta_q} e^{-j\beta_e z} \tag{22}$$

This expression must be set equal to zero at the initial plane ($z = 0$), and the result, combined with Eq. (21), yields

$$V_1 = V_2 = \frac{\alpha}{4} \frac{\sin (D/2)}{D/2} \frac{1}{I_0(\beta_e a)} \tag{23}$$

Assembling our results, we finally obtain for the velocities and displacement

$$\frac{v_z(r,z)}{v_0} = \frac{\alpha}{2} \frac{\sin (D/2)}{D/2} \frac{I_0(\beta_e r)}{I_0(\beta_e a)} \cos \beta_q z \, e^{-j\beta_e z}$$

$$\frac{v_r(r,z)}{v_0} = j \frac{\alpha}{2} \frac{\sin (D/2)}{D/2} \frac{I_1(\beta_e r)}{I_0(\beta_e a)} \cos \beta_q z \, e^{-j\beta_e z} \tag{24}$$

$$\Delta b(b,z) = j \frac{\alpha}{2} \frac{\sin (D/2)}{D/2} \frac{I_1(\beta_e b)}{I_0(\beta_e a)} \frac{\sin \beta_q z}{\beta_q} e^{-j\beta_e z}$$

It is evident that all initial conditions are satisfied by the superposition of the two $\rho = 0$ space-charge waves.

An interesting consequence of these equations for the velocity and displacement lies in the form of the current that they predict. Two current components result: one owing to displacements of the surface, the other to the volume current. The latter is not zero even though the r-f charge density is zero, since the existence of an axial component of r-f velocity contributes a volume current density of the form $\rho_0 v_z(r,z)$. The integral of this current density over the entire cross section gives the total volume current. The current resulting from displacements of the surface comes about because the rippled boundary is equivalent to a surface charge being transported at the d-c beam velocity; the product of the surface charge and the d-c beam velocity produces an r-f current. Numerically, consistent with the treatment in Chap. 4, the surface charge (integrated around the circumference) is given by $\rho_0 \Delta b(2\pi b)$. The corresponding surface current, which is merely this total surface charge multiplied by the beam velocity, is $\rho_0 v_0 \Delta b(2\pi b)$. If one compares this surface current with the above-mentioned volume current, two significant results become evident. First, the surface current is much larger than the volume current, and, second, the two are in time quadrature. Actually, the volume current is of the order of β_q/β_e times the surface current and may be neglected.

9

Coupled-mode Analysis

So far in the discussion of space-charge waves and the interaction of electron beams with traveling-wave circuits, we have not considered the change in the energy content of the electron beam itself. We have calculated the rate of growth of a growing wave in a traveling-wave tube, i.e., the gain of such a device, and also the gain of a backward-wave amplifier. These calculations involved (1) Maxwell's equations to determine the effects of the current in driving the circuit and (2) the equations of motion, equation of continuity, etc. to determine the converse effects of the electric fields in modifying the motion of the electrons and producing a current. Implicit in both of these calculations are certain consequences relating to the change both in the energy content of the electromagnetic field propagating on the circuit and in the energy of the electron beam. However, no attempt was made to extract these results from the equations.

A similar omission was made previously in the discussion of space-charge-wave phenomena in klystron drift tubes. The calculations made consisted of finding the amplitudes of the space-charge waves produced by a modulating voltage across a klystron gap; then by calculating the current at any distance from this input gap one could obtain the power transfer to a second gap. Again, a loss of energy by the beam (and presumably a change in the amplitude of the space-charge waves beyond the second gap) was implied. If the previously derived theory for space-charge waves was complete, we should expect (with suitable definitions of the energy content of an electron beam and of the energy delivered to either a propagating circuit or to a cavity) to find conservation of energy. The theory is not exact, however. It will be recalled that in deriving the space-charge-wave equations, we had to linearize the equations. Several terms were discarded for the purpose of obtaining linear homogeneous equations with constant coefficients that could be conveniently solved in terms of space-charge waves. However, this discarding of nonlinear terms has some special and possibly harmful implications for energy calculations.

As we shall see below, in making energy calculations it is necessary to construct certain quadratic functions either of the field amplitudes or of the space-charge-wave amplitudes. It will become apparent that in constructing such quadratic functions the validity of any expression proves to be questionable if nonlinear terms were omitted in the original equations. It seems plausible that in calculating energy (which is quadratic) one should calculate amplitudes to a higher order of approximation than in the linear theory used so far. Actually, it does prove to be possible to construct quadratic quantities based on the linear theory such that a conservation law does apply. This conservation law, which is known as the Chu small-signal power theorem,[1] turns out to be very useful and enables one to explain and to unify the treatment of various kinds of devices in a very illuminating manner. In fact, it does more: it permits one to solve, for quite general cases, some problems previously solved only for special cases, principally because the Chu theorem demonstrates that certain portions of the previous solutions that have been included are not really important and can be omitted without much error. Therefore, one can make calculations easily for a much wider range of parameters than with more involved theories.

The procedure in the following sections, then, will be first to indicate the exact form of a power conservation theorem for a system in which power flow is both in the form of electromagnetic energy and kinetic energy of the electron beam. From this definition, and with the small-signal approximations used previously, it will be possible to derive a conservation theorem of this same form that uses only small-signal quanti-

---

[1] L. J. Chu, A Kinetic Power Theorem, paper presented at AIEE–IRE Conference on Electron Tube Research, Durham, N.H., June, 1951.

ties and that defines so-called small-signal power in such a way that it can be easily calculated from the linear equations.

9.1 Small-signal Kinetic-power Theorem for Longitudinal Electron Beams

If we consider a general system in which energy is transported both in the form of electromagnetic waves and in kinetic energy, it is quite easy to demonstrate that the density of total power flow can be written as

$$\tfrac{1}{2} \operatorname{Re} \left(\mathbf{E} \times \mathbf{H}^* + \mathbf{J} \frac{v^2}{2\eta} \right) \tag{1}$$

where $\mathbf{J}$ is the current density and v the electron velocity. The first term is the well-known Poynting vector, which represents the electromagnetic power flow; the second term represents the flow of kinetic energy carried by the electron beam. It can be easily seen that the latter term represents this kinetic-energy flow (or, as we shall refer to it, kinetic power) if we rewrite the current

$$J = nev$$

where n is the number density. In this form the above expression for the kinetic-power flow merely represents the number of electrons crossing per unit area per unit time multiplied by the kinetic energy per electron.

If we consider a system without sources or sinks (i.e., if there is no increase or decrease in the energy stored per unit volume in any of the regions under consideration), then with the definition of power flow given above the divergence of this quantity must be zero:

$$\tfrac{1}{2} \operatorname{Re} \int\limits_{\text{vol}} \nabla \cdot \left(\mathbf{E} \times \mathbf{H}^* + \mathbf{J} \frac{v^2}{2\eta} \right) \cdot d\tau = \tfrac{1}{2} \operatorname{Re} \int\limits_{\text{surface}} \left(\mathbf{E} \times \mathbf{H}^* + \mathbf{J} \frac{v^2}{2\eta} \right) \cdot d\mathbf{s} \tag{2}$$

It is convenient to write this equation for the total power flow in a system in a new notation. We replace the kinetic power in the form written above by an equivalent expression

$$J \frac{v^2}{2\eta} \equiv JV \tag{3}$$

where $V = v^2/2\eta$ is the *kinetic voltage* and represents a convenient way of describing the kinetic energy. (It is important to note that, as defined here, this quantity is negative for electrons; thus, for a d-c beam of electrons starting from a cathode at zero potential and reaching an anode at a positive potential the kinetic voltage as defined here is the negative of the potential of this anode. With this definition, if the anode voltage is V_A, then $V + V_A = 0$.)

If we consider the conventional system with a-c currents and voltages, the energy stored in any volume does fluctuate with time sinusoidally. But on the *average* there is no increase or decrease in the energy stored in any portion of the volume, so that the above conservation theorem holds if averaged over time, although the integrals might not be zero instantaneously because of the time variations in the energy storage. On this basis, then, Eq. (1) represents the power flow. To apply it to any of the configurations we have been considering, we need only calculate the fields, currents, and velocities required for this expression. It is at this point that the difficulty mentioned earlier arises, since what we have available is a small-signal theory in which these quantities can be calculated only approximately.

Consider first the electromagnetic power. Let us assume that we have some system in which the interaction of the beam and a circuit generates an electromagnetic field at a frequency ω. From the small-signal equations such as we have used in all of our calculations previously, one can calculate this electromagnetic field. The appropriate equations are repeated here for the components at frequency ω.

$$\nabla \times \mathbf{E}_1 = -j\omega\mu\mathbf{H}_1 \tag{4}$$

$$\nabla \times \mathbf{H}_1 = j\omega\epsilon\mathbf{E}_1 + \mathbf{J}_1 \tag{5}$$

$$\mathbf{J}_1 = \rho_0\mathbf{v}_1 + \rho_1\mathbf{v}_0 + [\rho_1\mathbf{v}_1] \tag{6}$$

$$\nabla \cdot \mathbf{J}_1 = -j\omega\rho_1 \tag{7}$$

$$j\omega\mathbf{v}_1 + (\mathbf{v}_0 \cdot \nabla)\mathbf{v}_1 + (\mathbf{v}_1 \cdot \nabla)\mathbf{v}_0 + [(\mathbf{v}_1 \cdot \nabla)\mathbf{v}_1] = \eta E_1 \tag{8}$$

In these equations, the terms in brackets are nonlinear terms that must be omitted in order to make the equations linear. From these linear equations we may then calculate the electromagnetic fields correctly to first-order terms. With these quantities, as derived from the small-signal theory, one can calculate the electromagnetic power flowing out through some suitably chosen surface. If the device under consideration is a propagating circuit, the surface concerned may be a cylinder with two large end planes perpendicular to the direction of electron flow. For a cavity, the surface may enclose the cavity, including any output couplings from the cavity. The electromagnetic power flow P_e calculated would have the form

$$P_e = \tfrac{1}{2}\operatorname{Re} \int (\mathbf{E}_1 \times \mathbf{H}_1^*) \cdot d\mathbf{s} \tag{9}$$

Any correction to these fields that would arise from trying to use the theory more exactly would involve second-order terms that would be smaller than the first-order terms in the limit of very small signals. If we tried to include these second-order terms in the integral, at most we would obtain cubic terms or terms of still higher order that in the limit of very small signals could be made arbitrarily small. Therefore, in this limit (which is all with which we are really concerned at the moment)

Eq. (9) does represent the correct expression for the electromagnetic power flow; any other terms that are omitted are of higher order.

No difficulties with the small-signal theory thus arise from the electromagnetic power; but there are difficulties in formulating a suitable definition for the *kinetic power*. Suppose we attempt to write down the value of the kinetic power as given in Eq. (2), assuming that the current and electron velocity each consist of a d-c and an r-f component at the frequency ω, written as

$$\mathbf{J} = \mathbf{J}_0 + \mathbf{J}_1' \qquad \mathbf{v} = \mathbf{v}_0 + \mathbf{v}_1'$$

where $\mathbf{J}_1'$ and $\mathbf{v}_1'$ are the time-dependent r-f components; then the product representing the kinetic power would be of the form

$$\overline{\mathbf{J}(v^2/2\eta)} = \overline{[(\mathbf{J}_0 + \mathbf{J}')/2\eta](\mathbf{v}_0{}^2 + 2\mathbf{v}_0 \cdot \mathbf{v}_1' + \mathbf{v}_1'^2)}$$
$$= (1/2\eta)[\mathbf{J}_0\, v_0{}^2 + \overline{\mathbf{J}_1'v_0{}^2} + 2\overline{\mathbf{J}_0(\mathbf{v}_0 \cdot \mathbf{v}_1')} + 2\overline{\mathbf{J}_1'(\mathbf{v}_0 \cdot \mathbf{v}_1')} + \overline{\mathbf{J}_0 v_1'^2}$$
$$+ \overline{\mathbf{J}_1'v_1'^2}] \quad (10)$$

The bars represent some suitable time averages that need not be precisely defined at this point. If we consider only the a-c portion of Eq. (10), we note two terms that are quadratic in the r-f quantities and that, in principle at least, should be included in the kinetic power. More important still, since these r-f quantities were derived from the small-signal theory as given by Eqs. (4) to (8), it appears that a more precise theory that does not neglect the nonlinear terms in (6) and (8) would provide quadratic corrections to the linear theory. Without trying to calculate them in detail we can see that if we had calculated, for example, the r-f velocity from the linearized equation (8), we could obtain an approximate quadratic correction by merely inserting the missing quadratic term as a product of the first-order small-signal values. Similar statements could be made about the equation for the convection current, since one could get a quadratic correction to J_1' by merely inserting the small-signal values for $\rho_1 v_1$. If we then try to insert these quadratic corrections to the r-f current and r-f velocity into the expression for kinetic power, Eq. (10) becomes

$$J\frac{v^2}{2\eta} = \frac{1}{2\eta}\overline{(\mathbf{J}_0 + \mathbf{J}_1' + \mathbf{J}_2')(v_0{}^2 + 2\mathbf{v}_0 \cdot \mathbf{v}_1' + v_1'^2 + 2\mathbf{v}_0 \cdot \mathbf{v}_2')} \quad (10a)$$

where the subscript 2 denotes the quadratic corrections. If we perform the multiplications, two additional quadratic quantities result, $\overline{v_0{}^2 J_2'}$ and $2\overline{\mathbf{J}_0 \mathbf{v}_0 \cdot \mathbf{v}_2}$, which are of the same order as the quadratic quantities we had included previously. It is difficult to determine by inspection whether any of these terms is less significant than any other and ought to be omitted. However, a careful analysis (of the sort performed by Birdsall[1])

[1] C. K. Birdsall, Electron-stream Kinetic-power Second-order Terms as Obtained from MacColl's Mean Values, *J. Appl. Phys.*, **33**:236–237 (1962).

of second-order terms makes it possible to include them in a consistent fashion, a procedure that justifies the result that we shall derive by a more *ad hoc* approach in which a consistency argument is used only at the end. Instead of showing that these second-order terms, properly defined, actually cancel, we find that it is easier to proceed by constructing a form for the kinetic power, using *only* quantities derived from small-signal theory such that (together with the electromagnetic power defined previously, which is correct to the order to which we are interested) this form for the kinetic power does yield a conservation law.[1]

To derive the kinetic power, we use first the expression we have already used for the current correct to linear terms, with the time dependence stated explicitly, $J'_1 \equiv J_1 e^{j\omega t}$, $v'_1 \equiv v_1 e^{j\omega t}$. We write the kinetic voltage $V = (1/2\eta)(v_0 + v')^2$; and we keep only terms that are linear in the r-f quantities:

$$J = J_0 + J_1 e^{j\omega t} \qquad V = V_0 + V_1 e^{j\omega t} \qquad V_1 = \frac{\mathbf{v}_0 \cdot \mathbf{v}_1}{\eta} \qquad (11)$$

The second term in the expression for V is called the *a-c kinetic voltage;* it is used, together with the current, to calculate the kinetic power. From the definition of kinetic power in terms of current and kinetic voltage, we can write for the average kinetic power $\overline{P_k}$

$$\overline{P_k} = \frac{1}{2} \operatorname{Re} \int V \mathbf{J}^* \cdot d\mathbf{s} \qquad (12)$$

The time-averaged integrand yields

$$V_0 J_0 + \tfrac{1}{2} \operatorname{Re} (\mathbf{J}_1^* V_1) \qquad (13)$$

The first term represents the d-c kinetic power density. The second term may be called the small-signal kinetic-power density; the usefulness of this term still remains to be proved. Let us first try to interpret what is implied by this quantity. In particular, we wish to examine the sign of the quantity we have called the small-signal kinetic power. For simplicity, consider a thin filament of current flowing perpendicular to a surface da. The kinetic power flow through this surface is given by $\frac{1}{2} \operatorname{Re} (V_1 \mathbf{J}_1^* \cdot d\mathbf{s})$; the product $\mathbf{J}_1^* \cdot d\mathbf{s}$ represents, of course, the instantaneous current flowing through the surface, and the kinetic voltage depends on the instantaneous r-f velocity as indicated in Eq. (3). If the above product is positive, the nonquadrature components of current density and kinetic voltage are both positive (or both negative) at the same time; they are in phase. From the definition of V_1, in the case of electrons with negative charge, a positive instantaneous value of kinetic

[1] H. A. Haus and D. L. Bobroff, Small Signal Power Theorem for Electron Beams, *J. Appl. Phys.*, **28:**694–704 (1957).

voltage corresponds to a negative v_1, that is, an instantaneous velocity lower than the d-c velocity. For the electron-beam current, an instantaneous positive value of the r-f current corresponds to a number of electrons crossing ds that is smaller than the average (d-c). Therefore, when current and kinetic voltage are both positive, we have less than the average electron flow with less than the average kinetic energy per electron. A half cycle later, current and kinetic voltage both will be negative. By the same argument, this reversal corresponds to more electrons than the average number crossing the area with a positive v_1, that is, a velocity greater than the average. When the velocity is lower than the average, the number of electrons is below average; when the velocity is greater than the average, the number of electrons is above average. Therefore, the net total power carried by the beam averaged over a cycle is greater than under d-c conditions, since there are more electrons with an excess of energy than with a deficiency of energy. Similarly, when the above product is negative, there is a deficiency of electrons with a positive r-f velocity and an excess of electrons with a negative r-f velocity, relative to the d-c case. We can, therefore, speak of positive or negative kinetic power in the two cases according to whether the power flow in the beam is greater or smaller than under d-c conditions.

The distinction between the two signs of the kinetic power is a very important one, since most of the important properties of all amplifiers are a direct outgrowth of this distinction. For instance, if we may anticipate results to be derived later, it turns out that a slow space-charge wave carries negative kinetic power, whereas a fast space-charge wave carries positive kinetic power. The distinction between the two makes for important differences in their roles in various kinds of electronic devices.

Next, let us show (simply by algebraic manipulation of the small-signal equations) that with this definition for kinetic power and the previous form for the electromagnetic power, power conservation is obtained. By taking the dot product of Eq. (4) with $\mathbf{H}_1^*$ and of the complex conjugate of Eq. (5) with $\mathbf{E}_1$, we obtain after subtracting the two equations

$$\nabla \cdot (\mathbf{E}_1 \times \mathbf{H}_1^*) = -j\omega\mu\mathbf{H}_1 \cdot \mathbf{H}_1^* + j\omega\epsilon\mathbf{E}_1 \cdot \mathbf{E}_1^* - \mathbf{E}_1 \cdot \mathbf{J}_1^* \qquad (14)$$

This relation involves only small-signal amplitudes; in particular, the current density that appears here will be taken as the small-signal amplitude with all quadratic terms omitted. We wish to evaluate the last term of Eq. (14). First, we take the dot product of Eq. (8) with $\mathbf{J}_1^*$. The result contains a term $j\omega v_1 \cdot \mathbf{J}_1^*$, which can be rewritten as $j\omega v_1 \cdot v_1^* \rho_0 + v_0 \cdot v_1 \nabla \cdot \mathbf{J}_1^*$, using the properties of Eqs. (6) and (7), so that

$$\eta\mathbf{E}_1 \cdot \mathbf{J}_1^* = j\omega v_1 \cdot v_1^* \rho_0 + v_0 \cdot v_1 \nabla \cdot \mathbf{J}_1^* + [(v_0 \cdot \nabla)v_1] \cdot \mathbf{J}_1^* + [(v_1 \cdot \nabla)v_0] \cdot \mathbf{J}_1^*$$

For a one-dimensional flow the two velocities (d-c and r-f) and the current density are all parallel, so that we can combine the second, third, and fourth terms on the right-hand side of the equation to obtain

$$\mathbf{E}_1 \cdot \mathbf{J}_1^* = \frac{1}{\eta} [j\omega\rho_0\mathbf{v}_1 \cdot \mathbf{v}_1^* + \nabla \cdot (\mathbf{J}_1^*\mathbf{v}_0 \cdot \mathbf{v}_1)]$$

If we now substitute this equation for $\mathbf{E}_1 \cdot \mathbf{J}_1^*$ into Eq. (14), we obtain

$$\nabla \cdot \left[\mathbf{E}_1 \times \mathbf{H}_1^* + \frac{1}{\eta} (\mathbf{v}_0 \cdot \mathbf{v}_1)\mathbf{J}_1^* \right] = j\omega \left[\epsilon\mathbf{E}_1 \cdot \mathbf{E}_1^* - \mu\mathbf{H}_1 \cdot \mathbf{H}_1^* - \frac{1}{\eta} \rho_0\mathbf{v}_1 \cdot \mathbf{v}_1^* \right]$$

We integrate both sides over a volume, use Gauss's theorem on the left-hand side, and take the real part. Since the right-hand side of this equation is pure imaginary and, therefore, has zero real part, we finally obtain the following conservation law:

$$\tfrac{1}{2} \operatorname{Re} \int (\mathbf{E}_1 \times \mathbf{H}_1^*) \cdot d\mathbf{s} + \tfrac{1}{2} \operatorname{Re} \int \mathbf{V}_1 \cdot \mathbf{J}_1^* \, d\mathbf{s} = 0 \qquad (15)$$

This equation has been derived by using only the small-signal equations and is a consequence of them. It represents a small-signal conservation theorem which is usually known as the Chu small-signal-power theorem.[1] It defines a relation between the electromagnetic power and a quantity that has been previously discussed, namely, the small-signal kinetic power. Within the limits of the small-signal theory, then, assuming that this theory is an exact theory for some fictitious system that approximates a real system at sufficiently small signals, we now have a way of expressing the power, which is conserved, and we can draw whatever conclusions may be implied from this conservation law. To restate our previous result, the kinetic power can be either positive or negative, corresponding respectively to less or more power flow in the beam than in the d-c case. If the net kinetic power flow out of a volume is negative, the electromagnetic power flow must be positive; i.e., some electromagnetic power is generated within the volume at the expense of the kinetic power of the beam. This equation can be rewritten in still another form that is sometimes convenient. If the integration surface is a pair of planes a distance dz apart and perpendicular to the direction of flow of a one-dimensional electron beam, the remainder of the surface being a cylindrical surface connecting the planes at a radius sufficiently great that there is no electromagnetic power flow out across this surface, the equation can be written as

$$\frac{dP_e}{dz} + \frac{dP_k}{dz} = 0 \qquad (16)$$

[1] Haus and Bobroff, *op. cit.*

9.2 Kinetic Power in Space-charge Waves

To illustrate the application of these formulas, and in particular the definition of kinetic power, let us evaluate the kinetic power flow in a thin electron beam in a conducting drift tube. In this case, electromagnetic power flow can be shown to be negligibly small in comparison with the kinetic power, usually of the order of $(\omega_p/\omega)^2$, and we need to compute only the kinetic power. There are two space-charge waves (a fast wave and a slow wave), and from the relation between the current and velocity for each of these waves [Eqs. (4.51) and (4.63)], one can write the ratio of current to kinetic voltage for the fast and slow space-charge waves as

$$i_{f,s} = \pm Y_0 V_{f,s}$$

where $Y_0 = (i_0/V_0)(\omega/\omega_q)$, and $V_{f,s}$ are the voltage amplitudes of the fast and slow space-charge waves. Then the current and the kinetic voltage (instead of the r-f velocity) become

$$V_1 = (V_f e^{j\beta_q z} + V_s e^{-j\beta_q z})e^{-j\beta_e z}$$
$$i_1 = Y_0(V_f e^{j\beta_q z} - V_s e^{-j\beta_q z})e^{-j\beta_e z} \tag{17}$$

where β_q and β_e have the usual definitions. The kinetic power flow represented by these equations is given by

$$\tfrac{1}{2}\,\mathrm{Re}\,(Vi^*) = \tfrac{1}{2}\,\mathrm{Re}\,(V_f V_f^* - V_s V_s^* - V_f V_s^* e^{2j\beta_q z} + V_s V_f^* e^{-2j\beta_q z})Y_0 \tag{18}$$

The sum of the third and fourth terms is pure imaginary and the first two terms are pure real; therefore, the power flow is

$$P_k = \tfrac{1}{2}Y(V_f V_f^* - V_s V_s^*) \tag{19}$$

Two interesting conclusions can be drawn from the equation in this form. First, the power flow is the sum of two terms, one corresponding to the fast and the other to the slow space-charge wave, each term depending only on the amplitude of one kind of wave. Second, the power flow in the two waves is of opposite sign, the slow space-charge wave carrying negative power, the significance of which may be restated as follows. If one examines the relation between the current and velocity in a slow space-charge wave in detail, he will find that in the region where the electrons are traveling more slowly than the d-c beam velocity, the density of electrons is greater than the d-c density, and vice versa. Therefore, the beam has less energy in the presence of a slow space-charge wave than with no excitation. This situation may be described as the transport of a deficiency of kinetic energy in the positive z direction.

9.3   Application of the Power-flow Theorem to the Properties of Amplifiers

In terms of these properties of fast and slow space-charge waves, one may reexamine all the amplifiers considered in preceding chapters and reinterpret them in terms of the positive and negative kinetic-power flow in the beam. For all of the amplifiers, we shall find that (unlike in the drift-tube case we have just discussed) there is coupling between the circuit and the beam, and hence a transfer of power from the beam to electromagnetic fields. The conservation theorem we have derived above applies, with the result that an increase in the electromagnetic power produces a decrease in the kinetic power (i.e., an increase in the negative kinetic power) of the beam. For all such devices, electromagnetic power results from a net increase in the total amplitude of the slow space-charge waves in the beam, which increases the negative kinetic power in the beam.[1] In cases in which no transfer of power from the beam to an external circuit takes place, the fast and slow space-charge waves must have equal amplitudes, so that the negative power of the slow space-charge wave is compensated by the positive power of the fast, resulting in no net loss of power from the beam. Furthermore (to anticipate some later results), in cases in which the beam is coupled not to a cavity but to a propagating circuit, instead of simple space-charge waves, composite waves are obtained. The waves are the result of coupling between the beam and the propagating circuit, and they have both electromagnetic power and beam power. But in all these cases as well, electromagnetic power on the circuit is obtained only if the beam part of the wave has slow space-charge-wave characteristics.

One may distinguish two kinds of amplifier with this continuous interaction. In the first case, there is only one composite wave of importance. More precisely, several waves are obtained as the result of the coupling between the beam and the circuit, but the only significant one is a growing wave of both circuit power and beam power, the former being positive and the latter negative. This is the traveling-wave-tube case. In the second case, which includes the backward-wave amplifier and a particular type of forward-wave amplifier, there are two important waves, each being the result of coupling between a circuit and a slow space-charge wave. Neither wave grows, but the two waves travel with different velocities and a beat phenomenon takes place in such a way that the total power remains constant but transfers back and forth between the electromagnetic and kinetic forms (much as in a directional coupler or with coupled pendulums).

We can best start our consideration of the interaction between space-

---

[1] This statement does not apply to parametric amplifiers. in which power may be transferred from the pump to the circuit via the fast wave.

charge waves and electromagnetic fields by considering the simplest case, a beam passing through a planar r-f gap. The gap is taken to be short (i.e., the transit time of electrons across the gap is a small fraction of a cycle). From the previous discussion of the interaction of such a gap with the beam we know that the electrons emerge with a change in their velocity and no change in current. If we examine the velocity modulation produced by a gap and convert these results into equivalent ones using the concept of kinetic voltage, it will be apparent that, if the voltage across a gap is V_g with polarity as shown in Fig. 9.1, the change in the kinetic voltage of the beam is $-V_g$. Moreover, if V_g is a time-varying quantity, the kinetic-voltage change will obviously exhibit the same time dependence. As has been stated, this result can be derived from our earlier result (obtained in Chap. 3, in somewhat different notation) that the change in the velocity of a beam passing through a gap for small gap voltages is given by $v_0 V_g/2V_0$, which is readily converted into an equivalent change in kinetic voltage $\Delta V = -V_g$. The same result can be obtained by considering the change in the energy of the beam as it passes through the gap. The change in the energy is given by iV_g and must appear as a change in the kinetic power of the beam. Since current density does not change in passing through the gap, the kinetic voltage must change. If we examine this condition of an increment in the kinetic voltage and no increment in the current passing through the gap, we see that regardless of the excitation of the incident beam in terms of fast and slow space-charge waves, the change in the beam after passing through the gap must be of a form such that both fast and slow space-charge waves are increased by equal amounts in order to make the current increase zero. In terms of the notation used in calculating the kinetic power in a beam, if the total change in kinetic voltage is $\Delta V = -V_g$, this change must consist of equal increases in the voltage amplitude of fast and slow space-charge waves in the amount $\Delta V_f = \Delta V_s = -V_g/2$. The corresponding increments in the current-density amplitudes are given by $\Delta i_f = Y_0 \Delta V_f$, $\Delta i_s = -Y_0 \Delta V_s$, and because of the minus sign for one of these waves, the total increase in current density is zero, as it should be.

These results apply to any gap with small transit time, regardless of the composition of the waves incident on the gap. The question of

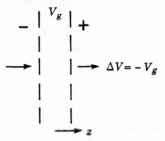

Fig. 9.1 Relation between kinetic voltage of beam and voltage across gap.

whether there is any increase or decrease in the average kinetic power transported by the beam after passage through the gap depends on the phases of the increments in kinetic voltage relative to the kinetic-voltage components already on the beam when it enters the gap. If the modulating voltage is produced by a beam passing through a gap with a suitable resistive impedance across it, then the voltage across the gap that results from the current in the beam has a phase relative to this current that results in an increment in the kinetic voltage of the proper sign to represent the loss of power by the beam in passing through the gap. The calculation can be carried out without a detailed analysis of the component waves by the use of some results derived previously regarding the effect of a convection current on a cavity. In Chap. 3 it was shown that a convection current passing through such a gap acts as an equivalent current generator and produces a voltage given by $V_g = iZ\sigma$, where Z is impedance across the gap and σ is the beam area. Accordingly, the increment in the kinetic voltage of the beam after passage through the gap is simply $V = -iZ\sigma$ and, since the current does not change in passing through the gap, the increment in the kinetic power of the beam is thus given by

$$\tfrac{1}{2}\operatorname{Re}(\Delta V i^*\sigma) = -\tfrac{1}{2}\operatorname{Re}(Zii^*\sigma^2)$$

It is apparent that for the normal passive impedance of a cavity with a positive real part this result, in general, corresponds to an increase in the *negative* power of the beam of just the right amount to provide conservation. This is really an example of the use of the small-signal power theorem derived above, even though we have used the terminology of lumped-constant circuit rather than calculating the Poynting vector.

It is also of interest to point out another consequence of this theorem. If we consider a d-c beam passing through a modulating gap with a *finite* transit angle, then, as shown earlier in Eq. (3.52), the change in the kinetic voltage of the beam (change in the r-f velocity) at the exit is accompanied by a nonzero value of the r-f current. If one uses these exit quantities of kinetic voltage and current as determined by the finite transit angle to calculate the amplitudes of the two space-charge waves launched on the exit side of the gap, the amplitudes will not, in general, be equal. Therefore, the net power will not be zero. A computation of the magnitude of this power flow gives a value equal to the beam-loading power, as calculated by other methods in Chap. 3. The small-signal kinetic-power theorem thus verifies a result obtained earlier in a different fashion.

9.4 Coupled-mode Equations

Let us next use the results just obtained to determine the effect of a continuous field such as is provided by a propagating circuit in modifying the behavior of space-charge waves. We need only specialize the results obtained above for the gap voltage to the case where the gap is of infinitesimal width and express the voltage in terms of an equivalent electric field. In this case, the voltage across a distance Δz is $\Delta V_g = -E \, \Delta z$. (The sign is again compatible with the polarity for the voltage as described in Fig. 9.1.) After an electron beam passes through this infinitesimal region Δz, the change in its kinetic voltage is $\Delta V = -\Delta V_g = E \, \Delta z$. There is no change in the current produced *by this voltage*. (There *are* changes in the current and kinetic voltage of a space-charge wave in a distance Δz arising from the normal changes of a propagating wave with distance. What we have just calculated here is an *additional* increment produced by the *externally* applied field.) As stated earlier, this increment in the kinetic voltage must result in equal increments of the kinetic voltage amplitudes of the fast and slow space-charge waves on the beam, so that no net increase in the current *due to the field* occurs. Therefore, for either the fast or the slow space-charge wave we have that the increment in the amplitude of that wave is given by $\Delta V_f = \Delta V_s = \frac{1}{2} E \, \Delta z$, or

$$\frac{\partial V_f}{\partial z} = \frac{\partial V_s}{\partial z} = \frac{E}{2}$$

This is the increment due to the field. The field involved here may be *any* field arising from any external source other than the field of the beam itself. For example, it could be the field due to a circuit or to the space-charge waves of another beam. In the absence of such an external field, a slow (say) space-charge wave which propagates as $e^{-j\beta_+ z}$, where $\beta_+ = \beta_e + \beta_q$, obviously satisfies a differential equation of the form

$$\frac{\partial V_s}{\partial z} + j\beta_+ V_s = 0$$

or $\Delta V_s = -j\beta_+ V_s \, \Delta z$. However, in the presence of an external modulating field such as we have been discussing there is an *additional* increment in the amplitude. One can essentially consider the above equation as representing the propagation of a free space-charge wave; when an extra term is added, it may be considered as a driving force, leading to an inhomogeneous equation for the space-charge wave:

$$\frac{\partial V_s}{\partial z} + j\beta_+ V_s = \frac{E}{2} \tag{20}$$

This is, then, one of the basic equations we shall use. It shows the effect of an external field (external in the sense described above) on the propagation characteristic of a slow space-charge wave. It is convenient, instead of using the amplitude of the kinetic voltage, to replace it by the amplitude of the corresponding current density:

$$i_s = -Y_0 V_s$$
$$i_f = Y_0 V_f$$
$$Y_0 = \frac{i_0}{2V_0} \frac{\beta_e}{\beta_q} = \frac{\eta \rho_0}{v_0} \frac{\beta_e}{\beta_q}$$

The equivalent equation for the current (for the slow space-charge wave) is

$$\frac{\partial i_s}{\partial z} + j\beta_+ i_s + \eta \frac{E}{2} \frac{\rho_0}{v_0} \frac{\beta_e}{\beta_q} = 0 \tag{21}$$

For the fast space-charge wave, the same equation applies with i_s replaced by $-i_f$ and β_+ by $\beta_- = \beta_e - \beta_q$.

To consider the interaction of such a space-charge wave with a propagating circuit (either backward or forward), one must write a corresponding equation for the effect of the current of the space-charge wave on the field of the circuit. So that the backward- and forward-wave cases may be considered simultaneously, it is convenient to modify slightly the derivation for the effect of the beam on a circuit originally given in considering traveling-wave tubes.

In any propagating circuit the electromagnetic power flow can be either in the positive or negative direction, described below for simplicity as to the right or to the left. In general, both are present, i.e., a wave with a group velocity to the left and another with a group velocity to the right. By convention, power flow to the right is called positive, so that the net power flow on a circuit is given by

$$P = \frac{E_R^2}{2\beta_0^2 K} - \frac{E_L^2}{2\beta_0^2 K}$$

In this equation E_R represents the amplitude of the field carrying *energy* to the right, and E_L to the left. The proportionality coefficients are, for convenience, defined in the same way as previously. For any mode carrying power to the right, power is proportional to the field amplitude squared; and similarly for the power to the left. It is to be noted particularly here that we are considering the direction of *power* flow, so that E_R could have a *phase* velocity in either direction, and similarly for E_L. Which of these two terms will be of interest to us will depend on which one has phase velocity in the same direction as the electron-beam velocity.

Given this relation for the power, if by some means we change the amplitude of both waves, then the rate of change of power with distance is

$$\frac{dP}{dz} = \frac{E_R}{\beta_0^2 K} \frac{dE_R}{dz} - \frac{E_L}{\beta_0^2 K} \frac{dE_L}{dz} \tag{22}$$

A note should be made of the signs. If dE_L/dz is positive, more energy is flowing to the left at $z + \Delta z$ than at z; therefore, this term with a positive dE_L/dz results in a negative contribution to dP/dz, which is the rate of increase of power to the right. If we now consider that the power increment described above is delivered by a thin electron beam passing through the field in question, then the rate of increase in power produced by the beam is

$$\frac{dP}{dz} = -\frac{iE\sigma}{2} \tag{23}$$

where σ is the area of the beam and E is the total circuit field at the beam The minus sign enters because a positive contribution of power results if the field and current have opposite signs; the factor $\frac{1}{2}$ reflects the fact that we are using time-average values, whereas E and i are peak values. Under these circumstances, by the same arguments used earlier in the traveling-wave-tube treatment, this power is split into equal increments of the waves carrying energy to the left and to the right, so that if the power increment is produced by a beam in this way, we must have $dE_R/dz = -dE_L/dz$. The reason for the minus sign is that, for an increase in the part of power flowing to the left, the field amplitude flowing to the left must have a negative derivative because of the direction we have taken for positive z. We can equate the two values we have written down for the rate of increase of power and thus write this equation in either of two forms:

$$-\frac{iE\sigma}{2} = \frac{E_R + E_L}{\beta_0{}^2 K}\frac{dE_R}{dz} = -\frac{E_R + E_L}{\beta_0{}^2 K}\frac{dE_L}{dz} \tag{24}$$

It must be remembered here that the field E that appears on the left is actually equal to the sum of the two fields present at the point z, namely, $E_R + E_L$. Which of the two alternative forms for the equations we have written above we use depends on whether we are interested in the amplitude of the field carrying energy to the left or to the right. If we are interested in a forward-wave circuit, in which the phase and the group velocity are in the same direction, then obviously the beam interacts mainly with E_R; if we are concerned with a backward-wave circuit in which the phase and group velocity are oppositely directed, the beam interacts mainly with E_L. (Interaction in a cumulative fashion is meant. There is also interaction between the beam wave and a circuit wave with negative phase velocity, but since the phase velocities are obviously completely different, in that case there is no cumulative coupling and this interaction can be ignored with complete justification.) Therefore, a forward-wave circuit (v_g positive) yields the relation

$$\frac{\partial E_R}{\partial z} = -\frac{i\sigma}{2}\beta_0{}^2 K \tag{25}$$

and a backward-wave circuit (v_g negative) gives us

$$\frac{\partial E_L}{\partial z} = \frac{i\sigma}{2}\beta_0{}^2 K \tag{26}$$

At this point, we can make the same statements about the field amplitudes as we made about the current or velocity amplitudes. The increments of E written above are those produced by the external currents. In the absence of such currents, these fields would propagate to the right with the cold propagation (phase) constant of the circuit β_0 and would satisfy a differential equation of the form

$$\frac{\partial E}{\partial z} = -j\beta_0 E$$

This would represent the homogeneous equation for the circuit. The presence of the beam current provides an extra driving term; in this case the driven equation (for a backward-wave circuit) is

$$\frac{\partial E}{\partial z} + j\beta_0 E = \frac{i\sigma}{2}\beta_0{}^2 K \tag{27}$$

(The sign of the current would be opposite for a forward-wave circuit.) Equations (21) and (27) represent the so-called *coupled-mode equations* for a slow space-charge wave interacting with a backward-wave circuit. By suitable changes in signs one can write down similar equations for the case of either a fast space-charge wave or a forward-wave circuit. We shall summarize all these equations below. Before doing so, however, it is convenient to redefine the variables in a particular way. Instead of using the field itself, we note that the electromagnetic power flowing in the circuit is given by $E^2/2\beta_0{}^2 K$, and it is more convenient to define $E' = E/\sqrt{2\beta_0{}^2 K}$ as the "field" amplitude. Similarly, the power carried by a slow space-charge wave in terms of the current density amplitudes can be written as

$$-\frac{i^2\sigma}{2Y_0} = -\frac{i^2\sigma V_0}{i_0}\frac{\beta_q}{\beta_e} = -\frac{\beta_q}{\beta_e}\frac{\sigma^2}{I_0}V_0 i^2 = -\frac{\beta_q}{\beta_e}\frac{\sigma^2}{G_0}i^2$$

and here, also, it is convenient to define a "current" which is the square root of this quantity, given by $i' = i\sigma\sqrt{\beta_q/(\beta_e G_0)}$. Obviously, as redefined here, the field and current are proportional to the true fields and currents and the corresponding differential equations then become simply

$$\frac{\partial E'}{\partial z} + j\beta_0 E' \pm i'\kappa = 0$$

$$\frac{\partial i'}{\partial z} + j\beta_\pm i' \pm E'\kappa = 0 \tag{28}$$

where

$$\kappa^2 = \frac{\beta_0{}^2 K G_0}{8}\frac{\beta_e}{\beta_q} \approx \frac{C^3\beta_e{}^3}{2\beta_q}$$

and C is the Pierce C defined in Chap. 6. In writing these equations, all possible combinations have been included. The *plus* sign in the current equation corresponds to a *slow* space-charge wave; the *minus* sign, to a *fast* wave. In the field equation the *plus* sign corresponds to a *forward* wave, the *minus* sign to a *backward* wave. The notation demonstrates that, in terms of these normalized units, we have a coupling coefficient between the two kinds of quantities that is symmetric. It displays the Pierce C parameter in an illuminating way and, furthermore, the power flow for either electromagnetic power or kinetic power is merely equal to the square of the amplitudes. The equations as now written for any choice of fast or slow space-charge waves, backward or forward circuit, represent first-order differential equations that can be solved quite easily for any combinations of β's and coupling coefficients, as we shall demonstrate below. For any amplifier, one usually has to consider three of these equations, i.e., the coupling of the circuit to both the fast and slow space-charge waves of a beam. However, as Gould has pointed out,[1] in many cases the important interaction is only between one of the space-charge waves and the circuit, so that approximate quantitative answers and illuminating qualitative descriptions may be obtained from a consideration of the coupling between one of the space-charge waves and the circuit. This approximation permits a great simplification in the mathematics and contributes considerably to better comprehension.

As examples we can examine the interaction between the slow space-charge wave and a forward-wave circuit at synchronism between the two waves, at departures from synchronism, as the coupling between them changes, etc. This method enables us to explore the behavior of devices over a much greater range of parameters by purely analytic means rather than by numerical computation of the roots. The reason for this simplicity is that we have "thrown away" certain parts of the problem that were included in the previous treatment (Chap. 6) but were not really essential; by their inclusion, the results became much more complex. In the previous treatment (such as the traveling-wave-tube case) consideration of the interaction between beam and circuit really included the interaction among four different waves; i.e., the backward and forward circuit waves and the fast and slow space-charge waves. (The same statement applies to the backward-wave oscillator treatment.) Even after we discarded the wave with negative phase velocity of the four that were found, the resultant equations were still too complicated to support any general conclusions. Actually, many important effects result from coupling between a pair of waves, namely, that pair which have approximately the same phase velocity. If the various velocities are sufficiently separated, it is thus possible to ignore the nonessential modes by con-

[1] R. W. Gould, A Coupled Mode Description of the Backward-wave Oscillator and the Kompfner Dip Condition, *IRE Trans. Electron Devices*, **ED-2:**37–42 (1955).

sidering the coupling to these other modes to be negligible, so that all the effects of these unimportant modes may be discarded to leave simpler equations. These simpler equations display in a much neater and more obvious fashion all the important features that are obscured by the presence of the lightly coupled waves. This is merely a consequence of the fact that the solution of a quadratic equation is of a sufficiently simple form that the result of any change in parameters may be examined quite easily, whereas the same thing is not true if the equation that determines the propagation constants is of third or higher order. Even in the analytic form of the solution of a cubic, the various constants enter in such complicated fashion that it is not easy to see the consequences of changes by inspection.

9.5 Application of Coupled-mode Theory

Let us consider in detail two particular cases to illustrate the use of these equations. First, consider the interaction of a slow space-charge wave with a backward circuit wave (i.e., a wave with a negative group velocity). The phase velocity, of course, must be positive to provide interaction with the beam. By only slight changes in some of the algebra, one can also treat other cases equally easily; examples are the traveling-wave-tube case, in which the interaction takes place between a forward circuit wave and a slow space-charge wave, and the so-called beating-wave amplifier, in which the interaction is between a slow space-charge wave and a forward circuit wave for a set of parameters for which there is no growing wave. Other examples that could be treated are the so-called Kompfner dip and the double-beam amplifier.

To consider the interaction between a slow space-charge wave and a backward circuit wave, we take the first of Eqs. (28) with a minus sign and the second with a plus sign. Before we proceed to solve these equations, it is interesting to point out a property of the equations which is quite illuminating. If we multiply the equation for the field by E'^* and the equation for the current by i'^*, take the complex conjugate of these equations, and add all four, we obtain the relation

$$\frac{\partial}{\partial z} (E'E'^* + i'i'^*) = 0 \tag{29}$$

This equation represents conservation of power, but if one remembers the nature of the waves involved, it also tells us a little more. Note that this is a relation between the *magnitudes* of the electromagnetic power and the kinetic power and involves their sum. We know (for the uncoupled case) that for the waves involved the electromagnetic power flows in the negative z direction, whereas the kinetic power is negative and flows in the positive z direction. This fact, together with the form of this equation, tells us that the amplitudes of the two quantities involved must vary with distance in such a way that in regions where the current is small, the fields are large, and vice versa, in order for conservation in this form to hold. It also appears that we cannot get growing waves from this system. Equation (29) applies to any solution for the system including a single wave. A single-growing-wave solution could not satisfy this equation, since in a single wave both E' and i' would grow together, so that the sum of their squares could not remain constant. Accordingly, for any single wave both E' and i' must have constant amplitudes along the entire length of the device. If there were to be any change in the amplitude of the fields with distance, one would need a pair of waves and a beat phenomenon such that interference that provided large E' at one place and large i' elsewhere would exist. This is, of course, precisely what we expect in a backward-wave amplifier. Equation (29) demonstrates it even before the nature of the solutions is known.

If we now assume that both E' and i' vary as $e^{-j\beta z}$, we can substitute into the differential equations, perform the differentiations, and find quite readily that the results reduce to the algebraic equations

$$
\begin{aligned}
(-j\beta + j\beta_0)E' - i'\kappa &= 0 \\
(-j\beta + j\beta_+)i' + E'\kappa &= 0
\end{aligned}
\tag{30}
$$

If we set the determinant of the coefficients equal to zero, we obtain a solution for the propagation constants of the form

$$
\beta_{1,2} = \frac{\beta_0 + \beta_+}{2} \pm \left[\left(\frac{\beta_0 - \beta_+}{2} \right)^2 + \kappa^2 \right]^{\frac{1}{2}}
\tag{31}
$$

The first thing that should be pointed out is that because of the plus sign in front of κ^2 the radical can never be anything but a real number (since κ is real), so that the β's will always be real and no growing waves can exist.

Before we go on to discuss these solutions further and to determine the starting conditions for a backward-wave oscillator, let us consider another case, the corresponding results that would have been obtained from Eq. (28) for the traveling-wave tube. In that case, the interaction is between a slow space-charge wave and a forward circuit wave: we take both of Eqs. (28) with a plus sign. A manipulation of the equations similar to that performed for the backward-wave amplifier case leads to an equation replacing (28) of the form

$$
\frac{\partial}{\partial z}(E'E'^* - i'i'^*) = 0
\tag{32}
$$

This also represents conservation, but in this case, since the electromagnetic power is positive flowing in the plus z direction, the form of the equation permits certain solutions for the traveling-wave tube that were not possible for the backward-wave amplifier. First, this form of the conservation law would permit constant-amplitude waves, just as for the backward-amplifier case. For such constant-amplitude waves, both the electromagnetic and the kinetic power are constant, as is indicated by Eq. (32). However, this equation does permit *growing* waves. A single growing wave in which both the field and the current grow at the same rate results in a growth in electromagnetic power and a growth in the (negative) kinetic power in such a way that their *algebraic sum* remains constant, which is permitted by the form of Eq. (32). Therefore, for the traveling-wave tube, one can expect that under some circumstances solutions representing constant amplitude can exist, but so can growing (and decaying) waves. All of these possibilities turn out to exist for various choices of parameters. If we pursue the consequences of this traveling-wave-tube case further, again assuming exponential solutions as we did for the backward-wave amplifier, we find that instead of (31) we obtain

$$\beta_{1,2} = \frac{\beta_0 + \beta_+}{2} \pm \left[\left(\frac{\beta_0 - \beta_+}{2} \right)^2 - \kappa^2 \right]^{\frac{1}{2}} \tag{33}$$

The major difference, of course, is that there is now a minus sign in front of κ^2. With this minus sign it is obvious that, depending on the relative magnitudes of $[(\beta_0 - \beta_+)/2]^2$ and κ^2, the radical can be either pure real or pure imaginary. In the former case, we have constant-amplitude waves; in the latter case, we have a pair of waves, one growing and one decaying, so that a new kind of behavior is possible for the traveling-wave-tube case, different from the backward-wave amplifier. Figure 9.2 indicates the differences in the possible power densities for the two cases. It might be pointed out that, for the conditions in Eq. (33) where the radical is purely real, the behavior of the waves is in many ways similar to that in a backward-wave amplifier; as a matter of fact, one can get gain under these conditions for forward-wave traveling-wave-tube devices by a beat phenomenon between two constant-amplitude waves. Oscillation is not

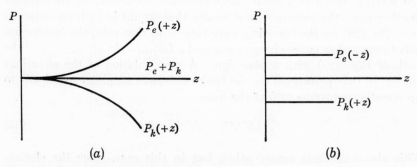

Fig. 9.2   Power densities for (*a*) **traveling-wave tube (growing wave) and** (*b*) **backward-wave amplifier (constant wave).**

possible because of the direction of the power flow in the traveling-wave tube.

We return now to treat the backward-wave amplifier in more detail, and we shall also derive the start-oscillation conditions for a backward-wave oscillator. If we take the roots given by Eq. (30), we can write the general solution for the field and the current as

$$i' = C_1 e^{-j\beta_1 z} + C_2 e^{-j\beta_2 z}$$
$$-j\kappa E' = C_1(\beta_1 - \beta_+)e^{-j\beta_1 z} + C_2(\beta_2 - \beta_+)e^{-j\beta_2 z} \qquad (34)$$

In writing the field equation we have used the ratio between the field and the current as given by the second of Eqs. (30). Of course, the ratio as given by the first of Eqs. (30) would be equally correct since their equality is really the condition imposed in deriving the roots given by Eq. (31). Equations (34) are the most general solutions for the field and current obtained by substituting the proper ratios for the two quantities as required by the equations. To proceed further, and particularly to find the oscillation conditions, the initial conditions are utilized. If the device is to be used as an amplifier, one specifies the fact that the current is zero at the entrance plane $z = 0$ and that an injected field amplitude exists at the plane $z = L$. To solve this problem, one would find the value of the two constants from these two conditions and then find the voltage gain by evaluating the amplitude of the field at $z = 0$. Instead, let us find the oscillation conditions, in which the situation is that the injected current at $z = 0$ is zero and the injected field at $z = L$ is also zero. We then wish to find a set of coefficients C_1 and C_2 that are nonzero and that still yield these initial conditions, which may be stated as follows:

$$z = 0 \qquad i' = 0 \qquad C_1 + C_2 = 0$$
$$z = L \qquad E' = 0 \qquad C_1(\beta_1 - \beta_+)e^{-j\beta_1 L} + C_2(\beta_2 - \beta_+)e^{-j\beta_2 L} = 0$$

These are two homogeneous linear equations for the C_1 and C_2; if there is to be a nontrivial solution, the determinant of the coefficients must vanish. This requirement results in the equation

$$\left\{ \frac{\beta_0 - \beta_+}{2} - \left[\left(\frac{\beta_0 - \beta_+}{2} \right)^2 + \kappa^2 \right]^{\frac{1}{2}} \right\} e^{-j\beta_2 L}$$
$$- \left\{ \frac{\beta_0 - \beta_+}{2} + \left[\left(\frac{\beta_0 - \beta_+}{2} \right)^2 + \kappa^2 \right]^{\frac{1}{2}} \right\} e^{-j\beta_1 L} = 0$$

This is a complex equation; if the values for the two propagation constants as determined by Eq. (31) are substituted, some rearrangement yields two resultant equations obtained by separately setting the real and imaginary parts equal to zero. These two equations are

$$\frac{\beta_0 - \beta_+}{2} \sin \left[\left(\frac{\beta_0 - \beta_+}{2} \right)^2 + \kappa^2 \right]^{\frac{1}{2}} L = 0$$

$$\left[\left(\frac{\beta_0 - \beta_+}{2} \right)^2 + \kappa^2 \right]^{\frac{1}{2}} \cos \left[\left(\frac{\beta_0 - \beta_+}{2} \right)^2 + \kappa^2 \right]^{\frac{1}{2}} L = 0 \qquad (35)$$

Examination of these equations indicates that the only way in which they can both be satisfied is if

$$\beta_0 - \beta_+ = 0$$

$$\left[\left(\frac{\beta_0 - \beta_+}{2} \right)^2 + \kappa^2 \right]^{\frac{1}{2}} L = (2n + 1) \frac{\pi}{2} \qquad (36)$$

or $$\kappa L = (2n + 1) \frac{\pi}{2} \qquad n = \text{integer}$$

These are, then, the starting conditions for a backward-wave oscillator. It is apparent that, first of all, synchronism between the circuit wave and the slow space-charge wave is required, which is the result cited in Chap. 7 without proof. Second, one obtains a relation between the space charge, the Pierce C parameter, and the length for starting which can, obviously, also be interpreted in terms of a starting current for a fixed length. It is to be noted that in solving these equations in this way, we have imposed additional conditions (36) on the system in order to obtain an oscillator. The *general* equation (31) for the roots would give us answers for other conditions but would not provide oscillation, although amplifier conditions are included in the sense described previously. These conditions (36) are precisely those required to obtain oscillation, i.e., nonzero output for a zero input.

The propagation constants obtained from Eqs. (36) are

$$\beta_{1,2} = \beta_0 \pm \kappa$$

and the value of the current and field are given by

$$i' = 2jC_1 e^{-j\beta_0 z} \sin \kappa z$$
$$E' = 2jC_1 e^{-j\beta_0 z} \cos \kappa z$$

It is apparent that these equations indeed satisfy the conditions imposed earlier of zero current at one end and zero field at the other. One can also see how current and field vary along the device; moreover, since $\cos^2 \kappa z + \sin^2 \kappa z = 1$, the power conservation result [Eq. (29)] that we derived from the differential equation is also satisfied. These solutions are valid approximations only when the fast and slow space-charge waves are sufficiently separated to permit us to consider coupling by pairs and not by triplets. Hence, for small space charge, small QC, the results obtained above are not valid, since the two space-charge waves have nearly the same velocity.

9.6   Application of Coupled-mode Theory to the Traveling-wave Tube

If we examine the behavior of the solutions given by Eq. (33) in detail, we can obtain a good deal of information about how the characteristics of a traveling-wave tube vary with changes in the parameters.   It is easy to determine, for example, how the gain of the growing wave depends on departures from synchronism.   It is immediately obvious that maximum gain occurs when the slow space-charge wave is synchronous with the circuit.   Under these circumstances, the coupling coefficient is also the rate of growth per unit length.   Departures from synchronism between the circuit and the slow space-charge wave reduce this rate of growth in a manner that is easily determined from the behavior of the radical.   It should be pointed out that this solution also contains the space-charge effects.   As defined, κ can be written as

$$\kappa^2 = \frac{C^2 \beta_e^2}{4 \sqrt{QC}}$$

and thus contains the effect of the space charge on the growth.   This result is to be expected, since the original theory was formulated in terms of space-charge waves, the expressions for which already contain the space-charge forces implicitly.   The formulation of Eq. (33) thus provides quite detailed information about the variation of propagation constants as the various parameters are changed.   It must be remembered that, in the original formulation of the equations, it was assumed that the coupling was only between the circuit wave and one of the space-charge waves (in this case, only the *slow* space-charge wave).   As one departs from synchronism between the circuit and the slow space-charge wave in such a way that the slow space-charge wave is slower than the circuit wave, the circuit wave comes closer to synchronism with the fast space-charge wave and the effects of the coupling between the two may become appreciable.   Departures from synchronism in the opposite direction would not be affected by the fast-space-charge-wave interaction in the same way.   Therefore, one would expect that, even though Eq. (33) predicts that gain varies symmetrically with departures from synchronism, actually this will not be true because the interaction with the fast space-charge wave produces an effect if the departure is in one direction and none if it is in the other.

If the departure from synchronism is in a direction in which the slow space-charge wave is faster than the circuit wave, that is, $\beta_+ < \beta_0$, a new kind of interesting behavior results.   Under these circumstances, of course, with the slow space-charge wave faster than the circuit wave, the fast space-charge wave is even further from synchronism, its effects are still negligible, and one can still consider the coupling between the circuit and the slow space-charge wave only.   If one then goes to sufficiently high beam velocity that the first term under the radical of Eq. (33) is larger than the second, then both roots are real and one no longer has growing waves. It is still possible, however, to get gain as a beat phenomenon between the two waves, just as in a backward-wave amplifier. A traveling-wave device operating under these circumstances, where gain results from beating between two waves, has been named the *crestratron*. (Experiments have been made on such a device and some numerical calculations of large-signal behavior have been performed, but it should be noted that the small-signal behavior would all be contained in the results described so far.) Any one of the waves given by Eq. (33) would, of course, have a constant amplitude, so that the result expressed by Eq. (32) would be valid but trivial. If one has two waves, interference between the two may result, so that a condition may arise when either the first or second term in the parentheses of Eq. (32) is zero and the other term is very small. At the output of the device both terms would be quite large because of the interference, with their sums still having the same value as at the input. The large value of the electromagnetic power at the output and a small value at the input represents amplification. Of course, gain in this case arises from interference, so that the two waves concerned (which both carry negative kinetic power) interfere in such a way that the kinetic power they carry is small at the input and large at the output. Similar statements can be made for the electromagnetic power at the input and output.

It might be pointed out that, from the pair of equations leading up to Eq. (33), one can not only obtain propagation constants but (by matching initial conditions on a device) also calculate the starting loss as a function of departures from synchronism, space charge, etc. Again, the results are subject to the fact that one is ignoring the interaction with the fast wave, but over some range of parameters these results will be valid and can be readily obtained from these equations. Finally, it should be noted that these equations would be almost as simple to handle if one included loss on the circuit in order to determine the effect of this loss on the rates of growth, etc. Adding loss merely corresponds to adding attenuation to the propagation constant for the circuit. Equations (28) are not drastically altered. Since there are only two equations, the equation for the roots is still quadratic and one can include the effects of attenuation readily. Again, the results are valid only for large space charge and do not apply when space charge is so small that the space-charge waves are very close to each other and coupling is not by pairs but by triplets.

9.7 Other Applications of the Coupled-mode Approach

It is of interest to point out at least one other application of the coupled-mode approach in which a particular problem can be handled much more readily than by means of the three-wave solution. The problem is that of the coupling between a circuit and a fast space-charge wave.   In this case, a forward-wave circuit and the fast space-charge wave are used. One takes the first of Eqs. (28) with the plus sign and the second with a minus sign.   The resulting conservation equation is of the same form as Eq. (29).   As before, this equation would apply to any solution of Eqs. (28) for the case under consideration (including a single wave) and, since the waves in this case carry positive electromagnetic power and positive kinetic power in the positive z direction, growing waves cannot exist. With a single wave, both terms in Eq. (29) correspond to power flow in the positive z direction.   If the sum is to be conserved, a growing wave in which both terms would grow is not possible.   However, with a pair of waves there may be a beat phenomenon in which the sum of the two terms has some fixed value at the input and is entirely in the form of electromagnetic power, and has the same fixed value at the output but is entirely in the form of kinetic power.   This is the basis of the so-called *Kompfner dip* phenomenon.   In this kind of operation of a traveling-wave circuit, the synchronism takes place between the circuit and the fast space-charge wave.   A small signal placed on the circuit and an entering unmodulated beam represent purely electromagnetic power at the input but no kinetic power.   At the correct distance along the circuit, one finds that there is no electromagnetic power left.   This phenomenon is used in measuring the properties of traveling-wave circuits. One injects a beam of a known amount of current, places a signal on the circuit, and varies the voltage until the signal disappears at the output. Under these circumstances, one has a quarter-beat wavelength ($\kappa L = \pi/2$) along the circuit.   From the theory, one can determine the value of C that was necessary to produce a quarter-beat wavelength for that length of circuit, at that voltage, at that current.   From this value of C one can then determine the interaction impedance.   The energy transfer that has taken place is evidently that all of the electromagnetic power has been transferred to the beam, so that the beam emerges with an equal amount of kinetic power.

It should be pointed out here that under these circumstances, if there were any excitation on the beam at the entrance, all of the excitation would be transferred to the circuit so that a complete interchange of excitation between the beam and the circuit would take place.   This idea, which originally was used for measuring circuit impedance, is also the basis of the so-called *fast-wave couplers* that are used in parametric amplifiers, in which the fast space-charge wave is responsible for providing gain.   The mechanism for coupling to the fast space-charge wave is exactly as described here.   In actual practice, something more complicated than has been described here is necessary for a fast-wave coupler. The coupling to the slow space-charge wave under these circumstances, while not large, is not actually zero; therefore, if one wants coupling only to a fast wave, the scheme as described above is not adequate.

10

Crossed-field Interactions

10.1 General Considerations

In a large number of electron devices, both amplifiers and oscillators (of which the best known is the magnetron oscillator), electron motion takes place in a region where static electric and magnetic fields are present at right angles to each other. The steady-state electron motion in such *crossed fields* has special characteristics that depend on the fields; and the fields also strongly affect the r-f behavior of the electrons under the action of r-f fields.

Before we go into any details of electron motion in such fields, it might be useful to describe the various devices that incorporate this particular combination of electric and magnetic fields. The best-known of these devices is the so-called cavity *magnetron oscillator* with a cylindrical configuration: a cylindrical cathode inside a cylindrical anode that is usually slotted periodically around the circumference (Fig. 10.1a), or else has some related periodic variation around the circumference. Electrons emitted from the cathode move in complex trajectories under the action of both the constant radial electric and the axial magnetic fields and of the r-f electric fields of the anode.   The trajectories are such that the electrons circulate in a particular sense around the cathode and interact with the electromagnetic fields.   The net result of the motion is that the energy imparted to the electrons by the constant accelerating electric field is transferred to the r-f field, resulting in the generation of r-f power.

Although the magnetron oscillator is the best known of all crossed-field devices, it is probably the most difficult to analyze at all quantitatively, since it always operates in a "large-signal" regime (large r-f amplitudes), so that the motion can at no time be described by simple equations.   There is an interplay among the d-c and r-f electric fields, the d-c and r-f space-charge fields, and the d-c magnetic field which results in highly nonlinear motion with crossing of trajectories; no real consensus of opinion has been reached to date as to even a qualitative description of the motion.   We shall be able to say a little more about that after characterizing the more elementary causes of electron motion in crossed fields; we shall then be able to describe (at least qualitatively) the phenomena that probably occur in an oscillating magnetron.

A device related to the magnetron oscillator is a type of crossed-field amplifier with a similar configuration but in which the anode is interrupted at some point.   It is possible to inject an input signal at some point along the anode circumference and to extract an output nearly 360° away.   The electrons still circulate in the same way under the action of d-c and r-f fields, but the injected signal determines the frequency and, to some limited extent, the amplitude.   In related versions of this crossed-field amplifier the structure is planar.   In that case, a planar anode faces a planar cathode, the static electric field is perpendicular to them rather than radial as in the cylindrical case, and the magnetic field is perpen-

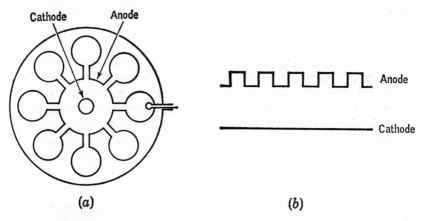

(a)   (b)

Fig. 10.1   Basic magnetron configurations: (a) cross section of cylindrical cavity magnetron; (b) planar magnetron.

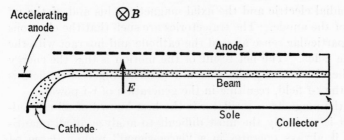

Fig. 10.2 Basic configuration of M-type tube.

dicular to the electric field and parallel to the cathode and anode surfaces (Fig. 10.1*b*).

In a third class of devices, either planar or concentric cylindrical in configuration, the electron beam is injected into the region between the anode and the negative electrode (called the *sole* in this case) and moves between the two electrodes under the action of crossed fields as shown in Fig. 10.2. The anode again comprises a periodic circuit, and the tube may be used as a forward- or backward-wave device; in the latter case, the tube can be an oscillator similar to that described in Chap. 7.

These devices have been designated by a variety of names. A common usage is to call them *M-type* amplifiers and oscillators. The M-type backward-wave oscillator is also generally known as a *carcinotron*. The M-type amplifier does permit operation in a small-signal regime, and a small-signal theory, which will be discussed later, has been developed for it. Because such a theory exists and is backed up by experimental evidence, and because some of the features of the theory apply to other M-type devices such as the magnetron oscillator, it is possible to obtain some indication of the sort of behavior that occurs in the other devices. (It must, nevertheless, be firmly kept in mind that oscillators, which always operate in a large-signal regime, cannot be described in numerical detail by small-signal theories.)

Before considering any of the r-f properties of such amplifiers or oscillators, we must investigate the problem of the steady electron motion in crossed static electric and magnetic fields. The analysis that follows is for the two-dimensional planar case only, because the algebra is somewhat simpler and most of the essential details of crossed-field devices are displayed by planar devices. Extensions to the cylindrical case can be plausibly made in many cases; we shall try to mention special features of the cylindrical case as the opportunity arises.

10.2 Motion of an Individual Electron in Static Crossed Fields

Let us first consider the case of the motion of a single, isolated electron in crossed fields (so that we need not consider space-charge effects), in the coordinate system shown in Fig. 10.3.   With the electric field in the y direction and the magnetic field in the x direction, the equations of motion for an electron are given by

$$m\ddot{z} = -e\dot{y}B_0 \tag{1}$$
$$m\ddot{y} = eE + e\dot{z}B_0 \tag{2}$$
$$m\ddot{x} = 0 \tag{3}$$

where the electric and magnetic fields are

$$E = E_y = -\frac{V_0}{s} \qquad B_0 \equiv B_x = \text{const}$$

Equation (1) can be integrated to yield

$$m\dot{z} = -eyB_0 + \text{constant} \tag{4}$$

It is convenient to set the constant of integration equal to zero by locating the origin of the y axis at the plane where the z component of the velocity is zero.   Substituting this value for the z component of velocity into Eq. (2), we obtain (with $\eta = e/m$)

$$\ddot{y} = -(\eta B_0)^2\left(y - \frac{E}{\eta B_0^2}\right) = -\omega_c{}^2\left(y - \frac{\eta E}{\omega_c{}^2}\right) \tag{5}$$

where we have defined the *cyclotron frequency*

$$\omega_c \equiv -\eta B_0$$

The general solution of Eq. (4) is

$$y - \frac{\eta E}{\omega_c{}^2} = A\cos\omega_c t + B\sin\omega_c t \tag{6}$$

Once again, it is convenient to pick a particular set of initial conditions that, although not necessarily the most general, lead to simpler results and contain all the essential features of the motion with which we

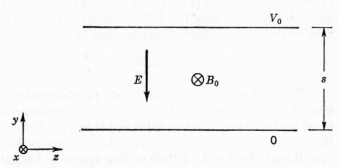

Fig. 10.3 Coordinate system for analysis of crossed-field tubes.

are concerned. A convenient initial condition is to assume that the electrons leave the plane at $y = 0$ at $t = 0$ with $\dot{y} = 0$. This condition, then, represents an emitting cathode surface. Equation (6) then becomes

$$y = \frac{\eta E}{\omega_c^2} (1 - \cos \omega_c t) \tag{7}$$

and again, if we had assumed that the z-directed velocity was not zero at the plane $y = 0$, we should have obtained an additional term in Eq. (7) corresponding to $B \neq 0$. Although the resulting change in the appearance of the trajectory would be quite drastic, such changes would not be important for our present purpose. (We shall return to this point after we have considered the z motion.) We now substitute the value for y obtained from Eq. (7) into Eq. (4) to obtain

$$\dot{z} = \frac{\eta E}{\omega_c} (1 - \cos \omega_c t) \tag{8}$$

and integration yields

$$z = \frac{\eta E}{\omega_c} \left(t - \frac{\sin \omega_c t}{\omega_c} \right) \tag{9}$$

In this case, we specify the initial value $z = 0$ at $t = 0$, which is a trivial specialization, since it merely defines the starting point of the electron. On the other hand, and less trivial, the presence of a sine term in Eq. (7) would add corresponding terms in Eqs. (8) and (9). The motion described by Eqs. (7) and (9) is shown in Fig. 10.4a; it represents a cycloid. Initial conditions different from those used here (zero y and z components of velocity at the plane $y = 0$) result in trajectories such as shown in Figs. 10.4b and c. These trajectories would correspond to electrons that did not start at the cathode, or to electrons injected from outside the region under consideration. However, the relevant result that we shall now derive applies to these more general conditions also. If we return to Eq. (8) for the instantaneous velocity, we can see that if we average it over a complete period of cyclotron frequency, the cosine term (as well as any sine terms that would be included in a more general case) averages to zero, so that the average velocity is given by

$$\dot{z} = \frac{\eta E}{\omega_c} = - \frac{E}{B_0} \tag{10}$$

This is the most significant result for the motion of a particle in crossed fields: its average drift velocity perpendicular to both fields is equal to the ratio of the two fields and is independent of the charge and the mass. This result applies to all the trajectories shown in Fig. 10.4, even though the details of their motion appear to be quite different. A special case of this condition on the average drift velocity that is of particular interest is the following. If by some means a particle is injected

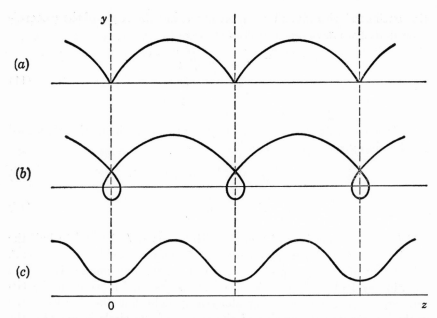

Fig. 10.4 Electron motion in crossed a-c fields: (a) basic cycloid, $y = \eta E/\omega_c^2$; (b) $y < \eta E/\omega_c^2$; (c) $y > \eta E/\omega_c^2$.

into a crossed-field region such that it has only a z component of velocity and that component satisfies the condition of Eq. (10), then the particle continues to travel in a straight line at this velocity. (This special case can be also derived directly from the equations by suitable choice of initial conditions.) The result of Eq. (10) is significant because, in the interaction of electrons with a circuit (or any multiple-stream interaction of one stream with another), it is this circumstance of a fixed average drift velocity in the direction perpendicular to the crossed electric and magnetic fields that permits synchronization between a circuit wave and the beam (or a multiple-stream interaction between several beam waves). The fact that the electrons may have other components of d-c motion in addition to this average motion does not destroy any effects that result from average drift velocity of the electrons being related to that of some other element in the device, such as the circuit. Without going into any further details at this point, we may see that cumulative interaction between an electron and a circuit would seem to be plausible for this reason, even though the electron may have additional superimposed components of motion that periodically vary its position relative to the circuit.

There is another means of describing the characteristics that we have just derived, which may also be illuminating. If instead of calculating the motion of the electron in a fixed frame of reference, fixed in the laboratory, we refer the motion to a frame of reference moving in the $+z$ direction with a velocity given by Eq. (10) and shift the origin of the y coordinate so that we have new coordinates given by

$$z' = z + \frac{E}{B_0} t$$
$$y' = y - \frac{\eta E}{\omega_c^2}$$

(11)

then (remembering that E is negative), we find that the motion described by the above equations is given by

$$y' = -\frac{\eta E}{\omega_c^2} \cos \omega_c t$$

(12)

$$z' = \frac{\eta E}{\omega_c^2} \sin \omega_c t$$

(13)

which are the equations of a circle with radius $\eta E/\omega_c^2$ equal to half the maximum value of y as given by Eq. (7) and centered at $y = \eta E/\omega_c^2$. This result may be interpreted in the well-known way commonly used to describe cycloidal motion: the electron moves as if it were on the circumference of a circle rolling along a straight line (in this case, the cathode); the linear velocity of the center of the circle is $-E/B_0$, the drift velocity given by Eq. (10); and the other two cases, shown in Fig. 10.4b and c, correspond to the electron being fixed at different radial distances from the same center point.

10.3   Effects of Space Charge on D-C Motion

The considerations of the preceding sections apply to the case when the number of electrons in the cathode-anode region is so small that space-charge forces may be neglected.   As we have seen, such an analysis leads to the interesting result of a constant drift velocity (superimposed on any angular motion) that would permit a cumulative interaction between a circuit and such a (small-space-charge) beam.   A similar calculation for a cylindrical configuration would lead to related results.   In that case, of course, the electric field between the cylinders is not constant and a centripetal acceleration must be taken into account, but it is once again possible to find a combination of magnetic and electric fields such that there is a constant angular velocity at a particular radial distance for which an equilibrium among all the forces involved results.

We have so far omitted the effect of space charge on the motion of the electrons in crossed fields.   We shall again treat the planar case; analogous results can be found for the cylindrical case, but in a mathematically more complicated form.   For the planar case, we shall show that it is possible to find a configuration that yields a consistent solution for the motion of the electrons, after space-charge forces, applied electric fields, and d-c magnetic fields have all been taken into account. We shall show that the solution represents a sheet of electrons in rectilinear motion perpendicular to both the applied electric and the magnetic fields. Within the sheet, the charge density is constant and the velocity perpendicular to the applied fields varies linearly with position across the sheet. Under these circumstances, all the equations of motion are satisfied and a self-consistent flow therefore results. This flow is known as *Brillouin flow*[1] (related to the Brillouin flow discussed in Chap. 2) and comprises the steady-state condition on the basis of which one may treat the r-f effects.

The configuration to be discussed, shown in Fig. 10.5, differs from the preceding case only in that we are now considering a beam of finite thickness with a finite space charge flowing between a pair of plates across which a potential is applied. We shall not attempt to indicate here how this sort of motion is actually established; to show that it is possible, we need only solve the equation of motion and Poisson's equation and show that they are consistent with the assumed conditions.

We assume as one of the conditions that the charge density in the beam is constant. Poisson's equation, then, is

$$\frac{\partial E_y}{\partial y} = -\frac{\partial^2 V}{\partial y^2} = \frac{\rho_0}{\epsilon_0} \tag{14}$$

in one-dimensional form. (It is assumed that the sheet of charge extends infinitely in the x and z directions, so that the only electric field that exists is in the y direction.) A solution inside the sheet of charge is then

$$E_y = E = \frac{\rho_0 y}{\epsilon_0} + \text{const} \tag{15}$$

where the constant can be determined from a boundary condition. Between the sheet of charge and the cathode $\rho_0 = 0$, so that the field is constant $(\partial E_y/\partial y = 0)$; let us call this constant value E_1. At the edge of the sheet of charge (at $y = d$), $E = E_1$, and Eq. (15) in the sheet thus becomes

$$E = \frac{\rho_0(y - d)}{\epsilon_0} + E_1 \tag{16}$$

[1] L. Brillouin, A Theorem of Larmor and Its Importance for Electrons in Magnetic Fields, *Phys. Rev.*, **67**:260–266 (1945).

Fig. 10.5 Beam of finite thickness at a distance $y = d$ from the cathode.

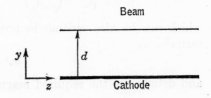

Beam

d

y

z

Cathode

A second integration provides the potential in the sheet:

$$V = - \left[\frac{\rho_0}{\epsilon_0} \frac{(y - d)^2}{2} + E_1 y \right] \tag{17}$$

In writing it in this form, we have already introduced a constant of integration; the first term inside the brackets contains a constant term so selected that potential is continuous at $y = d$, that is, $V = -E_1 d$.

We must next determine whether it is possible to find values of magnetic field B_0 and of the charge density ρ_0 that will satisfy, everywhere within the sheet of charge, the two relations determined by the equations of motion: first, that velocity is related to the total potential energy by

$$v^2 = -2\eta V \tag{18}$$

and second, that the net transverse forces on the electron vanish. As indicated by our previous discussion of the space-charge-free motion, this condition requires that everywhere within the charge sheet, for a fixed value of the magnetic field, we must have

$$v^2 = \left(\frac{E}{B_0} \right)^2 \tag{19}$$

These conditions impose two requirements on v^2, one in terms of Eq. (17) involving the potential and one in terms of Eq. (16) involving the fields. If we set these two values for v^2 equal to each other, we shall obtain a relation that must be satisfied if the flow is to be possible. We substitute for V from Eq. (17) into Eq. (18), and for E from Eq. (16) into Eq. (19), to obtain

$$v^2 = -2\eta V = 2\eta \frac{\rho_0}{\epsilon_0} \frac{(y - d)^2}{2} + 2\eta E_1(y - d) + 2\eta E_1 d$$
$$v^2 = \left(\frac{E}{B_0} \right)^2 = \left(\frac{\rho_0}{\epsilon_0 B_0} \right)^2 (y - d)^2 + \frac{2E_1}{B_0^2} \frac{\rho_0}{\epsilon_0} (y - d) + \left(\frac{E_1}{B_0} \right)^2 \tag{20}$$

where we have also written both equations for convenience as a polynomial in $(y - d)$.

The right-hand sides of the two equations must be equal for all values of y within the beam; if we consider them as two polynomials in $(y - d)$, we may equate coefficients term by term. If we equate the coefficients of the $(y - d)^2$ terms, we obtain

$$\frac{\rho \eta_0}{\epsilon_0} = \left(\frac{\rho_0}{\epsilon_0 B_0} \right)^2 \qquad \text{or} \qquad (\eta B_0)^2 = \frac{\eta \rho_0}{\epsilon_0} \tag{21}$$

which can be also written in terms of the cyclotron and plasma frequencies as

$$\omega_c^2 = \omega_p^2 \tag{21a}$$

and determines the required magnetic field for a given charge density.

In the form of Eq. (21a), this result means that the cyclotron frequency must be equal to the plasma frequency in the beam.

From the constant term of Eqs. (20), we obtain

$$\left(\frac{E_1}{B_0}\right)^2 = 2\eta E_1 d \qquad \text{or} \qquad E_1 = 2\eta B_0^2 d = 2\frac{\rho_0}{\epsilon_0} d \qquad (22)$$

which determines the value of the field at the lower edge of the electron sheet and, therefore, in the region between $y = 0$ and $y = d$.

The remaining corresponding terms of both expressions, linear in $(y - d)$, yield no additional information: it may be seen that equating them gives the same result as Eq. (21), so that by satisfying that equation one automatically makes the linear terms in Eqs. (20) equal to each other.

With these conditions met, we may go back to Eqs. (16) and (17) for the field and potential inside the beam. With the value for E_1 determined by Eq. (22), these equations reduce to

$$E = \frac{\rho_0}{\epsilon_0} (y + d) \qquad (23)$$

$$V = - \frac{\rho_0}{\epsilon_0} \frac{(y + d)^2}{2} \qquad (24)$$

At the upper edge of the beam, subject to having the proper value of charge density inside the beam, the potential and the field correspond to the value of y at that upper edge. Above the sheet, for continuity of field, the field must have a constant value given by the value at the upper edge, with the potential above the sheet increasing linearly according to this field. Therefore, any electrode (the anode) placed above the sheet and adjusted to the potential as determined by these conditions is a possible electrode choice. Under these circumstances, for a given potential difference between cathode and anode, the field above and below the sheet of charge adjusts itself to the value of E_1 and (say) E_2, respectively, as determined by the maximum value of Eq. (23). The potential variation inside the beam, as given by Eq. (24), provides the correct boundary conditions at the upper and lower edges of the beam; the motion of the electrons, under the action of the magnetic field as determined by Eq. (21) and of the electric field as determined by Eq. (23), is rectilinear and also satisfies the condition of conservation of energy, Eq. (18). We have thus demonstrated (essentially, by construction) the existence of a solution of the equations of motion and Poisson's equation that is consistent with all requirements; therefore, this is a possible state.

One further result should be pointed out. Since Eq. (19) requires that the velocity should be proportional to E everywhere inside the sheet, then according to Eq. (23), the velocity in the z direction also varies linearly with the y coordinate, from a minimum value at the lower edge of the sheet to a maximum value at the upper edge. For this reason, the

Brillouin-flow pattern is also sometimes known as *slipping-stream flow*. (Figure 10.6 is a schematic representation of the variation of E, V, and v as a function of y.)   The existence of slipping-stream motion in crossed fields leads to interesting consequences in r-f behavior.   One is that in considering interaction with a circuit (the anode replaced by an r-f structure) the problem becomes complicated because of the dependence of velocity on the transverse coordinate.   Another consequence is that it is possible in such a stream to obtain a behavior analogous to double-stream interaction (cf. Sec. 4.4) between the two edges with no external circuit.

It is interesting to compare the y-z motion just described with that obtained in a "Brillouin-focused" sheet beam,[1] which moves in the x direction through the same field and potential distribution in the yz plane. In a Brillouin-focused sheet beam, the beam moves with a constant x-directed velocity that is the same for all electrons; the focusing action in the yz plane does not depend on the x-directed motion, but, rather, depends on a combination of space-charge fields and magnetic fields in the presence of the same kind of shearing velocity as we have just described. In the Brillouin-focused sheet beam, the field would be generally symmetrical about the center plane of the beam, being directed toward the wall on either side of this symmetry plane.   All properties within the beam, except the motion in the x direction, are similar to the case we have just described.

A similar statement may be made about the motion of electrons in a

---

[1] Brillouin, *op. cit.*, discusses both the sheet-beam case and the rotational-symmetry case described in Sec. 2.5.

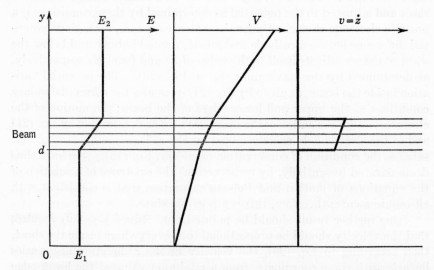

Fig. 10.6   Schematic representation of E, V, and v as a function of distance across beam.

cylindrical configuration with a cylindrical cathode concentric with a cylindrical anode. One can then find a steady-state motion with a constant *angular* velocity for all the electrons in a space-charge ring of a finite thickness such that the combination of centripetal acceleration, magnetic forces, and electric fields all balance everywhere within the electron cloud and a steady-state motion is possible, corresponding to the constant angular velocity of this ring of finite thickness. This case is also analogous to the corresponding Brillouin-focused cylindrical beam,[1] which also has a velocity in the x direction that does not contribute to the focusing forces. In the crossed-field configuration under consideration in the present chapter, the field required at the inner boundary of the rotating ring is provided not by other electrons as in the Brillouin-focused beam, but by the cylindrical cathode on the inside of the ring.

10.4 Crossed-field Amplification

Having treated some aspects of the motion of electrons under the action of static magnetic and electric fields, we now wish to examine what sort of characteristics may be found if a stream in the presence of such electric and magnetic fields also interacts with a slow-wave circuit. The treatment will be similar to that of traveling-wave tubes, in that we shall first consider the interaction of a beam of this kind with a circuit in the absence of r-f space-charge effects and then take the effects of the space-charge fields into account. We follow this procedure not merely for the sake of completeness but because in the case of crossed fields, one actually finds quite new phenomena occurring when one takes the space-charge fields into account.

Some preliminary remarks of a general nature about crossed-field tubes may be in order. In some ways, their behavior is similar to the behavior of traveling-wave tubes and backward-wave oscillators (of the sort discussed in Chaps. 6 and 7), in which there is no electrostatic field but in which a magnetic field along the direction of motion is provided for focusing. It is customary to designate such tubes, in which the magnetic field plays no essential part except to hold the beam together, as O-type tubes, whereas the crossed-field tubes are, as already noted, called M-type tubes. The behavior of M-type tubes, as stated, is in many ways similar to that of O-type tubes. For example, if a circuit is located near the beam in a crossed-field tube and if at some frequency the circuit velocity and the beam velocity are in approximate synchronism, interaction results as in an O-type tube, and the fact that space charge is present in the beam leads to r-f space-charge forces that are to some extent similar to those in an O-type tube. The presence of space charge introduces a natural resonant frequency, the plasma frequency, into the theory of both O- and

[1] *Ibid.*

M-type tubes. However, another natural frequency is also present in a crossed-field device, the cyclotron frequency. Both frequencies have already appeared in the analysis of the motion of an electron beam in static crossed fields, in the so-called Brillouin-flow case (Sec. 10.2). One might expect that the cyclotron frequency (just like the plasma frequency) might also manifest itself somehow in the r-f behavior; and, as a matter of fact, it does so in a rather drastic way, providing certain kinds of interaction which do not exist in O-type tubes. In addition, the space-charge forces as represented by the plasma frequency also produce a new phenomenon known as the *diocotron effect*, which results in growing waves being possible in the beam even in the absence of a circuit.

The analysis of the motion in constant fields has already demonstrated certain phenomena that are closely related to these types of r-f behavior. In static-field motion, two kinds of behavior are present: (1) a steady drift perpendicular to both the electrostatic and magnetic fields, with a velocity equal to the ratio of the two fields [Eq. (10)], and (2) a superimposed rotational motion at a frequency ω_c. The counterparts of these constant-field motions exist under the action of r-f fields. As a counterpart of (2) we shall find that if the electron, because of its average velocity and the velocity of the waves on the circuit, moves in a field that has an effective frequency (as seen by the electrons) equal to ω_c, a resonant behavior (and, consequently, rotational motion) results. As the counterpart of (1), because of the peculiar property that the average velocity of an electron is perpendicular to the electric field, we shall find that (unlike in the O-type tube) an r-f field acting in the z direction affects the motion of the electron in the y direction. In the simplest possible case, that of electrons moving under d-c conditions at the same velocity as a wave on the circuit so that the electron sees a steady circuit field in the z direction, this field looks like a constant field to the electron and causes a constant drift in the y direction. We shall analyze this effect in more detail, but it is immediately obvious that the resulting behavior in crossed fields is quite different from the O-type case. It might be also pointed out here that it is the y components of the fields that cause the variations in the z components of the velocity and hence bunching. This cross coupling between fields and velocities is an effect of major importance. Actually, it is this cross coupling that is responsible for the diocotron effect mentioned above; it is the *space-charge fields* producing orthogonal velocities that produce this effect.

Since the r-f field component E_y perpendicular to the steady motion thus plays an important role in the behavior of crossed-field devices, we shall have to include this component in any analysis. Moreover, since the z components of the field cause y velocities (and therefore y displacements), we shall also have to take into account variations of E_z with the y coordinate. To illustrate the nature of these fields, a common struc-

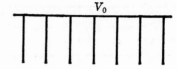

V_0

$V = 0$

**Fig. 10.7 Typical crossed-field r-f struc-
ture, nonsymmetric.**

ture used in crossed-field devices is shown in Fig. 10.7. The symbols
indicate the voltages applied to the two electrodes, the top one of which
is the propagating circuit made up of conducting vanes. It is apparent
from the circuit that E_z is zero at the lower electrode (the sole). One can
also imagine a circuit such as shown in Fig. 10.8, which consists of two
such vane structures symmetrically arranged, with potentials as shown.
This structure has two modes that are related (and velocities that are
quite close), but one of them has an electric-field pattern of the form
shown in Fig. 10.9a, with $E_z = 0$ on the symmetry plane; whereas the
other is as shown in Fig. 10.9b, with $E_y = 0$ on the symmetry plane.
The upper half of the field pattern of Fig. 10.9a is the same as one obtains
with the configuration of Fig. 10.7. We shall find that the electron
behavior depends on the ratio E_y/E_z, which in turn depends on the mode
and on the location of the beam in the field.[1]

[1] It should be pointed out here that we have already discussed, in Chap. 8,
transverse effects arising from a combination of a magnetic field and space charge
for the case of the space-charge waves that could exist in an O-type beam in Brillouin
flow. In that case, we were concerned with a cylindrical beam and a magnetic field
in the direction of beam flow. The r-f fields and the displacement transverse to the
steady motion of the beam in that case are both symmetric with respect to the beam
axis, i.e., the radial displacements of all electrons at a given radius are the same.
This circumstance leads to certain consequences described in Chap. 8, which are,
however, of a drastically different nature from the transverse displacements that
occur in crossed-field devices—particularly such as might occur in a circuit of the
form shown in Fig. 10.7, with a field configuration like the upper half of Fig. 10.9a.
In this case, the transverse electron displacement is not in an axially symmetric field
and the results are quite different.

V_0

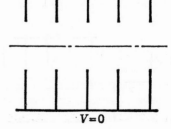

$V = 0$

**Fig. 10.8 Typical crossed-field r-f struc-
ture, symmetric.**

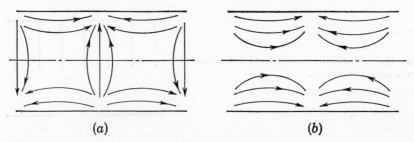

$$(a) \qquad\qquad\qquad\qquad (b)$$

Fig. 10.9 **The electric-field modes in the circuit of Fig. 10.8:** (*a*) $E_z = 0$ at symmetry plane; (*b*) $E_y = 0$ at symmetry plane.

Although we have previously indicated the importance of space charge, we shall first treat the case of the interaction between a beam in a crossed field and a circuit when the effect of space charge is ignored; i.e., just as we did in the initial work with the O-type tube, we shall assume that the only r-f fields present are those of the circuit.

10.5 Traveling-wave Interaction When Space Charge Is Negligible

Let us first write the equations of motion of the circuit in their complete form; then we shall make the various approximations that are necessary if we are to obtain simple solutions, and we shall try to justify these approximations, or at least indicate the range of their validity.

The equations of motion refer to a configuration such as shown in Fig. 10.10. We consider an electron beam of thickness t with the origin of the y coordinate on the center line of the beam. The sole is at a distance $y = -a$ and the circuit is at a distance $y = +b$ from this center line. The magnetic field B_0 is in the x direction, into the paper. We consider all quantities as having no variation with the x coordinate and no motion in the x direction. Under these conditions, the equations of motion of any electron in terms of the y and z velocities are given by

$$\frac{d^2y_1}{dt^2} = \frac{dv_y}{dt} = \eta[E_y + E_{0y} + (u_0 + v_z)B_0] \tag{25}$$

$$\frac{d^2z_1}{dt^2} = \frac{dv_z}{dt} = \eta(E_z - v_yB_0) \tag{26}$$

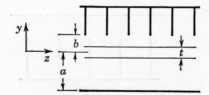

Fig. 10.10 Beam of thickness t in nonsymmetric structure.

These equations are in Lagrangian variables, in which we follow the motion of individual electrons and y_1 and z_1 represent the displacement of the electrons; so that the fields should be evaluated at the displaced electron positions $y_0 + y_1$, $z_0 + z_1$, where y_0 and z_0 would be the electron positions under d-c conditions. In Sec. 10.6, where the behavior of a thin beam with space-charge forces taken into account is considered, we shall calculate the average forces (and velocities) for all the electrons in the beam, and the above formulation will be then more useful than one in Eulerian variables. If the fields vary with time and coordinates as $e^{j(\omega t - \beta z)}$, then the time dependence (to the first order in r-f magnitude) of these fields as seen by a *moving electron* at z is given by $e^{j(\omega - \beta u_0)t}$, where r-f velocity terms in the exponential that would give quadratic terms in the final result have been dropped.

With this time dependence, we obtain

$$\frac{d^2 y_1}{dt^2} = \frac{dv_y}{dt} = j(\omega - u_0\beta)v_y = -(\omega - \beta u_0)^2 y_1 \qquad (27)$$

$$\frac{d^2 z_1}{dt^2} = \frac{dv_z}{dt} = j(\omega - u_0\beta)v_z = -(\omega - \beta u_0)^2 z_1 \qquad (28)$$

and we can rewrite Eqs. (25) and (26) in terms of the r-f velocities. In doing so, we must recall that in order to obtain a flow of the sort shown in Fig. 10.10, under d-c conditions the magnetic field and the electric field at each electron must satisfy the relation

$$u_0(y)B_0 + E_{0y}(y) = 0 \qquad (29)$$

Accordingly, these two terms would cancel in Eq. (25). However, if there has been an r-f motion in the y direction, resulting in a displacement y_1, then the electron is in a position where the d-c field acting on it is different from that in an unperturbed beam; the cancellation represented by Eq. (29) then leaves this term as a residue. Thus, if the variation in the d-c field because of space charge is $\partial E_{0y}/\partial y$, then Eqs. (25) and (26) become[1]

$$j(\omega - u_0\beta)v_z = \eta(E_z - v_y B_0) \qquad (30)$$

$$j(\omega - u_0\beta)v_y = \eta(E_y + v_z B_0 + y_1 E_0') \qquad (31)$$

[1] In Eulerian variables, where v_y, v_z represent *field variables* (i.e., velocities as functions of the coordinates y, z), the corresponding equations would be

$$j(\omega - u_0\beta)v_z + v_y \frac{\partial u_0}{\partial y} = \eta(E_z - v_y B_0) \qquad (30a)$$

$$j(\omega - u_0\beta)v_y = \eta(E_y + v_z B_0) \qquad (31a)$$

Here the velocities and fields are evaluated at y, z rather than at $y_0 + y_1$, $z_0 + z_1$. There is no force term of the form $y_1 \partial E_0/\partial y$, which is characteristic of following an individual electron to a point other than its d-c position. However, there is an acceleration term $v_y \partial u_0/\partial y$, since describing the passage of an electron from one y position to another in Eulerian variables requires assigning different values of d-c velocity at the two points, as represented by $\partial u_0/\partial y$.

where, for the case of Brillouin flow,

$$E_0' = \frac{\rho_0}{\epsilon_0} \tag{32}$$

as could be obtained from Eq. (23). (The primes denote partial differentiation with respect to y.)

We shall assume in what follows that the displacement y_1 and the velocity v_y are constant over the cross section of the beam. This assumption is tantamount to saying that we shall consider a *thin* beam, which will limit the validity of our results accordingly. Under the thin-beam assumption, the y component of the current also does not vary with y, that is, $\partial i_y/\partial y = 0$, and the equation of continuity then becomes

$$\frac{\partial i_z}{\partial z} = -\frac{\partial \rho}{\partial t} = -j\omega\rho \tag{33}$$

Equations (30) and (31) or (30a) and (31a) in the form given do not lead to any simple result; further development, most conveniently carried on from Eqs. (30a) and (31a), would yield equations that would have to be solved numerically. This circumstance arises from the fact that u_0 in these equations is actually a function of y. It is this functional dependence that, when carried on through the other equations, leads to complicated results.[1] In particular, one obtains linear differential equations in which the coefficients are not constants (as in all the cases discussed previously), but functions of y. These equations lead to the so-called slipping-stream solutions. One can find rather complicated behavior, but some of the interesting cases require numerical solutions of the equations.

Instead, we shall proceed as follows. We shall take the steady velocity as a constant independent of y; or, stated perhaps more rigorously, we shall assume that the variation is so small over the cross section that we can take the velocity as approximately constant. The Brillouin-flow condition with associated velocity variation (derived in Sec. 10.3) is not the only flow possible. If we assume that the electrons originate at a nonequipotential cathode, it is in principle possible to have a beam with finite space charge, finite thickness, and with only a small variation in velocity over the cross section.[2] That is hardly a practical method of

[1] G. G. McFarlane and H. G. Hay, Wave Propagation in a Slipping Stream of Electrons: Small Amplitude Theory, *Proc. Phys. Soc.* (*London*), **B63**:409–427 (1950).

[2] To show that the assumption of a constant velocity over the cross section is not implausible, we must generalize the problem of the steady-state motion of electrons in crossed fields beyond the treatment given earlier in this chapter For steady-state motion, we must have for each electron.

$$\frac{d\mathbf{u}}{dt} = \eta(\mathbf{E} + \mathbf{u} \times \mathbf{B}_0) = 0 \tag{i}$$

For an infinite strip beam, E has only one component, E_y. The space charge pro-

generating such a beam, but it at least serves to indicate that what we postulate here does not violate any physical principles. In practice one can imagine a beam with a very low density for which this constancy of the velocity is approximately true, as against the hypothetical case of some peculiar sort of cathode for which it could be actually true.

With this approximation, then, of a constant d-c velocity, and using the relation between the displacement y_1 in the y direction and the value

duces a y variation within the beam

$$\nabla \cdot \mathbf{E} = \frac{\partial E_y}{\partial y} = \frac{\rho}{\epsilon_0} = -\nabla \cdot (\mathbf{u} \times \mathbf{B_0}) \tag{ii}$$

where we have used Eq. (i). With $u = u_z = u_0$ and $B_0 = B_x$, so that $\rho/\epsilon_0 = -\beta_0 \, \partial u_0/\partial y$, we can write

$$\omega_p{}^2 = \omega_c \frac{\partial u_0}{\partial y} \tag{iii}$$

If the beam comes from a *unipotential* cathode at $V = 0$, then $mu_0{}^2/2 = -eV$ and

$$u_0 \frac{\partial u_0}{\partial y} = -\eta \frac{\partial V}{\partial y} = \eta E_y \tag{iv}$$

The equilibrium condition (i) can be written as

$$\eta E_y = -\eta u_0 B_0$$

so that from Eq. (iv),

$$\frac{\partial u_0}{\partial z} = -\eta B_0 = \omega_c \tag{v}$$

and with the use of Eq. (iii) we have

$$\omega_p{}^2 = \omega_c{}^2 \tag{vi}$$

That is the condition for Brillouin flow derived previously in this chapter and includes the well-known slipping-stream condition (v).

However, if we assume that the electrons originate from a *nonequipotential* cathode, then for each electron $mu_0{}^2 = -e(V - V_c)$, where V_c is the cathode potential for that electron. We then have the condition for the y variation of velocity in the beam,

$$-mu_0 \frac{\partial u_0}{\partial y} = e \left(\frac{\partial V}{\partial y} - \frac{\partial V_c}{\partial y} \right) = -eE_y - eV_c' = eu_0 B_0 - eV_c'$$

Here $V_c' \equiv \partial V_c/\partial y$ is the variation in the beam region of the cathode potential associated with the electrons at each point in the beam. Instead of Eq. (v) we now have

$$\frac{\partial u_0}{\partial y} = \omega_c + \eta \frac{V_c'}{u_0}$$

and Eq. (iii) becomes

$$\omega_c \frac{\partial u_0}{\partial y} = \omega_p{}^2 = \omega_c{}^2 + \eta \frac{V_c'}{u_0} \omega_c \tag{vii}$$

By a suitable variation in V_c at the cathode we could therefore get an arbitrarily small $\partial u_0/\partial y$ (and $\omega_p{}^2$) in the beam and are not restricted to the velocity variation given in Eq. (v).

of v_y given by

$$\frac{dy_1}{dt} = v_y = j(\omega - u_0\beta)y_1 \tag{34}$$

we can replace y_1 in Eq. (31) by its value from Eq. (34); and Eqs. (30) and (31) reduce to linear algebraic equations relating the velocity components of an electron to the field components. If we introduce the notation $\omega_c \equiv -\eta B_0$, $\Omega \equiv \omega - u_0\beta$, and $\omega_p{}^2 \equiv \eta\rho_0/\epsilon_0$, Eqs. (30) and (31) become

$$v_z = -\frac{\eta[(j/\Omega)(\Omega^2 - \omega_p{}^2)E_z + \omega_c E_y]}{\Omega^2 - \omega_p{}^2 - \omega_c{}^2} \tag{35}$$

$$v_y = -\frac{\eta[j\Omega E_y - \omega_c E_z]}{\Omega^2 - \omega_p{}^2 - \omega_c{}^2} \tag{36}$$

We note again that the two components of velocities each depend on *both* components of the electric field.

The equations as written are exact (except for the assumption of constant d-c velocity over the cross section) and could be applied to the case where E_z and E_y include the r-f effects of the space charge. These equations, together with the equation of continuity and the definition of current, eventually lead to an electronic equation. We shall also have to derive a circuit equation, i.e., to find the effect of the r-f beam current in producing circuit fields. Before we do so, however, it is of interest to point out even at this stage a peculiar consequence of the dependence of each component of velocity on both components of the field. Consider a case for which

$$\Omega = \omega - u_0\beta \ll \omega_p \qquad \omega_p \ll \omega_c \tag{37}$$

This is a case that occurs when there is interaction with a circuit and the circuit velocity is approximately equal to the beam velocity, and it results in waves with velocities approximately equal to the beam velocity. This is the most important case, since it represents normal conditions in crossed-field amplifiers. Equations (35) and (36) then reduce to the very simple forms

$$v_z = -\frac{E_y}{B_0} \qquad v_y = \frac{E_z}{B_0} \tag{38}$$

This is a very interesting and significant result. Under the conditions of Eq. (37), the two r-f velocities are proportional to the electric fields which are *perpendicular* to them, so that the total r-f velocity is perpendicular to the r-f field. These equations really describe a relatively simple phenomenon. If the beam is in approximate synchronism with the circuit, then it travels at about the same velocity as the circuit wave, the r-f field looks to the synchronous electrons like an additional *steady* field, and just as in the case of a static electric field and a static magnetic field the velocity is perpendicular to both, here the additional velocity is again

at right angles to this added field.   We shall return to these results later.
We might also note in connection with Eq. (37) that usually $\omega_p < \omega_c$,
so that the approximation of Eq. (37) implies that $\Omega < \omega_c$.   Dropping
terms from Eqs. (35) and (36) to obtain Eq. (38) corresponds to representing the actual motion (Fig. 10.11a) by smoothed trajectories (Fig.
10.11b); under the conditions of Eq. (37) the rapid variations are unimportant and may be safely ignored.   This approach is known as the *adiabatic
approximation.*

In deriving a circuit equation, i.e., the relation between the driving
currents in the beam and the field induced in the circuit, we shall have to
take the transverse fields and transverse displacements into account, since
they play an essential role in the effect of the beam on the circuit.   We
have already said something about that, but it may be now pointed out
that in the second of the Eqs. (38) we can see that E_z, the component of
r-f field along the direction of steady beam motion, produces a velocity
perpendicular to it, i.e., either toward or away from the circuit.   Since
there is a d-c field E_y in this direction, the velocity v_y produced by E_z
results in the electron moving into a region of higher (or lower) d-c potential, with a consequent gain or loss of kinetic energy.   This is a mechanism by which the velocities produced by the r-f fields can result in a

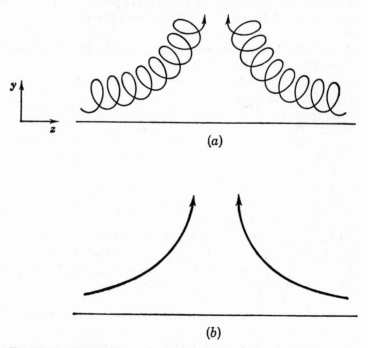

(a)

(b)

Fig. 10.11   Adiabatic approximation: (a) actual motion; (b) approximate motion.

change of the d-c energy of the beam. This effect represents actually *the* important mechanism in the most common kind of interaction in a crossed-field device: electrons continually gain energy from the d-c fields and lose it to the r-f fields, so that the kinetic energy of the electrons remains approximately constant but there is a net transfer of energy from the steady fields to circuit fields. Thus in deriving the circuit relations, we shall have to derive the current induced in the circuit by the beam current just as we did in the O-type case, except that now we must add the effect of transverse motion of the electrons, which also results in an induced current.

We can derive the induced current, taking the transverse motion into account, by two methods. It is perhaps of value to demonstrate both. The first method goes back to the treatment given in Chap. 3 (and Appendix 2) of the current induced in a circuit by the motion of charges in the neighborhood of the circuit. We derived [Eqs. (3.26) and (A2.13)] the charge induced on an electrode by the presence of a charge in the space outside the electrode. This relation is given in terms of the position of the charge in the space and the potential distribution that exists outside the electrode when it is maintained at some fixed potential. We shall restate the equation here with some slight changes in notation. Since this equation is expressed in terms of potentials, it will be convenient to express the fields on the circuit in terms of a quasistatic potential also. Let us assume that the potential $V(z)$ at the boundary between the circuit and the interaction region, at $y = b$ in Fig. 10.10, varies as $e^{-\Gamma z}$ (where $\Gamma = j\beta$) and in the interaction space the variation is given by $V\Phi(y)$; that is, Φ reduces to unity at the circuit. We now consider the effect of a small segment of a thin strip beam of length dz at position z in the space outside the circuit in producing an induced charge on the circuit. The changes with time of the amount of charge in this little segment *and of its position* (y coordinate) relative to the circuit cause changes in the induced charge on the circuit; it is these changes that constitute the induced current that we are trying to calculate. The new feature here is the effect of changes in the y position. Let the beam have a cross-sectional area σ. We denote, as usual, the d-c charge density by ρ_0 and the r-f charge density by ρ; the average position of the beam (with no r-f) will be y_0 (actually $y_0 = 0$ for the coordinate choice we have made in Fig. 10.10), and the displacement caused by r-f will be y_1. Then the charge density δQ_1 per unit length induced on the circuit by the segment of beam in this interaction space is given by

$$\delta Q_1 = \sigma(\rho + \rho_0)\frac{1}{V}\,[V\Phi(y_0) + y_1 V\Phi']\,dz$$

$$\delta Q_1 = \sigma(\rho + \rho_0)[\Phi(y_0) + y_1\Phi']\,dz \tag{39}$$

where $\Phi' = \partial\Phi/\partial y$ evaluated at $y = y_0$; this is a rewritten version of Eq.

(3.39). The time-varying part of this expression, to terms in the first order, is given by

$$\delta Q_1(t) = \sigma(\rho\Phi + \rho_0 y_1 \Phi') \tag{40}$$

where besides omitting the d-c term (which is merely the product of the d-c charge density and the potential Φ at the equilibrium position y_0), we have dropped a term quadratic in r-f quantities, the product ρy_1. Of the two terms on the right, the first represents the change in the induced charge on the circuit owing to varying charge density at the position z, and the second term represents the induced charge owing to the variation in the y position of the d-c beam. The induced current on the circuit is given by the time derivative of this quantity, which we can write as

$$I = \sigma j\omega(\rho\Phi + \rho_0 y_1 \Phi') \tag{41}$$

where we have used the fact that both the charge density and the varying y position have the same time dependence. It might be pointed out here that the first term on the right is one that normally occurs in O-type tubes (although it has never been written in this form previously); it represents the effect of a varying charge density flowing through the reference point z. The second term, which is new, involves the transverse displacement of the beam and provides a contribution to the induced current even if there is no varying charge density in the beam.[1]

We can now use this result for the induced current in a circuit equation of exactly the same form as we used for O-type tubes in Chap. 6. There we were considering a thin beam with no transverse motion and no marked variation in field or potential transverse to the beam; this case corresponds to $\Phi = 1$. The circuit equation derived in Eq. (6.16b) is written in terms of E_z rather than potential. Since $\Phi = 1$, we may write

---

[1] It is interesting to compare this result with the case of a solid cylindrical beam under Brillouin-focused conditions (cf. Chap. 4). In that case, we obtained space-charge waves for which the charge density did not vary in the interior but the beam boundary fluctuated. The effect of such a beam current in inducing a current in a circuit would be all contained in terms of the first kind in Eq. (41). If we consider the region near the unperturbed boundary of the beam and assume that Φ does not vary markedly near this unperturbed boundary (which is a good approximation for axial symmetry), then the only nonzero terms arising from the whole beam occur near this beam boundary owing to terms of the first kind. Just outside the unperturbed beam boundary, a periodic charge appears where there is normally no charge; slightly inside the original beam boundary we shall have a periodic dearth of charge where there is normally a constant charge. Both effects give rise to terms similar to the first term of Eq. (41), where the charge density ρ would represent either the alternating appearance or disappearance of charge. Only a small error results from taking Φ to be constant over this region of the fluctuating boundary; for sufficiently small fluctuations, this error approaches zero. There is no bodily displacement of the beam as a whole into regions of different Φ and, therefore, no term of the second kind results.

$E_z = -\partial(V\Phi)/\partial z = \Gamma V$, so that we obtain for Eq. (6.16b) in terms of the potential

$$V = -\frac{\Gamma_0 \Gamma K_0}{\Gamma^2 - \Gamma_0^2} i\sigma \qquad (42)$$

where i is the *beam* current density.

The circuit equation for an O-type tube given by Eq. (42) can be written in terms of the charge density in the beam for the O-type case (where the beam is close to the circuit and $\Phi = 1$) by using the equation of continuity, $\Gamma i = j\omega\rho$, to provide a relation between current and charge density:

$$V = -\frac{\Gamma_0 K j\omega\rho}{\Gamma^2 - \Gamma_0^2} \qquad (43)$$

If there is a significant variation in the potential transverse to the beam— as there is in the cases with which we are concerned here—and transverse motion of the entire beam, then ρ in Eq. (43) must be replaced by the entire expression in parentheses in Eq. (41):

$$V = -\frac{\Gamma_0 K_0 j\omega\sigma}{\Gamma^2 - \Gamma_0^2} (\rho\Phi + \rho_0 y_1 \Phi') \qquad (44)$$

The result is a circuit equation for the M-type tube including transverse motion. It can be seen quite readily that this expression reduces to the O-type case when $y_1 = 0$ and $\Phi = 1$.

It might be of some interest to derive the same result by a power-transfer argument of the sort that we used in deriving the induced field in the O-type tube in Chap. 6. Essentially, we wish to derive the results of Sec. 6.3 for the case where transverse displacements are important. We have again power flow to the left and to the right given by

$$P_L = -\frac{E_{L0}^2}{2\beta_0^2 K_0} \qquad P_R = \frac{E_{R0}^2}{2\beta_0^2 K_0} \qquad (45)$$

where K_0 and the fields E_{L0}, E_{R0} are defined right at the circuit, where $\Phi = 1$. For conservation of power, the total power flow in the circuit plus the power P_E in the beam must be a constant:

$$dP_E = -(dP_R + dP_L) = -\frac{E_{R0} dE_{R0} - E_{L0} dE_{L0}}{\beta_0^2 K_0} \qquad (46)$$

The increase in power in the circuit must be equal to the decrease in power in the beam. Moreover, the total field in the circuit is the sum of the two fields,

$$E_{z0} = E_{R0} + E_{L0} \qquad (47)$$

Finally, the effect of any beam current on the circuit is to increase the amplitudes of the waves traveling to the left and to the right by equal amounts, so that the increments have opposite signs:

$$dE_{R0} = -dE_{L0} \tag{48}$$

Therefore, Eq. (46) becomes

$$dP_E = -\frac{(E_{R0} + E_{L0})\, dE_{R0}}{\beta_0^2 K_0} = -\frac{E_{z0}\, dE_{R0}}{\beta_0^2 K_0} \tag{49}$$

The above equations are all expressed in terms of field at the circuit. If we assume as before that we have a potential of the form $V(z)\Phi(y)$, where $\Phi = 1$ at the circuit, then the z component of the field at any other value of y is given by the z component at the circuit multiplied by Φ:

$$E_z(y) = -\frac{\partial V}{\partial z}\Phi(y) = E_{z0}\Phi(y) \tag{50}$$

In the presence of this field the power gained by the beam is given by an expression similar to that in Sec. 6.3, but with an additional term allowing for a transverse displacement of the whole beam:

$$dP_E = \left(\frac{iE_z\sigma}{2} + \frac{I_0}{2}y_1\frac{dE_z}{dy}\right)dz \tag{51}$$

Here the first term is of the same form as that derived in Sec. 6.3 and the second term represents the transfer of power from the beam owing to an r-f displacement y_1 of the entire beam in a field in which E_z varies with y. Figure 10.12 shows an example of a field configuration and a beam shape that obviously represent such mechanism of power transfer. The wavy band shown represents the beam shape in a field that reverses sign in the midplane, and it can be seen that even if the density in the beam does not vary along the beam at all, there can be a continuous transfer of power if the wave shown and the beam move in synchronism. To be sure, this example is a special case, but it illustrates the principle involved.

For a field derivable from a potential, we must have relations between z and y components given by $(\nabla \times \mathbf{E})_x = 0$, or

$$\frac{\partial E_z}{\partial y} = \frac{\partial E_y}{\partial z} = -\Gamma E_y \tag{52}$$

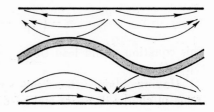

Fig. 10.12 Mechanism of power transfer from beam owing to its r-f displacement.

From the definition of potential, we also have

$$E_y = -\frac{\partial(V\Phi)}{\partial y} = -V\Phi' \qquad E_z = -\frac{\partial(V\Phi)}{\partial z} = \Gamma V\Phi \qquad (53)$$

so that

$$\frac{E_y}{E_z} = -\frac{\Phi'}{\Gamma\Phi} \equiv j\alpha \qquad (54)$$

where we have defined a new constant α; we shall discuss its significance later.

In terms of the quantities as specified in Eqs. (53) and (54), we can rewrite Eq. (51) as

$$dP_E = \tfrac{1}{2}E_z\, dz\, (i\sigma - I_0\Gamma j\alpha y_1) \qquad (51a)$$

It must be remembered that the E_z that appears here is the field at the beam, which is related to the field at the circuit by Eq. (50). If we rewrite Eq. (49) in terms of the field at the beam using Eq. (50), we obtain

$$dP_E = -\frac{E_z\, dE_R}{\beta_0{}^2 K_0 \Phi^2} \qquad (49a)$$

In equating Eqs. (51a) and (49a), we obtain

$$\frac{dE_R}{dz} = -(i\sigma - I_0\Gamma j\alpha y_1)\beta_0{}^2 K_0 \Phi^2$$

$$\frac{dE_R}{dz} = \frac{dE_{R0}}{dz}\Phi \qquad (55)$$

for the rate of increase of the induced field at the beam, which can also be written for the induced field at the circuit from the subsidiary equation on the second line of Eq. (55). It is this equation that would replace Eq. (6.34) and would lead to the appropriate circuit equation for a beam with transverse displacement. As written here and by straightforward substitution we would not get quite the same form as Eq. (44). But we can obtain this form by using Eq. (43) for the relation between the current density i and the charge density, by using $I_0 = \rho_0 u_0 \sigma$, and by using the fact that the propagation constant Γ is approximately given by

$$\Gamma \approx \frac{j\omega}{u_0} \qquad (56)$$

With these relations, Eq. (55) can be rewritten as

$$\frac{dE_{R0}}{dz} = -\left(\frac{j\omega\rho\sigma}{\Gamma} + \frac{\Phi'}{\Gamma\Phi}j\omega\rho_0\sigma y_1\right)\beta_0{}^2 K_0 \Phi \qquad (55a)$$

This equation would lead to a circuit equation exactly of the form of Eq. (44).

Having obtained the circuit equation (44) for the circuit potential in terms of charge densities and r-f displacements, we now wish to obtain an electronic equation relating the same quantities. We first refer back to Eqs. (35) and (36) for the r-f velocities. If we were going to solve these equations completely (as we do later), we would take the fields written there as the total fields at the beam including the effect of space charge; and the equations contain a factor ω_p, which also represents a space-charge effect arising from the displacement of the electron (y_1) in the d-c space-charge field. If we wish to drop all space-charge fields consistently, the quantities E_z and E_y appearing in Eqs. (35) and (36) will be only the circuit fields derivable from the potential that we have just been discussing in deriving the circuit equation, and we must drop the ω_p factors in Eqs. (35) and (36) also. We can now take these equations, as modified by omitting the ω_p terms, and write expressions for the fields in terms of the potential. From the modified Eq. (36) and from Eq. (34) we can get a relation between y_1 and the potential. Similarly, from the modified Eq. (35) and from Eq. (43), and from the equation for the current density written in the form

$$i = \rho u_0 + \rho_0 v_z \tag{57}$$

we can get another relation between the charge density and the potential.[1]

By combining the two relations, we then obtain the electronic equation between the potential, the charge density, and the displacement, which will have the same form as Eq. (44). We thus have two equations, circuit and electronic, which we shall rewrite with the following notation. Let

$$\beta_e = \frac{\omega}{u_0} \qquad \beta_m = \frac{\omega_c}{u_0} \qquad \Gamma = j\beta \qquad \Gamma_0 = j\beta_0 \qquad m = \frac{\beta_m}{\beta_e} = \frac{\omega_c}{\omega}$$

and the unknown

$$\Delta = \frac{\beta}{\beta_e}$$

Then

$$\frac{\sigma(\rho\Phi + \rho_0\Phi'y_1)}{V} = \frac{(\beta_0/\beta_e)^2 - \Delta^2}{K_0\omega\beta_0/\beta_e} \tag{58}$$

which is Eq. (44) rewritten; and

$$\frac{\sigma(\rho\Phi + \rho_0\Phi'y_1)}{V} = -\frac{\eta I_0}{u_0^3} \frac{\Delta^2[(1 + \alpha^2)(1 - \Delta) + 2\alpha m]}{(1 - \Delta)[m^2 - (1 - \Delta)^2]} \tag{59}$$

[1] Strictly speaking, the continuity equation in the form used in (43) (involving field variables) can be used only with Eulerian equations of motion, Eqs. (30a) and (31a). However, under the assumptions used here—thin beam, y_1 and v_y constant over the cross section, space-charge forces neglected—Eqs. (30) and (31) and Eqs. (30a) and (31a) lead to the same relations between v_y, v_z and E_y, E_z. These relations essentially represent statements about velocities and fields *averaged* over the beam cross section, and Eq. (57) represents a similar statement about average values. It is in this sense of averages that subsequent equations must be interpreted.

which is the electronic equation derived from the motion of the electrons, etc. It is also convenient to rewrite the components of the r-f velocity in terms of the same notation.[1]

$$v_z = - \frac{\eta \beta V \Phi}{\omega} \frac{(1 - \Delta) + m\alpha}{(1 - \Delta)^2 - m^2}$$
$$v_y = - \frac{\eta \beta V \Phi}{\omega} \frac{(1 - \Delta) - m\alpha}{(1 - \Delta)^2 - m^2} \tag{60}$$

In these equations α and Φ are the values at the beam position (for the coordinate system we have chosen here, at $y = 0$). By equating the right-hand sides of Eqs. (58) and (59), one obtains the determinantal equation for the propagation constant β or Δ. As in Chap. 6, one may plot each side as a function of β and look for the intersection of the two sets of curves; cases for which some intersections in the plane of real β disappear represent the region where β has an imaginary component and, therefore, possibly growing and attenuating waves. Equating the right-hand sides of Eqs. (58) and (59) results in a quintic equation in Δ and hence five roots, as discussed by Muller[2] in terms of the graphical solutions that have just been described.

We shall follow a slightly different procedure, similar to one given originally by Pierce.[3] We note, first, that this is a fifth-degree equation, rather than a fourth-degree equation as for the ordinary traveling-wave tube, and that this is the result of the additional degree of freedom arising because transverse beam motion is allowed (which, as we have already pointed out, is significant). We might thus expect that the waves that arise will be different in kind from those in the O-type case because of this extra added degree of freedom. The second significant factor that should be noted is the appearance in the equations of the quantities Φ and α, both of which are related to the transverse variations of the fields. Since the values of α will prove to play a significant role in determining the sort of waves that result, it is important to discuss the significance of α [defined in Eq. (53)] a little further. It describes the ratio E_y/E_z of the transverse to the axial r-f field at the location of the beam; and it is of some interest to see what values α takes for particular circuit configurations. Figure 10.8 shows a typical circuit for a crossed-field amplifier and Fig. 10.9 the corresponding mode configurations. In general, if we describe the fields by a potential as before, the potential anywhere within the interaction space varies as

$$V_{y,z} \sim \Phi(y)e^{-\Gamma_0 z} \qquad \Gamma_0 = j\beta_0 \tag{61}$$

[1] M. Muller, Traveling-wave Amplifiers and Backward-wave Oscillators, *Proc. IRE*, **42**:1651–1658 (1954).

[2] *Ibid.*

[3] J. R. Pierce, "Traveling-wave Tubes," 2d ed., chap. 15, D. Van Nostrand Company, Inc., Princeton, N.J., 1954.

If we are considering a propagating mode, Γ_0 must be pure imaginary and Laplace's equation for the potential requires Φ to be of the form

$$\Phi(y) = A e^{-j\Gamma_0 y} + B e^{j\Gamma_0 y} \tag{62}$$

where the exponents $j\Gamma_0$ are, of course, pure real. The values of A and B are determined by the boundary conditions, and as previously stated, two modes are possible in a configuration of the sort shown in Fig. 10.8, namely, Fig. 10.9a and b. For the field of Fig. 10.9a, which is antisymmetrical (odd in y), the field component E_z must be zero on the axis ($y = 0$), so that we obtain the relation $A = -B$. Conversely, if we are considering the symmetric mode shown in Fig. 10.9b, where E_z is symmetric about the axis, we must have the condition $A = B$. Let us summarize the characteristics of these fields: for Fig. 10.9a, $E_z = 0$ on the axis, $E_y \neq 0$; for Fig. 10.9b, $E_z \neq 0$ but $E_y = 0$ on the axis. For the two cases, then, where we have labeled (a) the transverse mode ($E_z = 0$ at $y = 0$) and (b) the longitudinal mode ($E_y = 0$ at $y = 0$), we have for α

$$\begin{aligned} \alpha &= \coth \beta_0 y & E_z &= 0 \text{ at } y = 0 \\ \alpha &= \tanh \beta_0 y & E_y &= 0 \text{ at } y = 0 \end{aligned} \tag{63}$$

so that $\alpha = \infty$ at $y = 0$ in case a and $\alpha = 0$ at $y = 0$ in case b. In both cases, α is positive above the axis and negative below the axis. It follows that for the case of Fig. 10.7, if $y = 0$ is taken to be along the sole, then in the interaction region between the sole and the circuit we have a field configuration such as in Fig. 10.9a. As we shall see later, these field configurations have important effects on the amplification properties of this crossed-field device.

To examine some of these amplifying properties, it is convenient to examine the relation obtained by equating the right-hand sides of Eqs. (58) and (59) in the form

$$\left[\left(\frac{\beta_0}{\beta_e} \right)^2 - \Delta^2 \right] (1 - \Delta)[m^2 - (1 - \Delta)^2]$$

$$= - \frac{\eta I_0}{u_0{}^3} \Delta^2 [(1 + \alpha)^2 (1 - \Delta) + 2\alpha m] \Phi^2 \omega \left(\frac{\beta_0}{\beta_e} \right)^2 K_0 \tag{64}$$

We may compare this equation with the corresponding result obtained in Chap. 6 for the O-type tube. If one goes to the limiting case of no magnetic field and no variation in the electric field (which corresponds to letting $m \to 0$, $\alpha = 0$, and $\Phi = 1$), this equation reduces to the ordinary traveling-wave-tube equation and the right-hand side reduces to the second term in Eq. (6.18), or the term containing C^3 in Eq. (6.19). The right-hand side thus represents the coupling between the circuit and the beam. This is a small quantity, so that we shall be looking for values of β that make the left-hand side also small. Additional insight into the system is obtained by a consideration of the waves that exist in the absence of beam-circuit coupling, i.e., when K_0 vanishes and the left-hand side has to be set equal to zero. In that case, five waves are obtained. Two of them are the normal circuit waves,

$$\beta = \pm\beta_0 \tag{65}$$

one is a beam wave at the velocity of the beam,

$$\beta = \beta_e \tag{66}$$

and two, beam waves given by

$$1 - \Delta = \pm m \quad \text{or} \quad \beta_e = \pm\beta_m \tag{67}$$

represent the so-called cyclotron waves. These waves are necessary to describe the wavelike behavior of the beam if one applies transverse modulation at a frequency ω.

The interpretation of these waves becomes simpler when we consider the coupling to the circuit. The useful interactions in which we are interested are, of course, not those for which the coupling approaches zero, but rather the cases in which the beam waves described by Eqs. (66) or (67) couple to the circuit; i.e., in which the values of the β's given by (66) and (67) are approximately equal to one of the cold-circuit β's, either forward or backward. If none of them approaches the value of a cold-circuit propagation constant, no interesting interactions result; even when the interaction impedance does not vanish, one gets essentially the same waves as given by Eqs. (65) to (67), with some slight perturbations produced by the coupling.

What we wish to examine, then, are the cases when the uncoupled wave velocities are close to the circuit velocity. It is then more convenient to introduce a slightly different notation. If we assume that the propagation constant of the composite system will be close to the cold-circuit propagation constant, we can write

$$\Gamma \equiv j\beta = j\beta_0(1 + p) \tag{68}$$

where p is assumed to be a small quantity and we look for imaginary values of p. If we substitute this expression into Eq. (64) and discard terms in p that are small compared to unity, we obtain a relation for p

$$p\left(\frac{\beta_e}{\beta_0} - 1 - p\right)\left[\left(\frac{\beta_e}{\beta_0} - 1 - p\right)^2 - \left(\frac{\beta_m}{\beta_0}\right)^2\right]$$
$$= -\frac{\beta_e}{2\beta_0}\left[\left(\frac{\beta_e}{\beta_0} - 1 - p\right) + \frac{2\alpha\beta_m}{(1 + \alpha^2)\beta_0}\right]H^2 \tag{69}$$

where
$$H^2 = \frac{(1 + \alpha^2)\Phi^2 K_0 I_0}{2V_0}$$

H^2 as defined here is similar to the definition of C^3 for the O-type tube, but differs from it in two respects: first, it contains values of α and Φ related to the location of the beam in the transverse fields, and second, the ratio of the interaction impedance to beam impedance is proportional to H^2 rather than C^3 as in the O-type case. (The significance of the different exponent will appear when we determine the roots.)

We shall be interested in possible imaginary values of p with magnitudes of the order of H.[1] Since the right-hand side of Eq. (69) is small, of the order of H^2, the factor p on the left-hand side can be of the order of H only if the factors multiplying it on the left-hand side are also of the order of H. This requirement may be met under one of two conditions. First, let us take the condition

$$\frac{\beta_e}{\beta_0} - 1 = 0 \quad \text{or} \quad \beta_e = \beta_0 \tag{70}$$

i.e., the beam velocity is synchronous with the circuit velocity. This case is quite similar to that of the O-type traveling-wave tube. In this case, the circuit field seen by the electrons looks like a *constant* field (since the electrons are traveling at about the same velocity as this field) that is only slightly modified by the change in the propagation constants of the "hot" waves owing to interaction. Stated in another way, in the electron frame of reference, the frequency seen by the electrons is approximately zero. If we insert the condition (70) in Eq. (69), we obtain

$$p^2 \left[p^2 - \left(\frac{\beta_m}{\beta_0} \right)^2 \right] = \frac{1}{2} \left[-p + \frac{2\alpha\beta_m}{(1 + \alpha^2)\beta_0} \right] H^2 \tag{71}$$

Since we assume $p \ll 1$, we can neglect the terms in p inside the brackets on both sides of the equation, so that a simple quadratic in p results. Though we are apparently discarding two roots, we note that these roots would have violated our original condition (which we have already used) that p would be small, so that the approximations we have used would not be valid if we tried to keep all four roots. The two remaining roots can be written as

$$p = \pm j \left[\left(\frac{\alpha}{1 + \alpha} \right)^{1/2} \left(\frac{\beta_0}{\beta_m} \right)^{1/2} \right] H \tag{72}$$

and are of the order of H as expected. We also see from this equation that two imaginary roots result for p if α is *positive*, one representing a growing wave, the other a decaying one.

Although the condition that we have used to obtain growing waves (that the beam is in approximate synchronism with the circuit velocity)

---

[1] This requirement is also analogous to the O-type case, where the increments of the propagation constants owing to interaction are of the order of C.

is similar to that which holds in an O-type tube, several features in the growing waves obtained here are quite different and must be discussed. Before doing so, we should also point out that the growing wave that results from Eq. (72) is the one that represents the usual gain mechanism in a crossed-field amplifier. We shall later discuss certain other conditions that yield growing waves, but circumstances for such cases occur much more rarely in practice.

Three important features concerning the growing waves represented by Eq. (72) should be mentioned: first, the characteristics of the electron motion, i.e., the r-f velocities and accelerations; second, the dependence on beam position represented by α; and third, the dependence on beam current represented by H.

We consider first the r-f electron velocities for these waves. We know from Eq. (72) that p is a small quantity; therefore, the propagation constants for the combination of beam and circuit are approximately equal to the circuit propagation constant, which by Eq. (70) is also equal to the beam propagation constant. Under these circumstances, we have satisfied approximately the condition of Eq. (37), $\omega - u_0\beta \approx 0$; the plasma frequency is here equal to zero, as had been assumed in writing Eqs. (58) and (59). With conditions (37) valid, we have Eqs. (38) for the relation between the r-f velocities and the r-f fields. [It might be pointed out that the same results would arise from Eq. (60) if we let $1 - \Delta = 0$.] Under these circumstances, the growing waves for this mode of operation thus have the peculiar property that the r-f velocity is *perpendicular* to the r-f field. We have previously mentioned this kind of motion, and we now see that it occurs under important circumstances. What it amounts to is that under synchronous conditions, the beam sees the r-f field as a constant field (approximately, except for the growth factor). This field is superimposed on the electrostatic field applied to the device but has components in both directions. The resultant velocity of the beam, as indicated in the general discussion of electron motion in crossed fields, is then perpendicular to the magnetic field and to the *total* electric field, which in this case consists of the d-c field and the r-f field. We see here that r-f field E_z in the direction of the d-c beam motion acts in such a way as to displace the beam toward or away from the circuit, so that the beam either loses or gains potential energy from the d-c field by this action. On the other hand, any bunching owing to r-f velocities v_z in the direction of the d-c motion derives from E_y. This behavior is, of course, quite unlike that of the electron beam in an O-type tube. Moreover, the behavior represented by Eq. (38) is intimately connected with the dependence of the roots of p on the magnitude and sign of α. We shall return to this point presently, but it might be worth pointing out first one additional property of the kinematics of the beam. From the equations of motion we can evaluate approximately the acceleration of the electrons in this type of interaction. We have

$$\frac{dv_z}{dt} = \left(\frac{\partial}{\partial t} + u_0 \frac{\partial}{\partial z}\right) v_z = j(\omega - u_0\beta)v_z$$

$$\frac{dv_y}{dt} = \left(\frac{\partial}{\partial t} + u_0 \frac{\partial}{\partial z}\right) v_y = j(\omega - u_0\beta)v_y \tag{73}$$

We see that the accelerations are proportional to the corresponding r-f velocities. However, under the conditions (70) and because p is small, the multiplication factors on the right-hand sides of Eqs. (73) are very small, so that the accelerations are also small. This type of behavior, in which the magnitude of the velocities is changing very slowly, is called *adiabatic motion;* the strong interaction between the beam and the circuit is the result not of large r-f velocities being imposed on the beam, but of the fact that the velocities have a cumulative effect in producing displacements that result in motion toward the circuit and also bunching.

The second feature of this crossed-field interaction, closely related to what we have already said about the velocities given by Eq. (38), has to do with the dependence of the roots on the value of α. According to Eq. (72), α must be *positive* for a growing wave, so that if we use a circuit of the sort shown in Fig. 10.8, the beam must be *above* the central axis; Eqs. (63) show that α is positive for both modes under these circumstances. (Such interaction would obviously be also possible in a circuit such as shown in Fig. 10.7, for which α is also positive.) The reason for this condition on α is related to the motion as described by Eqs. (38), as can be best illustrated with reference to Fig. 10.13. This figure shows the instantaneous distribution of the r-f and static fields in solid lines (a) above and (b) below the axis of a circuit such as that of Fig. 10.8. In Fig. 10.13c and d we have added dotted lines that indicate the direction of motion of the electrons as given by Eq. (38). Both diagrams apply to either the symmetric or antisymmetric mode in such a circuit. The difference between these two modes is largely in the relation between E_z and E_y near the axis of the circuit. This difference is not significant for the behavior with which we are concerned and which depends on the relation between the fields and the electron motion near the circuit; this behavior is the same for both modes under consideration.

As indicated in Fig. 10.13c, the action of the r-f fields is twofold. The y components of the field tend to push the electrons into the region marked R, where the z component of the field is a retarding one on electrons. In this retarding z field, however, because of the static electric field, the electrons travel at a slight angle with the axis, moving toward the anode at potential V_0. Thus, the energy (and velocity) they lose because of being in a retarding r-f field is regained from their motion in

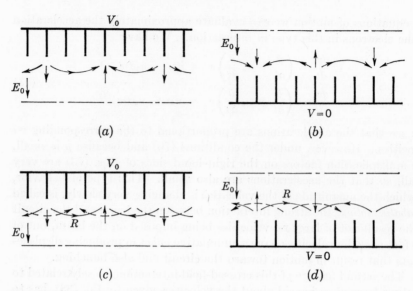

Fig. 10.13 Instantaneous fields in circuit of Fig. 10.8: (a) above axis; (b) below axis; (c) with direction of electron motion indicated in dashed lines, above axis; (d) below axis.

the constant electric field.   This process, then, of bunching in the z direction owing to the y components of the field and motion toward the anode at V_0 owing to the z components of the field results in a continual exchange of energy via the electrons from the electrostatic to the r-f field.   Inspection of Fig. 10.13d shows just the converse: the y components of the field push the electrons toward accelerating regions of the z component, which pushes these electrons toward the circuit at zero potential.   The electrons are then accelerated by the r-f field and transfer this energy by being pushed toward the most negative electrode at zero potential.   The difference in these two kinds of behavior, of course, is a consequence of the fact that in Fig. 10.13c the retarding region (marked R) has a positive y component of the field ahead of it and a negative component behind it, whereas in Fig. 10.13d the converse is true.   Because of the nature of Eqs. (38), this fact reverses the motion and causes the drastic difference between the two cases described by the quantity α, which is the ratio of the two fields E_y/E_z and changes sign between the two regions.

It should also be pointed out that in cases for which α is positive, as in Fig. 10.13c, so that there is gain, α behaves quite differently close to the axis for the two possible modes of the circuit of Fig. 10.8.   In one case α approaches infinity on the axis, in the other case, zero; but it can be observed from the dependence of p on α and H that the *gain* will go to zero on the axis of the circuit of Fig. 10.8 for either mode.   This fact can be most readily seen by carrying out the multiplication indicated in

Eq. (72):

$$p = \pm j \left(\alpha K_0 \Phi^2 \frac{I_0}{2V_0} \frac{\beta_0}{\beta_m} \right)^{\frac{1}{2}} \tag{74}$$

We recall that K_0 is the normal interaction impedance involving E_z at the *circuit*; $K_0\Phi^2$ as defined here gives the corresponding interaction impedance at the position of the *beam*. Keeping in mind the definition of α, we note that the first three factors in the product written in Eq. (74) really represent the *product* of $E_y E_z$ at the position of the beam. For each mode of Fig. 10.8, one component or the other vanishes on the axis, so that zero gain results for both modes. The closer one gets to the circuit the higher the gain, since the product increases as one approaches the circuit. Maximum gain at $\alpha = 1$, with both components equal, could be achieved only at infinite distance from the axis. This behavior, which indicates the dependence on the *product* of the two field components, again illustrates the importance of both field components in producing gain in this kind of interaction, and the description of the diagrams of Fig. 10.13 indicates why both components are necessary.

The third feature of this interaction that should be pointed out is the dependence of p on the beam current. As can be seen, p is proportional to H, which is proportional to the square root of the current. Since p determines the rate of growth, we see that this rate is proportional to the square root of the current, whereas in the O-type tube, it is proportional to the cube root.

We have just determined one condition [stated in Eq. (70)] under which Eq. (69) will give growing waves. The resultant interaction depends on a particular kind of motion in crossed fields, namely, that in which the electron drifts at right angles to the magnetic field and the total electric field (both d-c and r-f), with the velocity proportional to the electric field. In considering motion in steady fields, we also found that there could be another type of motion superimposed on any drift, namely, a rotation of the electrons at the cyclotron frequency. This would be superimposed on any steady motion. A corresponding motion is possible under the action of r-f fields.

The motion at the cyclotron frequency is characteristic of one of the other waves that comes from the solution of Eq. (69). For this case, as before, the propagation constant of the combined circuit-beam wave is still approximately equal to that of the circuit, so that Eqs. (68) and (69) are still appropriate, but the beam is *not* in synchronism with the circuit. Instead, we consider the condition

$$\frac{\beta_e}{\beta_0} - 1 = \pm \frac{\beta_m}{\beta_0} \qquad \text{with } \beta \approx \beta_0 \tag{75}$$

This condition when used in Eq. (69) results in the second factor that multiplies p on the left-hand side of the equation being small and, therefore, one can again get a relatively large value of p (of the order of H) as a solution. If we substitute the condition (75) into (69), we can simplify the resulting equation, taking into account the fact that p is small compared to unity and also small compared to the ratio β_m/β_0. Under these conditions, we get

$$p^2 = \pm \frac{1}{4} \frac{(1 \pm \alpha)^2}{1 + \alpha^2} \left(\frac{\beta_0}{\beta_m} \pm 1 \right) H^2 \tag{76}$$

The two sign combinations in (76) correspond to the two sign choices in Eq. (75). We obviously cannot get an imaginary value for p with the choice of the positive signs. The other choice, of negative signs, requires that $\beta_e = \beta_0 - \beta_m$ and

$$\beta \approx \beta_0 \approx \beta_e + \beta_m \tag{77}$$

If we insert this choice of sign into Eq. (76), we get

$$p = \pm \frac{j}{2} \frac{1 - \alpha}{(1 + \alpha^2)^{\frac{1}{2}}} \left(\frac{\beta_e}{\beta_m} \right)^{\frac{1}{2}} H \tag{78}$$

Condition (77) implies that the circuit velocity (and the "hot" wave velocity) are both slower than the beam velocity, since β_0 (and β) are greater than β_e. We shall discuss this point further. Equation (78) shows that growing waves result for any value of α except $\alpha = 1$. Furthermore, maximum gain occurs at $\alpha = -1$, below the axis of Fig. 10.8 and far from the axis. However, gain also occurs above the axis, but decreases as we move away from the center line and approaches zero as α approaches unity. These statements apply to both symmetric and antisymmetric modes.

Although this interaction under the conditions of Eq. (77) is less important than the one we have described previously, under the conditions of Eq. (70), which is the kind that normally occurs in crossed-field devices, it is still worth interpreting the results we have derived here. First, we may point out that the statement of Eq. (77), the condition for the relation between β_e, β_0, and β_m, is the condition for synchronism between the circuit wave and one of the beam waves previously found in Eq. (67), known as the *slow cyclotron wave*, with propagation constant $\beta_e + \beta_m$. The use of the word "slow" here implies that it is a wave with a phase velocity slower than the beam velocity. The question then arises as to what kind of wave this is which is involved in the interaction. We may gain some insight by considering, first, the relative velocity of the *circuit wave* and the *beam*. Let us call the circuit velocity v_p, which is, of course, related to the phase constant by

$$\beta_0 = \frac{\omega}{v_p} \tag{79}$$

Then the velocity of the beam relative to the circuit wave is merely $u_0 - v_p$. With this relative velocity, the frequency of the waves *on* the circuit as seen by the electrons is given by

$$\omega_{el} = (u_0 - v_p)\beta_0 \tag{80}$$

where we have used the obvious relation between the phase constant β_0 and the wavelength of the circuit wave. Equation (80) can be written as

$$\omega_{el} = \beta_0 u_0 - \omega \tag{80a}$$

Under conditions when Eq. (77) holds, we see by comparison with that equation (and using the definition of β_m) that this would be merely the cyclotron frequency. Accordingly, the condition of Eq. (77) that we have imposed is merely that the electron and circuit velocity are such that as the electrons run past the waves on the circuit, the apparent frequency they see is the cyclotron frequency. This is the basic effect involved in this interaction. If the apparent frequency is the cyclotron frequency, a cumulative effect on the electron motion results, since the electrons are being driven at a frequency corresponding to their natural rotational frequency in the magnetic field. Another way of saying the same thing is that in the frame of reference moving with the electrons, the waves in the circuit have a Doppler-shifted frequency equal to ω_c. In the presence of these waves, individual electrons undergo circular motion at the frequency ω_c. If these waves are growing waves, the size of the orbit for each individual electron increases with time or, if one inspects the beam along its path, the size of the orbit increases with distance.

We can say something about the difference between the motion involved in this kind of wave and the waves resulting from Eq. (70) if we look at the velocities given by Eqs. (35) and (36). For the condition implied by Eq. (77) and at $\omega_p = 0$, the denominators in both Eqs. (35) and (36) are essentially equal to $2pu_0$, which is a small quantity and leads to relatively large r-f velocities. We shall not write out the detailed results here. Perhaps a more illuminating result is to consider the electron accelerations characteristic of these waves. We write out Eq. (73) as before for the acceleration but remember that the resultant differentiation now gives ω_c as the factor multiplying the velocities on the right of those equations rather than a very small quantity of the order of $\beta_0 p u_0$, as was the case for the waves given by Eq. (72). This difference means that one will have large accelerations, unlike in the case of the waves described by Eq. (72). This difference in the motion represents an important difference between the two kinds of waves given by (78) and (72) or by conditions (70) and (77). Condition (70), which describes the kind of wave that usually occurs in crossed-field amplifiers, results in a gradual drifting of the beam toward the anode. The power delivered to the field or circuit comes from the change in the potential energy of the electrons but, compatible with the small accelerations, there is never any appreciable change in their kinetic energy. The kinds of waves described by Eqs. (77) and (78), on the other hand, do exhibit relatively large kinetic energies in the beam, and any transfer of power to the circuit is at the expense of the d-c kinetic (rotational) energy.

Some further insight into the nature of these waves may be gained by looking at the individual particle motions and, more particularly, at the sort of initial launching conditions that can produce such waves. Let us assume that at some initial plane at $z = 0$, $y = 0$ there is a means for producing velocity modulation of the beam in *two* directions so that in addition to the drift velocity, the initial velocity at t_0 of any electron is given by

$$\dot{y} = v \cos \omega t_0 \qquad \dot{z} = v \sin \omega t_0 \tag{81}$$

The subsequent motion of these electrons will then be described by

$$
\begin{aligned}
y &= -\frac{v}{\omega_c} \{\sin [(\omega + \omega_c)t_0 - \omega_c t] - \sin \omega t_0\} \\
z &= \frac{v}{\omega_c} \{\cos [(\omega + \omega_c)t_0 - \omega_c t] - \cos \omega t_0\} \\
\dot{y} &= v \cos [(\omega + \omega_c)t_0 - \omega_c t] \\
\dot{z} &= v \sin [(\omega + \omega_c)t_0 - \omega_c t]
\end{aligned}
\tag{82}
$$

which can be shown to satisfy the equations of motion in the crossed field. The average drift motion is also present, but is omitted from the equations. We are assuming here that there is no r-f field but that the motion as described by Eqs. (82) is merely a result of the initial velocities given by Eq. (81). This description represents the motion of electrons in a cyclotron wave that does not interact with a circuit (beyond the initial modulation) for a wave that propagates as

$$e^{-j(\beta_e + \beta_c)z} e^{j\omega t}$$

In terms of wave motion, this would be a description in Eulerian variables, whereas Eqs. (82) describe the motion in Lagrangian variables. Each electron has a motion described by Eqs. (82), of course with different values of t_0 corresponding to different starting times and, therefore, different initial velocities as given by Eq. (81). Equations (82) represent motion in a circle (superimposed on the average drift). All electrons move in such circles. To find what constitutes a single wavelength, we must find the spatial separation between two electrons which have instantaneously the same *vector* velocity. Any electron after it leaves the plane $z = 0$, $y = 0$ rotates *counterclockwise* at the frequency ω_c. The motion of its velocity vector would be then described by Fig. 10.14a, where we are looking at the velocity, at the time t, of a particular electron which left the initial plane at t_0. Electrons leaving the initial plane subsequently have initial velocity vectors as given by Eq. (81), with a suitable change in the initial time. Equation (81) describes a variation of this initial velocity that has a *clockwise* rotation at frequency ω. Thus, at a time t, when the electron that left the initial plane at t_0 has a velocity as represented in Fig. 10.14a, the electron now leaving the initial plane has a velocity as indicated in Fig. 10.14b. The phase difference between the velocity of the electron that left the initial plane at t_0 and any subsequent electron crossing this initial plane is thus $(\omega + \omega_c)(t - t_0)$. When this phase difference equals 2π, the distance between the position of the reference (t_0) electron and the initial plane equals one wavelength, given by the product of the drift velocity u_0 of the electron and its transit time, $2\pi/(\omega + \omega_c)$. The corresponding propagation constant of this kind of wave would be $(\omega + \omega_c)/u_0$. It might be pointed out that whereas for the *slow* cyclotron wave the initial velocity vector of successive electrons rotates *clockwise* and leads to this particular wavelength, another kind of wave known as the *fast* cyclotron wave can also be set up (by changing the initial modulation) so that initial velocity vectors of successive electrons rotate *counterclockwise*. In this case, the phase between our reference (t_0) electron and the electron crossing the initial plane is $(\omega - \omega_c)(t - t_0)$. Therefore, since the t_0 electron will have to travel for a longer time and longer distance than in the previous case before there is a full cycle between it and the electron at the initial plane, the wavelength will be longer, corresponding to a faster wave.

One more point might be made about these waves, which concerns the dependence of the growth factor on α as given by Eq. (78). Two features of this dependence were mentioned previously. Gain approaches zero for $\alpha = 1$ and is a maximum for $\alpha = -1$. This is a consequence of the fact that in order to amplify waves of this kind (cyclotron waves) the effective field acting on the beam has to have both E_y and E_z components, with a proper magnitude and phase relation. It turns out that this proper relation between field components corresponds to a *circularly* polarized field, which is plausible on the basis of what we have said about the circular nature of electron motion in cyclotron waves. It is well known that an arbitrary field can be always represented as a super-

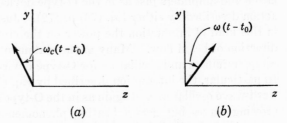

(a)   (b)

Fig. 10.14 **Representation of electron velocities:** (a) **electron that left initial plane at t_0;** (b) **electron now leaving initial plane. (The value of t_0 shown is such that $\sin \omega t_0 = 0$.)**

position of two circularly polarized fields with the field vectors rotating in opposite directions. A simple example is a linearly polarized field, which is the superposition of two equal-amplitude circularly polarized fields. The statements made above about the values of α merely represent the fact that to amplify the slow cyclotron wave requires a circularly polarized field with one sense of rotation. This is the one described by $\alpha = -1$; whereas $\alpha = 1$ represents a circularly polarized field of the opposite polarization and is the only polarization that contains no component of the opposite circular polarization (and, therefore, cannot amplify this wave). For any other value of α, the gain is less than for $\alpha = -1$ because only a portion of the field is effective.

From Eq. (69), one can get imaginary values of p for propagation constants that are close to the backward circuit wave, namely, for

$$\Gamma = -j\beta_0 \qquad (83)$$

with the subsidiary condition that

$$\beta_e + \beta_0 = \beta_m \qquad (84)$$

Under these conditions, it turns out one gets the same equation (78) for the value of p except that $1 + \alpha$ replaces $1 - \alpha$. Apparently, this condition leads to growing waves. However, this solution is misleading. It has been shown by Haus and Bobroff[1] that a more careful consideration of the power flow involved indicates that the above condition actually does not represent true gain. It might be pointed out that this statement about the consequence of Eqs. (83) and (84) concerns an interaction with a wave that has a *negative* phase velocity opposite to the beam velocity. This is a situation different from any we have encountered previously. It is not to be confounded with backward-wave interaction, in which the *group* velocity is opposite to the beam velocity. Such backward-wave interaction can also occur in M-type devices: all the results previously obtained for the waves described by Eqs. (72) and (76) would also apply to circuits with a forward phase velocity and a negative group velocity. One can, with this kind of circuit, get backward-wave oscillators and amplifiers just as in the O-type device using the kinds of interaction described by either Eq. (76) or (72). Just as in the O-type device, in this kind of interaction the power on the circuit flows opposite to the direction of beam flow. Many of the statements made about backward-wave amplifiers and oscillators for O-type devices would also apply here. In particular, the interaction described by Eq. (72) can also lead to backward-wave oscillators and again as in the O-type case, one does not require growing waves but gets a beating phenomenon. We shall say a little more about that in the next section.

[1] H. A. Haus and D. L. Bobroff, Small Signal Power Theorem for Electron Beams, *J. Appl. Phys.*, **28**:694–704 (1957).

10.6   Interactions with Space-charge Fields Considered

We wish to discuss now some of the effects of space-charge fields on the interactions that can occur in a crossed-field device.   More specifically, we shall want to describe in detail a new phenomenon that can occur in a crossed-field device as a consequence of space-charge fields.   In an O-type device, the space-charge fields merely modify the numerical results, but all the qualitative information can be obtained by omitting space-charge fields.   For crossed-field devices that is not true.   The space-charge field does modify some of the numerical results previously obtained, but more importantly, a new phenomenon occurs; it is responsible for a different gain mechanism and also modifies the behavior of crossed-field devices drastically.   In this section we shall be mainly concerned with this new phenomenon and the new gain mechanism that results, and then we shall briefly refer to its effect on the interaction with a circuit.

Before going into detail, we might point out that the existence of this new phenomenon should not be too surprising.   We have already seen the effect of the crossed fields in coupling two field components and the two velocity components, so that the z component of the electric field produces a y component of velocity and vice versa.   The phenomenon we now wish to describe depends on a similar action, except that the fields involved are the space-charge fields rather than the circuit fields. We shall consider anew the problem of a thin beam moving in the space between a circuit and a sole and indicate how the interaction equations should be modified by the presence of space-charge fields in the beam. However, we shall apply our results only to a special case, one in which the circuit is also a smooth plane (i.e., a short circuit).   Surprisingly enough, one shall find growing waves even in that case.   This is known as the diocotron effect.[1]   Although most simply demonstrated in the case of a short circuit, the effect also has important consequences for the waves in the presence of a propagating circuit with nonzero fields.

We shall again use Eqs. (30) and (31) for the velocity components of the electrons.   We still consider a thin beam with thickness such that any variations in velocity across the cross section can be neglected and any fields, space-charge or otherwise, existing in the beam can be taken to vary only slightly over the beam cross section, so that we can use average values.   This is an approximation, but it simplifies the calculation greatly and can be shown to give results very similar to those obtained by a more exact calculation, which assumes that the beam is not thin and takes into account variations in the fields across the cross section.   The problem, then, is to find what these average fields are

[1] G. G. McFarlane and H. G. Hay, Wave Propagation in a Slipping Stream of Electrons: Small Amplitude Theory, *Proc. Phys. Soc. (London)*, **B63**:409–427 (1950)

inside the beam, including the effect of space charge. We must match the fields inside the beam to those outside the beam, and in turn match the latter to the circuit. Since both z and y components of field and velocity occur in the beam, transverse displacements also result and have an important effect. Just as for the fields, we shall assume that the transverse displacement is constant across the cross section. The treatment to be given here follows that given by Gould.[1] Figure 10.15 indicates the beam configuration under consideration and some of the nomenclature to be used. The beam has a thickness t with charge density per unit volume ρ_0 and charge per unit length per unit width of σ_0. The fields described will be needed in finding the average field inside the beam as well as in matching this field to the fields outside the beam. The transverse displacement of the beam is y_1. We can relate the fields inside and outside the beam by means of this displacement. The displacement y_1 as shown results in a scalloped beam boundary along both the top and the bottom of the beam, so that charge is alternately present and absent in regions where in the unperturbed beam it is absent and present, respectively. For displacements y_1 small enough compared with the thickness t we can make the approximation that this excess or dearth of charge is located exactly *at* the unperturbed boundary, as a surface charge—much as we did in treating space-charge waves in Brillouin flow—a procedure that permits us to apply boundary conditions at the smooth surface of the unperturbed beam.

The surface charge density appears at every point on the upper and lower surface, and its sign depends on the direction of the displacement. An excess charge on the upper surface is accompanied by a deficiency of charge on the lower surface of the same amount, since we are assuming

[1] R. Gould, Space Charge Effects in Beam-type Magnetrons, *J. Appl. Phys.*, **28**:599–605 (1957).

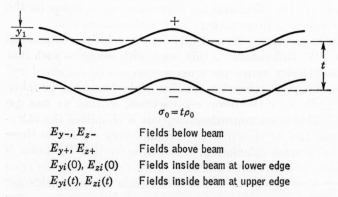

$$\sigma_0 = t\rho_0$$

E_{y-}, E_{z-}	Fields below beam
E_{y+}, E_{z+}	Fields above beam
$E_{yi}(0), E_{zi}(0)$	Fields inside beam at lower edge
$E_{yi}(t), E_{zi}(t)$	Fields inside beam at upper edge

Fig. 10.15 Beam configuration and nomenclature used in Sec. 10.6.

equal displacements at the two surfaces. We can write, for the relations of the y components of the field inside and outside the beam,

$$E_{yi}(0) - E_{y-} = -\frac{\rho_0 y_1}{\epsilon_0}$$

$$E_{y+} - E_{yi}(t) = \frac{\rho_0 y_1}{\epsilon_0}$$

(85)

These equations simply represent discontinuities in the transverse field due to the surface charge. The average y component of the field E_{yi} in the interior of the beam is merely the average of the interior field at the bottom and the top, namely,

$$\bar{E}_{yi} = \frac{E_{yi}(0) + E_{yi}(t)}{2} = \frac{E_{y+} + E_{y-}}{2} - \frac{\rho_0 y_1}{\epsilon_0} = \bar{E}_y - \frac{\rho_0 y_1}{\epsilon_0} \qquad (86)$$

If we insert this value for the average y component of the field in Eq. (31), using also Eq. (32), we obtain

$$\eta \bar{E}_y = j\Omega v_y + \omega_c v_z \tag{87}$$

Note that the last term in Eq. (86) just cancels the last term of Eq. (31).

Here we have used the notation which we introduced preceding Eq. (35). For the z fields, it is convenient to introduce a quasistatic potential both above and below the beam, as well as inside. We shall assume that all of these potentials propagate as $e^{-j\beta z}$. We also assume that in the beam some bunching has been taking place so that there is a volume charge density of σ_1 per unit length per unit width. In terms of this volume charge density, we can write (for a thin beam) the equation for the *discontinuity* in the y component of the field above and below the beam as

$$E_{y+} - E_{y-} = \frac{\sigma_1}{\epsilon_0} \tag{88a}$$

and we can write

$$E_{z+} = E_{zi}(t) \qquad E_{z-} = E_{zi}(0)$$

$$E_{z+} - E_{z-} = -\frac{\partial}{\partial z}(V_+ - V_-) = j\beta(V_+ - V_-) \qquad (88b)$$

for the *continuity* of the z components of the field inside and outside the beam. We have written the equations for the z components in terms of the potential above and below the beam. Owing to the displacement of the beam boundary as shown in Fig. 10.15, we shall have a discontinuity in this potential. The displacements produce a double layer, and it is known from fundamental electrostatic theory that such a double layer produces a discontinuity in potential. The strength of this layer (the dipole density) is given by the charge density on each surface multiplied by the thickness. Therefore, the discontinuity potential is given by[1]

$$V_+ - V_- = \frac{y_1 \rho_0 t}{\epsilon_0} = \frac{y_1 \sigma_0}{\epsilon_0} \tag{88c}$$

From the discontinuity of the potentials in Eq. (88c) we can also get the discontinuity in the z components of field above and below the sheet, given by

$$E_{z+} - E_{z-} = j\beta \frac{y_1 \sigma_0}{\epsilon_0} \tag{88d}$$

We now define an average z component field in the interior of the beam given by

$$\bar{E}_{zi} = \frac{E_{zi}(0) + E_{zi}(t)}{2} = \frac{E_{z+} + E_{z-}}{2} = \bar{E}_z \tag{89}$$

which can be written in terms of the fields outside because of the relations (88b). In terms of this average field, we can rewrite Eq. (30) as

$$\eta \bar{E}_{zi} = \eta \bar{E}_z = j\Omega v_z - \omega_c v_y \tag{90}$$

We shall also need the equation of continuity in the form[2]

$$j\omega \sigma_1 - j\beta(u_0 \sigma_1 + \sigma_0 v_z) = 0 \tag{91a}$$

and the equation for the transverse displacement

$$y_1 = \frac{v_y}{j\Omega} \tag{91b}$$

is obtained from Eq. (34). It should be pointed out that we are going to be concerned with waves such that the beam is close to synchronism with the circuit; therefore, Eqs. (37) apply ($\Omega \ll \omega_c$) and Eqs. (87) and (90) will reduce to equations of the form of Eqs. (38) with the fields being replaced by the averages that appear in Eqs. (87) and (90). We can now write Eq. (91a) and (91b) in terms of these averages under the condition (37). For the equation of continuity, we can solve for the charge density

[1] A useful way of regarding this problem is to remember that we are looking for the r-f potential, which can be obtained from the *total* potential by superimposing on the beam a thin sheet of ions of the same thickness as the beam and with the same charge density. The ion sheet effectively cancels the d-c fields and leaves only the r-f fields. Under these circumstances the top and bottom layers of the beam would have an excess charge density whose sign depends on the sign of the displacement at that surface. In addition, we also have the field produced by the interior charge density σ_1. These considerations thus lead to Eqs. (88a) to (88c).

[2] Since we are really considering averages over the beam cross section, we may use this form for the equation of continuity here even though as a point function of field variables it would be appropriate only with Eulerian equations of motion. [See also footnote at Eq. (57).]

in terms of v_z and write v_z from Eq. (87) to get

$$\sigma_1 = -\frac{\sigma_0 \beta}{B_0} \frac{\bar{E}_y}{\Omega} \tag{92a}$$

Similarly, Eqs. (90) and (91b) lead to

$$y_1 = \frac{1}{B_0} \frac{\bar{E}_z}{j\Omega} \tag{92b}$$

We can now combine Eqs. (92a) and (88a) with the definition of $\bar{E}_y$ from Eq. (86) to get a relation between the y components of the field above and below the beam:

$$E_{y+} = \frac{\Omega - (\sigma_0 \beta/2\epsilon_0 B_0)}{\Omega + (\sigma_0 \beta/2\epsilon_0 B_0)} E_{y-} \equiv T E_{y-} \tag{93}$$

We can get a similar result for the z components above and below using Eqs. (92b), (88d), and the definition of $\bar{E}_z$ from Eq. (89):

$$E_{z+} = \frac{E_{z-}}{T} \tag{94}$$

It is useful at this point to summarize what we have done. We have used the properties of the beam, its displacement (transversely and axially), and the equations of motion to get conditions that relate the fields below the beam to those above the beam. In this derivation, the space-charge forces due to the beam have been involved through the various boundary conditions and in the equations of motion. The two relations, then, Eqs. (93) and (94,) contain all the effects of the beam on the fields outside the beam. These fields, of course, must in addition satisfy boundary conditions at the circuit and at the sole. It is convenient to use the same α nomenclature we used previously for the ratio of the y to the z components of fields. Since we are now going to be interested in these fields, as perturbed by the beam, both above and below the beam, we shall have to introduce subscripts defined for the two ratios as

$$\frac{E_{y+}}{E_{z+}} = j\alpha_+ \qquad \frac{E_{y-}}{E_{z-}} = j\alpha_- \tag{95}$$

We can get a relation between these ratios from Eqs. (93) and (94) in the form

$$\alpha_+ = T^2 \alpha_- \tag{96}$$

The difference between what we have here and what we have done in the previous calculation (in which we neglected space charge) is that previously we have used α's as determined merely by the field configurations due to the circuit. For a very thin beam, α_+ would have been equal to α_-, since we are assuming that the bottom and top surfaces are almost in coincidence and we had been neglecting the effect of the beam in perturbing the fields. The essential new addition is that we have introduced this discontinuity.

Having thus derived a relation between the fields above and below the beam, we must now consider the conditions imposed on the fields by the circuit and the sole. The formal procedure would be to set up the most general expression for the fields in the space below the beam and above the beam, in terms of the unknown propagation constant β. For E, these general expressions, for planar circuits such as we are considering here, would be of the forms

$$E_{z\pm}(y,z) = (A_{\pm}e^{-\beta y} + B_{\pm}e^{\beta y})e^{-j\beta z} \qquad (97)$$
$$E_{y\pm}(y,z) = -j(A_{\pm}e^{-\beta y} - B_{\pm}e^{\beta y})e^{-j\beta z} \qquad (98)$$

Here the subscript $\pm$ refers to the region above or below the beam. The equations are of the same form above and below but in general with different constants. The form of E_y relative to E_z is such that curl $\mathbf{E} = 0$ as it should if we are assuming a quasistatic potential. One can then determine the ratio A_-/B_- below the beam by the condition that E_z must vanish at the sole. This is straightforward and results in the value for α_-

$$j\alpha_- = \frac{E_{y-}}{E_{z-}} = j \coth \beta(a - \tfrac{1}{2}t) \approx j \coth \beta a \qquad (99)$$

This is the same form that we would have for the cold circuit without a beam except for β being replaced by β_0. If we knew the details of the propagating circuit above the beam, we could use a similar procedure and actually analyze what is the condition imposed on the ratio E_y/E_z at the circuit boundary for any value of β. This would permit us to evaluate α_+, and after inserting this value and the value of α_- derived from Eq. (99) into Eq. (96) we would get a transcendental equation for β. As described here, this is the straightforward, exact method of taking into account conditions imposed on the fields by the *boundaries* of the interaction region. The solution of the transcendental equation would give us the waves we are looking for. All that would be possible if we knew the detailed behavior of the circuit as a function of β. However, there is a way of evading this detailed calculation, which we shall use. We should perhaps outline briefly what we shall do. We are primarily interested in obtaining an expression for the change produced in the ratio α *at* the circuit by the change in propagation constant produced by *interaction with the beam*. If we assume that the variation in the field ratio at the circuit is a slowly varying function of β, we may use a power-series expansion and then try to evaluate the derivative in this equation by finding the change in β produced in a *known* case, namely, the interaction of a very thin beam carrying only longitudinal currents and located very close to the circuit. Application of the conditions on the discontinuity in the r-f magnetic field produced by such a current and use of a result obtained from normal O-type traveling-wave-tube theory leads to an equation exactly in the form of such a power-series expansion. By comparison of these two equations, it is therefore possible to evaluate the unknown derivative in the first equation, which thus provides us with the necessary result for proceeding further with the problem we are trying to solve.[1]

The procedure we shall use depends on the fact that the propagation constants of the system differ only slightly from the cold propagation constant of the circuit. If β differs only slightly from β_0, the ratio E_y/E_z at the circuit (at $y = b$) for propagation constant β differs only slightly from the condition imposed by the circuit for β_0. We may thus write the value of E_y/E_z as a power series in $(\beta - \beta_0)$:

$$\alpha_\beta{}^b = \alpha_{\beta_0}{}^b + \left(\frac{\partial \alpha}{\partial \beta}\right)_{\beta_0} (\beta - \beta_0) + \cdots \tag{100}$$

where α has the usual meaning as defined previously but is now being evaluated at the circuit, $y = b$. (The subscripts indicate the appropriate values of β.) If in Eq. (100) we know the left-hand side, $\alpha_\beta{}^b$, then it is only a matter of simple algebra to show from Eqs. (97) and (98) that α_+ is given by[2]

$$\alpha_+ = \frac{\alpha_\beta{}^b - j \tanh \beta b}{1 + j(\tanh \beta b)\alpha_\beta{}^b} \tag{101}$$

Thus, given the ratio α at the circuit, by means of Eq. (101) we can find it above the beam and by combining this result with Eqs. (96) and (99), we can get the desired transcendental equation for β. Of the two terms on the right-hand side of Eq. (100), we already know the first since this is merely the field ratio E_y/E_z at the circuit with no beam interaction. It is given by

$$j\alpha_{\beta_0}{}^b = j \coth \beta_0(b + a) \tag{102}$$

The problem then is to find the second term of Eq. (100) or, more specifically, the derivative. What we need is the rate of change of α with β. If we can find this derivative in any way, we shall have the ingredients to solve our present problem. For this purpose, we shall use the known results for the interaction with a beam of a particularly simple kind, obtained previously. We consider a thin, flat beam passing very close to the circuit, with the current in the beam so small that its space charge

---

[1] It may be pointed out that even if one did have all the details of the circuit, so that one could write down the exact equations, the resulting transcendental equation is very often so inconvenient that an approximation is necessary before a solution can be obtained. This approximation also involves a power series and is actually equivalent to the procedure we shall use, but it is applied at a later stage in the calculation.

[2] In writing Eq. (101), we have taken the top surface of the beam to be at a distance b from the circuit, rather than at $b - (t/2)$, obviously a minor error for $t \to 0$.

can be neglected, and restrained in some way so that there is no transverse motion. We already know the propagation constant for the combination of such a beam and the circuit. We use this information and formulate it in a particular way to get the result we want. Let us then assume such a modulated thin beam carrying an r-f current per unit width I_z; the total width of the circuit is w. We know that with this current, there will be a discontinuity in the r-f magnetic field which we can write in the form

$$\frac{H_x(b_-) - H_x(b_+)}{E_z} = \frac{I_z}{wE_z} \tag{103}$$

Here $H_x(b_-)$ represents the r-f magnetic field just below the beam and $H_x(b_+)$, just above the beam, which is assumed to be very thin. It can be shown[1] from the equation for curl $\mathbf{H}$ that we have

$$H_x = -\frac{\omega\epsilon_0}{\beta_0} E_y \tag{104}$$

Using this result for the relation between E and H, we can rewrite Eq. (103) as

$$\frac{E_y(b_+)}{E_z} = \frac{E_y(b_-)}{E_z} + \frac{\beta_0}{\omega\epsilon_0 w} \frac{I_z}{E_z} \tag{105}$$

The second term on the right involves the ratio of the r-f current in the beam to the longitudinal field at the beam. This is exactly the quantity derived in the simple treatment of the O-type traveling-wave tube in Eq. (6.69) and can be written as

$$\frac{I_z}{E_z} = \frac{\Gamma_0^2 - \Gamma^2}{\Gamma_0\Gamma^2 K_0} = \frac{\beta^2 - \beta_0^2}{-j\beta_0\beta^2 K_0} \tag{106}$$

Since we are considering cases where β will be approximately equal to β_0, this result can be also written as

$$\frac{I_z}{E_z} \approx \frac{(\beta - \beta_0)2\beta_0}{-j\beta_0^3 K_0} = \frac{2(\beta - \beta_0)}{-j\beta_0^2 K_0} \tag{106a}$$

If we now insert expression (106a) into (105), we obtain

$$\frac{E_y(b_+)}{E_z} = \frac{E_y(b_-)}{E_z} - \frac{2(\beta - \beta_0)}{j\beta_0 K_0 \omega\epsilon_0 w} \tag{105a}$$

[1] Deriving a magnetic field component in this way from the electric field is not inconsistent with our original statement about deriving the electric fields from a quasistatic potential. The r-f magnetic fields for slow waves are small and can be neglected in the equation for curl $\mathbf{E}$, which permits us to use a quasistatic potential; but then it is possible to obtain an approximate value for these magnetic fields by using the equation for curl $\mathbf{H}$. The fact that the magnetic field is small can be seen from the factor β_0 in the denominator of Eq. (104). For slow waves, β_0 is, of course, a large number, which is the measure of the accuracy of the approximation we made in having used a quasistatic potential.

which is exactly of the form written in Eq. (100).   As I_z approaches zero, β approaches β_0, the first term on the right has the value given by Eq. (102), and the first-order term in the difference $(\beta - \beta_0)$ in Eq. (100) is just equal to the value given by Eq. (105a).   We are here using the fact that in Eq. (105a) the value of α just below the beam, some distance above the short circuit, is not a very sensitive function of β and, therefore, the first term on the right of Eq. (105a) is essentially equivalent to the cold value that one would get at the circuit, which is given by Eq. (102).[1] Since Eq. (105a) under these circumstances is just of the form of Eq. (100), giving us the behavior of α at the circuit as a function of β, we can use the result given by Eq. (105a) to evaluate the derivative in Eq. (100):

$$\left(\frac{\partial \alpha}{\partial \beta}\right)_{\beta_0} = \frac{2j}{\beta_0 \epsilon_0 \omega w K_0} \tag{107}$$

It should be pointed out that the form of the derivative given by Eq. (107) indicates why we were able to get an answer apparently without specifying all the details of the circuit.   Actually, the relevant properties of the circuit are really contained in the factor K_0, which is the interaction impedance measured right at the circuit; that is, K_0 as used in Eq. (107) has the usual definition with the electric field involved being E_z *at the circuit*.   Therefore, Eq. (107) does contain circuit properties, and this relation that we have obtained for the change in α with β holds quite generally for any circuit.

Given this result, we can now combine Eqs. (107), (101), and (102) to obtain α_+; and with Eq. (96) and the definition of α_- given in Eq. (99), we can get the transcendental equation to determine β.   (It should be recalled that the effects of the current in the beam are contained in the factor T, which was derived from the various equations of motion including space-charge fields and represents the discontinuities in the fields as produced by the beam.)   This transcendental equation has been derived by Gould and then written in a simplified form.[2]   We shall quote his algebraic results here with some changes in notation to make it consistent with our own.   Let

$$\beta \equiv \beta_e(1 + jD\delta) \qquad \beta_0 \equiv \beta_e(1 + Dc)$$

$$D^2 \equiv j\frac{\omega}{\omega_c}\frac{I_0}{2V_0}K_0\Phi^2\alpha \qquad S \equiv \frac{|\sigma_0|}{2\epsilon_0 B_0 u_0 D} \tag{108}$$

$$g = \frac{\tanh \beta_e b - \tanh \beta_e a}{\tanh \beta_e b + \tanh \beta_e a}$$

Here D is an interaction parameter similar to the Pierce parameter C of

---

[1] For usual choice of parameters $\beta_0(b + a) \geq 1$, this is a good approximation; the error is much smaller than the first-order term in $(\beta - \beta_0)$, which we are taking as contributing *all* of the change in the ratio α just above the beam.

[2] Gould, *op. cit.*

O-type traveling-wave-tube theory. Note that it is D^2 which is proportional to beam current. Therefore, the incremental propagation constant due to beam-circuit interaction (which is proportional to D) is proportional to $I_0^{\frac{1}{2}}$ (as is the corresponding H factor that appears in the M-type theory neglecting space charge) rather than to $I_0^{\frac{1}{3}}$ as in O-type theory ($C^3 \sim I_0$). Note also that in the above definition, K_0 is defined at the circuit, whereas Φ^2 and α are the cold parameters defined at the position of the beam. The product $K_0\Phi^2$, then, is really the interaction impedance measured at the beam. With these definitions, one can take the transcendental equation derived in a way we have indicated above and obtain

$$(\delta + jc)(\delta^2 + 2jgS\delta - S^2) = \delta \tag{109}$$

It might be pointed out that this equation was obtained for a forward wave on a circuit. For a backward-wave circuit any change arises from the fact that the right-hand side of Eq. (106) has a sign reversal which results in a minus sign in Eq. (107) and a minus sign on the right-hand side of Eq. (109). Here D has been assumed to be small compared to unity. Gould has considered the solutions of this equation in some detail, both for forward- and backward-wave interaction. We do not propose to discuss these solutions in detail here; rather, we shall discuss the most important effect, which also appears in the solutions obtained by Gould.

The effect we wish to discuss now is the existence, as displayed by this equation, of growing waves far from synchronism with a circuit. This corresponds to $c \gg 1$ [see the definition of β_0 in Eq. (108)] and signifies negligible interaction with the circuit. For this condition, and for the beam taken for simplicity as centered between circuit and sole (so that $g = 0$), we obtain

$$\delta^2 - S^2 = 0 \tag{110}$$

which obviously has the roots $\delta = \pm S$, or

$$\beta = \beta_e \left[1 \pm j \frac{\sigma_0}{2\epsilon_0 B_0 u_0} \right] \tag{110a}$$

where we have returned to the definitions of δ and S in writing the propagation constants.

Since this result represents negligible interaction with the circuit, it turns out that the same roots result for the case of a beam located symmetrically between smooth conducting plates, i.e., when both the top and bottom surfaces of the circuit are merely short circuits. In that case we have for α_- the value given by Eq. (99) at $y = 0$ and we get α_+ from Eq. (101). We note that α at the top circuit surface α_β^b is infinite and that for a symmetrically located beam $b = a$; then Eq. (101) gives simply the negative of Eq. (99), or

$$\alpha_- = -\alpha_+ \tag{111}$$

Therefore, Eq. (96) leads to

$$T^2 = -1 \tag{112}$$

From the definition of T, we find that we get the same roots as written in Eq. (110a). One of these roots represents a growing wave. It is this wave that can exist in a crossed field even when there is *no* interaction with a circuit (zero circuit field)—which is the important new effect that is different from the behavior of O-type tubes. The principal reason for developing space-charge theory for M-type devices was to obtain this result. The existence of this wave means that a beam in a crossed field can be unstable in a way that does not depend on the circuit characteristics. The phenomenon is called the diocotron effect, and we shall have occasion to speak of it below.

It is convenient to rewrite the result for the imaginary part of β in terms of other variables. If we remember the relation between volume charge density ρ_0 of the beam, the thickness t, and the total charge density σ_0 ($\sigma_0 = \rho_0 t$), we can rewrite the imaginary portion of the roots in Eq. (110a) as

$$\pm \frac{\beta_e \sigma_0}{2\epsilon_0 B_0 u_0} = \pm \frac{\omega_p^2 \beta_e t}{2\omega_c u_0} = \pm \frac{\beta_p^2 t}{2} \frac{\beta_e}{\beta_m} \tag{113}$$

where $\omega_p^2 = \eta \rho_0 / \epsilon_0$ as usual, with $\rho_0 = \sigma_0 / t$.

Several important features about this result should be pointed out. First, the rate of growth as given by Eq. (113) agrees with a more precise calculation made by Gould and others[1] in which the beam is taken, not to have a uniform velocity as we have taken it, but rather to exhibit slipping-stream behavior. As indicated earlier in this chapter for the static solutions, equilibrium for a stream with space charge requires a linear variation with y of the z component of velocity. The analysis of the r-f behavior of such a stream is difficult, and we have not tried to describe it here at all. However, the analysis of such a stream by Gould and others has shown that one gets a growing wave of exactly the kind described here and that for a sufficiently thin beam ($\beta_e t < 0.4$) the rate of growth is numerically the same as derived here. A detailed study of that analysis also shows that the fields, transverse displacements, charge density, and all other physical aspects of the slipping stream are the same as obtained from this simplified treatment of a thin, constant-velocity beam. This agreement is important for two reasons. First, it indicates that despite the approximations made (such as the nonslipping behavior and averaging

[1] Gould, *op. cit.*; McFarlane and Hay, *op. cit.*; R. W. Gould, A Field Analysis of the M-type Backward Wave Oscillator, *Calif. Inst. Technol.* (*Electron Tube and Microwave Lab.*), *Tech. Rept.* 3, Sept. 1953.

of fields), we have not lost any of the essential characteristics of such a beam in a crossed field.   Second, the treatment given here demonstrates in a conclusive way that the instability we have found does *not* depend on the slipping nature of the beam.   Originally, when the slipping-stream problems in crossed fields were first solved, it was thought that the growth phenomenon found was in some way connected with the two-stream behavior treated in Chap. 4, since electrons in a slipping stream have different velocities.   However, rather than having a double-stream inter-action as was thought, the instability found here depends on a different phenomenon, which will now be explained.   The explanation also follows that of Gould.

The growing space-charge waves we have found here are embodied in a beam perturbation of the kind shown in Fig. 10.16.   Imagine the beam displaced as shown in the figure.   Under the unperturbed condition of rectilinear flow for the beam, the electrostatic forces due to the applied voltage and the magnetic forces just balance so that one gets rectilinear flow.   Under the displaced conditions shown, electrons at position (*a*), for example, have some additional electrostatic forces acting upward due to the other electrons, such as at (*d*) and (*c*), and to the image charges in the electrodes.   Similarly, the electrons at (*b*) would have downward forces (we are assuming that the displacement shown is symmetrical around the unperturbed position of the beam, shown by a dashed line).   Because a beam is in a magnetic field, any electric field at (*a*) upward will, as is characteristic of a crossed field, produce an *additional* compo-nent of motion at right angles to the magnetic field and to the *additional* electric field.   Therefore, this upward field at (*a*) causes a drift of the electrons at (*a*) in the direction shown by the arrows, and similarly for the electrons at (*b*), also shown by the arrows.   Such a motion, therefore, results in a bunching around position (*c*) and a decrease in density around positions (*d*).   This increase in the charge at (*c*) and decrease at (*d*) result in longitudinal fields at (*a*) and (*b*) and (by the same argument we have just used) result in a vertical displacement.   If one goes through the details of the directions, it will be found that the result is an *increase* of the displacements at (*a*) and (*b*).   Thus, the perturbation and the instability described by Eq. (110*a*) represent a combination of longi-tudinal bunching and transverse displacement that grows because of the presence of the magnetic field.

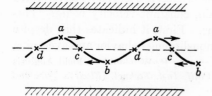

Fig. 10.16   Schematic representation of beam perturbation.

Further insight into the nature of these waves can be obtained by looking at the dependence of the rate of growth in the operating parameters. As shown by Eqs. (110a) or (113), a decrease in the magnetic field with unchanged d-c velocity results in an increase in the rate of growth. The reason for this relationship is a consequence of the nature of motion in crossed fields. The d-c velocity can be kept constant under a decreasing magnetic field only by correspondingly decreasing the applied electrostatic field. Then any given perturbation of the beam that produces an additional (space-charge) field results in a larger perturbed velocity, since the ratio of the electric field produced by the perturbation to the magnetic field is now larger (for the smaller applied magnetic field).[1]

The instabilities represented by this wave have been observed in many crossed-field devices. Any initial disturbance in the cathode region where the beam originates, such as noise, or any improper injection that results in initially nonrectilinear motion increases because of this instability, and one gets large perturbations in the motion. The displacements shown in Fig. 10.16 can indeed become so large that the electrons can strike the sole. The energy that enables the electrons to strike an electrode at zero potential with a finite energy comes, of course, from the interaction among the electrons. This same instability can also appear as an excessive noise output from a crossed-field device with no input. Under these circumstances, presumably the instability we have just described builds up to large amplitude at a frequency which may be close enough to synchronism with the circuit that power can be transferred to the circuit which then appears in the output.

This same growth phenomenon due to space charge, which we have just demonstrated for the case in which the circuit is irrelevant, also strongly affects the interaction of the beam with a circuit that is synchronous with the beam. In that case, one has to look at the solutions of Eq. (109) for either the backward- or forward-wave case (with the appropriate choice of sign on the right). Various cases have been analyzed by Gould. He does find that in the presence of space charge, the gain for the forward-wave case is increased apparently because of this growth mechanism inherent in the beam itself. Applied to an M-type backward-wave oscillator, the same phenomenon is shown to result in a marked decrease in starting current, since again the effect of the beam instability is to increase the interaction with the circuit. This behavior is, of course, unlike the effects of space charge in the O-type tubes, where

---

[1] An equivalent interpretation can be obtained from the factor σ_0/B_0u_0 which appears in the imaginary part of the propagation constant in Eq. (113). For any beam perturbation, the space-charge field is proportional to σ_0, and B_0u_0 is equal to the applied electrostatic field. Therefore σ_0/B_0u_0 states that the ratio of growth starting from any beam displacement is proportional to the ratio of the perturbation field to the applied field.

the effect of space charge is to decrease the gain in traveling-wave tubes and increase the starting current in backward-wave oscillators. The experiments on M-type backward oscillators seem to bear out, at least qualitatively, this prediction of the effect of space charge on starting currents (or starting lengths). It is found that the starting currents predicted by the theory omitting space-charge effects are *higher* than experimental values by a large factor. This discrepancy is in a direction that is unusual in that one would normally expect any approximate theory to predict too low a value.

The existence of the diocotron effect is a plausible explanation of the discrepancy. The Gould theory including space charge and resulting in much lower starting currents is closer to the experimental results. A precise comparison cannot be made easily. The experimental results can be strongly affected by injection conditions. It is doubtful whether the electron flow is purely rectilinear in any practical device, and in general the initial conditions on the beam would require a superposition of *all* the possible waves we have considered, including the cyclotron waves. In the absence of detailed knowledge of the electron flow it is not possible, therefore, to make precise calculations of the initial conditions.

Appendix **1**

Lagrangian and Eulerian Hydrodynamics

In all treatments of microwave devices, one is continually concerned with the interaction of beams of electrons and electromagnetic fields, static or dynamic. In every such problem, one is ultimately interested in finding the current and/or the charge density at various points in space as determined by the equations of motion of the particles and the electromagnetic fields. The motion of the particles is, of course, determined by the fields to which the particles are subjected, and the electromagnetic fields are in turn produced by the currents and charge densities that exist at all points in the system. In obtaining the current and charge densities from the motion of the particles, one is essentially always considering the electrons as a fluid and applying hydrodynamical notions.

In hydrodynamics there are two approaches, one known as the Lagrangian, the other as the Eulerian. In the Lagrangian approach, one follows the motion of the individual charges throughout space. From the motion of these individual particles, one can calculate the current and charge density the particles contribute at any point in the space when they arrive at this point. This approach thus consists of "labeling" the particles, following them, and calculating their contribution as they traverse various regions of the system. The variables of interest are the coordinates of the individual particles; charge densities and currents are always calculated by following a group of particles and finding how this particular group expands or contracts as it moves through space. In the Eulerian approach, one starts by defining certain field quantities as functions of the coordinates and of time; i.e., at each point in space there is a charge density, a current, and a velocity of the fluid and one relates these quantities at any *fixed* point to the dynamical properties of the particles *passing through* the point at every instant in time. Of course, one must use the equations of motion of individual particles; but by a transformation of variables, one can arrive at the contribution that the motion of these particles makes to the field quantities at particular points in space. One does not continue to follow the same particles along their trajectories.

The relation between these two approaches can perhaps be best seen by considering the equation of motion of a particle. For any particular particle, this equation can be written as $m\,dv/dt = eE$. If we integrate these equations, we can obviously find the position of a particle as a function of time. It is this equation and the integration of this equation that are used in treating the elementary theory of velocity modulation in the first part of Chap. 3 and also throughout Chap. 5 on the Llewellyn-Peterson equations. The basic equation used in relating individual electron motion to currents comes from the fact that, if one follows a particular (infinitesimal) group of particles through space (i.e., a particular amount of charge), one can calculate from the motion the time (infinitesimal) that this group will take in passing across a given surface. This calculation provides the instantaneous current through the surface given by

$$dq = I_1\,dt_1 \tag{1}$$

and from a knowledge of the subsequent motion, one can calculate that this same group of particles (which may have expanded or contracted its extent in space), passing through some other surface during an interval of time that is larger or smaller, constitutes an instantaneous current given by $I_2\,dt_2$. If one knows the current given by the first equation at some point in space for all electrons and can calculate the motion of all the electrons subsequently, one can also determine the current at the second point. In particular (and this is the important advantage of the Lagrangian formulation) if the subsequent motion is such that some trajectories cross, there is in principle no problem. We merely find that several groups of charges may be simultaneously passing through surface 2 even though they left surface 1 at different times. Since we follow individual particles and their current contributions, all are always automatically included, since the summation is over all electrons.

The deficiencies of this approach become more apparent when we consider the Eulerian approach. In this method, one is interested not in following the velocity of particular particles through space but in determining the velocities (as functions of time) of the *various* particles that pass through a given point as time goes on. The velocity, the density, and the current are field variables (like electric field or magnetic field). We define these quantities as functions of space and time, and the problem is to show how these field variables are determined by the motion of the charges that successively pass through the region. One observes the charges merely as they pass through a point and one is not interested in following the identical particles.

The transition from the Lagrangian formulation to the Eulerian is obtained by transforming the equation of motion. If velocity v is defined as a function of the coordinates and time for the fluid we are examining, then the acceleration of any particle that passes through the point in question at the time in question is related to the spatial and time derivatives of field variable velocity by the well-known relation between the so-called particle derivative and the two partial derivatives:

$$\frac{d\mathbf{v}}{dt} = \frac{\partial\mathbf{v}}{\partial t} + (\mathbf{v}\cdot\nabla)\mathbf{v} \tag{2}$$

where $\mathbf{v}$ is the velocity of the particle passing through the point in question, i.e., the value of the field variable at that point. By transforming the equation in this way, we are essentially stationing ourselves at one position in space and calculating the accelerations of the particles that pass through that point. This procedure is sufficient to determine the field quantities, and we are then no longer interested in following that particle after it has passed through. We now look at a succession of particles at the same point in space and their accelerations. The advantage of this approach is that we now have field variables that are functions of space and time and we have a set of differential equations for these field variables. This set includes the equation of continuity expressed in these variables

$$\nabla \cdot \mathbf{i} + \frac{\partial \rho}{\partial t} = 0 \tag{3}$$

which states merely that the net flow of current out of any infinitesimal volume must be equal to the rate of decrease of charge density in that volume. Note that we speak here not of conservation of charge of a set of particles that we are following through space, but of conservation of charge in a fixed volume in space. With these equations one has greater flexibility. It is easier to solve problems with complicated configurations and to put in boundary conditions, since all quantities (electromagnetic fields as well as currents, densities, and velocities) are on the same basis as dependent variables that are functions of space and time and can be treated by means of standard methods of solving partial differential equations.

The principal disadvantage of the Eulerian approach is that it cannot handle crossing of electron trajectories. By definition, the velocity must be a single-valued function of the coordinates. Trajectory crossing obviously violates this condition and makes the equations unmanageable. (The condition when trajectories are just beginning to cross at a particular point in space would correspond in hydrodynamical terms to the formation of a shock wave; it is well known that such waves offer great mathematical difficulties.)

Another difficulty with the Eulerian treatment, though less serious, is that it is not particularly suited for large amplitudes. The actual equations that one gets as outlined above and used widely in the text have nonlinear terms in them. These terms are omitted for the small-signal case and one obtains very manageable linear equations that enable one to solve a whole variety of problems. If one keeps the nonlinear terms, it is still possible by successful approximations to get some answers, but the analysis becomes more difficult. (Note that nonlinearity is not the same problem as crossing trajectories. The nonlinearity can be handled, at least approximately, but the crossing of trajectories is a much more serious problem; actually, it is necessary to go back to the Lagrangian formulation in this case.) Since the Eulerian formulation utilizes all field variables, the effects of space charge on the fields are particularly easy to handle and almost all space-charge-wave problems handled in the text are based on the Eulerian approach (for example, Chap. 4 with the exception of Sec. 4.1, which is Lagrangian). On the other hand, if one is interested in large-signal effects where there is crossing of trajectories *and* space-charge effects, one has to go back to the Lagrangian formulation. In this case, the problem can be always solved in principle even though the solution may require using numerical methods or computers. The means of solution are merely to follow all electrons: one calculates a step along each trajectory and at each interval in time one stops, locates all the electrons, finds the space-charge effects due to the electrons at these locations, calculates the resulting forces, carries the motion one step farther in the process, and so on. This is the basis of all the numerical large-signal calculations. It is laborious but does, in principle, provide all the answers.

Induced Currents—
General Configuration

The result derived in Sec. 3.4 for a parallel plane gap, although sufficiently general for most purposes, can be generalized to apply to the motion of a charge in the neighborhood of a number of electrodes, without restrictions on the shape of the electrodes. To derive this equivalent result, we shall use a theorem of electrostatics which is known as Green's reciprocation theorem. If at a number of points in space $P_1, P_2, \ldots, P_n$ we have a system of charges $q_1, q_2, \ldots, q_n$, then the potentials V_i at each of these points will be proportional to the charges situated at all the other points and inversely proportional to the distance from those other points. Thus

$$V_1 = 0 + \frac{q_2}{r_{12}} + \frac{q_3}{r_{13}} + \cdots + \frac{q_n}{r_{1n}} \tag{1}$$

$$V_2 = \frac{q_1}{r_{21}} + 0 + \frac{q_3}{r_{23}} + \cdots + \frac{q_n}{r_{2n}} \tag{2}$$

$$\cdots \cdots \cdots \cdots \cdots \cdots \cdots \cdots$$

where $r_{12} = r_{21}$ is the distance between points 1 and 2, and similarly for the other subscripts. If the charges $q_1, q_2, \ldots, q_n$, which we have assumed to exist at these points, are replaced by another, different set of charges $q_1', q_2', \ldots, q_n'$, then, of course, the potentials V_i will be given by a similar set of equations with each q_i replaced by q_i', the distances remaining as before. In other words, given a distribution of charge, the potential produced by this distribution is proportional to the charge; and if the charges are changed, the potentials are changed correspondingly. If we multiply (1) by q_1', (2) by q_2', etc., we obtain a set of equations

$$q_1'V_1 = 0 + \frac{q_1'q_2}{r_{12}} + \frac{q_1'q_3}{r_{13}} + \cdots + \frac{q_1'q_n}{r_{1n}} \tag{3}$$

$$q_2'V_2 = \frac{q_2'q_1}{r_{21}} + 0 + \frac{q_2'q_3}{r_{23}} + \cdots + \frac{q_2'q_n}{r_{2n}} \tag{4}$$

. . . .

The sum of the terms on the left-hand side is $\displaystyle\sum_{i=1}^{n} q_i'V_i$. If we now add each column separately, we obtain for the sum of column 1, for example,

$$0 + q_1\left(\frac{q_2'}{r_{12}} + \frac{q_3'}{r_{13}} + \cdots + \frac{q_1'}{r_{1i}}\right) = q_1V_1' \tag{5}$$

Similarly, the sum of column 2 yields q_2V_2', etc., so that adding all these sums gives $\displaystyle\sum_{i=1}^{n} q_iV_i'$. Since the total sum of all the terms on the right-hand side of the equations must be the same no matter in what order we sum them, we finally obtain

$$\sum_i q_i'V_i = \sum_i q_iV_i' \tag{6}$$

This equation is known as *Green's reciprocation theorem*. If certain of these charges $q_1, q_2, \ldots, q_i$ are located on the same conductor, we can group the charges together (to obtain a single charge Q), since they are then all necessarily at the same potential. We may then write (6) in another form, namely

$$\sum_j Q_jV_j' = \sum_j Q_j'V_j \tag{7}$$

where the summation is now over all separate conductors.

Let us now use these equations to find how the charge on any one electrode is affected by the presence or absence of a charge in the space between the electrodes. We shall have to pick particular special values of the q's and V's to arrive at the result we desire. It is convenient to rewrite Eq. (7) so that we are considering the case of k electrodes and one point in space P which is occupied by a charge of magnitude q_p (Fig. A.1). The equation then becomes

$$q_pV_p' + \sum_j Q_jV_j' = q_p'V_p + \sum_j Q_j'V_j \tag{8}$$

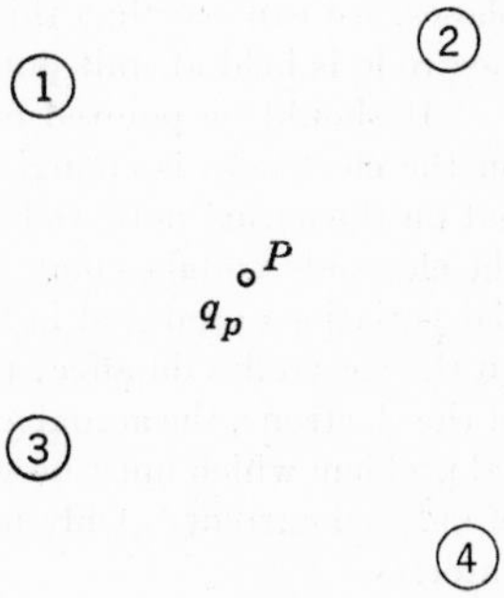

$\textcircled{1}$ $\textcircled{2}$

Fig. A.1 Distribution of charges around a point charge q_p at P.

$\overset{\circ}{}\!P$
q_p

$\textcircled{3}$

$\textcircled{4}$

One choice of values for this equation is that for which all $V_i = 0$ except V_1 and V_1', and $q_p' = 0$. Then the equations reduce to

$$Q_1'V_1 = Q_1V_1' + q_pV_{p1}' \tag{9}$$

Similarly, one can deduce an equation

$$Q_2'V_2 = Q_2V_2' + q_pV_{p2}' \tag{10}$$

and so on. The significance of V_{p1}', V_{p2}', etc., in these equations is that the potential V_1' (and the corresponding charge Q_1') produces the potential V_{p1}' at P, the potential V_2' produces the potential V_{p2}' at P, etc.; i.e., each charge produces a potential V_{pi}' at the point P due to the charge Q_i' on the ith electrode. If we add all these equations, we obtain

$$\sum_i Q_i'V_i = \sum_i Q_iV_i' + q_pV_p' \tag{11}$$

where we have written $V_p' = \sum_i V_{pi}'$. This result describes the effect of all the potentials V_i' in producing the potential at the point P (i.e., superposition will apply). Let us again consider, however, only one of these equations and let $V_1 = V_1'$, or

$$Q_1'V_1' = Q_1V_1' + q_pV_{p1}' \tag{12}$$

This equation thus gives us the difference which exists in charge on electrode 1 according to whether the point charge at P is present or absent:

$$\delta Q_1 = Q_1 - Q_1' = -q_p \frac{V_{p1}'}{V_1'} \tag{13}$$

Here δQ_1 is the increment in charge on electrode 1 produced by the charge q_p at the point P and V_{p1}' is the potential at P (due to the charge Q_1' on the electrode) in the absence of the charge at point P. If the charge q_p changes its position, then δQ_1 will also change, resulting in a current given by the following equation:

$$i = \frac{d}{dt}(\delta Q) = -\frac{d}{dt}\left(q_p \frac{V_{p1}'}{V_1'}\right) = -q_p \frac{d\mathbf{r}}{dt} \cdot \frac{\nabla V_p'}{V_1'} = -q_p\mathbf{v} \cdot \frac{\nabla V_p'}{V_1'} \tag{14}$$

Thus current is independent of the effects of the other electrodes, since superposition applies. It is to be noted that the current is independent of the potential of the electrode. The factor $\nabla V_p'/V_1'$ which appears in (14) is a geometrical factor which merely describes the distribution of the fields in the neighborhood of the electrodes and is independent of absolute magnitude. Just as in the special case of parallel planes, we can see that this factor is really the gradient of the field at P when the electrode is held at unit potential.

It should be pointed out that the above derivation applies even if the voltage on the electrodes is changing during the motion, since the induced current depends not on the actual potentials, but merely on the geometric configuration. Changes in the electrode voltages may be due to other currents flowing in the circuit or to potential variations produced in the circuit by the flow of induced current. (The voltages on the electrodes do affect the *motion* of the electrons; i.e., in calculating the velocity of the electrons, the actual existing voltages must be used. This is a separate dynamical problem which must be solved in any application of this equation to the calculation of induced current. Only in this particular dynamical problem do the actual voltages enter.)

Index

A

Accelerated motion, 120
Acceleration, 261, 265
Adiabatic approximation, 249
Adiabatic motion, 261
Admittance, 80
  circuit, 109, 151
  electronic, 109, 151
Alekseev, N. F., 3
Amplification, 151
  crossed-field, 241
Amplifier, 214
  backward-wave, 214, 223–225, 228
  beating-wave, 222
  crossed-field, 231, 260
  double-beam, 222
  M-type, 232
  magnetron, 12
Angular momentum, 44, $46n.$
Anode, 6, 16, 21
Arrival time, 62
Arsenjewa-Heil, A., 3
Attenuating wave, 111
Axial velocity, 48, 49

B

Backward wave, 181, 218
  interaction, 178
Barkhausen, oscillator, 6, 12

Beam, 16, 17, 31, 34
  Brillouin, $112n.$, 202
  circular, 33
  confined, 97–103
  converging, 34
  electron, 16–21
  hollow, 56
  ion-focused, 202
  laminar, 38
  magnetically focused, 50
  nonconvergent, 44
  rectangular ("strip"), 32
Beam boundary, 114
  scalloped, 115, 270
Beam conductance, 79
Beam-coupling coefficient, 78, 193–195
Beam focusing, 42–52
Beam formation, 14
Beam loading, 68, 79
Beam production, 11
Beam radius, 50
  maximum and minimum values of,
    50, 51
Beam shape, 50
Beam-spreading curve, 40
Beam transmission, 40
Beam wavelength, 105
Beam waves, 258
Beat phenomenon, 228
Birdsall, C. K., viii, 155, 161, $163n.$,
  $173n.$, $209n.$
Blodgett, K. B., $23n.$, 24–26
Bobroff, D. L., $210n.$, $212n.$, $268n.$

Boot, H. A. H., 3
Bowen, A. E., 138
Bowman-Manifold, M., 33n.
Brewer, G. R., 155, 161, 173n.
Brillouin, L., 44, 45, 46n., 48–50, 84, 113, 117, 118, 202, 237, 237n., 240, 240n., 241, 243n., 246, 270
Brillouin flow, 44, 45, 48–50, 84, 113, 117, 118, 202, 237, 240, 243n., 246, 270
Brillouin focusing, 202, 251
Bunching, 5, 8, 13, 60, 61, 78, 79, 87, 260, 262, 271
  longitudinal, 280
Busch's theorem, 45, 46n.

C

C, 154, 170, 173, 221, 226, 229, 259, 277
Carcinotron, 232
Cathode, 6, 16, 21
  cylindrical, 30
  oxide-coated, 18
Cavity, klystron, 59
Cavity resonator, 3
Child, C. D., 22n., 127
Child's law, 127
Chodorow, M., 194n., 202n.
Chu, L. J., 143n., 206n.
Chu small-signal-power thoerem, 206, 212
Circuit, 229
  backward-wave, 182, 183, 219
  forward-wave, 219
  propagating, 145, 147, 178, 218, 274
  resonant, 8
  "slow-wave," 4, 8, 241
  traveling-wave, 8
  traveling-wave-tube, 191
Circuit admittance, 109
Circuit boundary, 274
Circuit curve, 152
Circuit equation, 20n., 74, 107, 108, 144, 150, 157, 161, 163, 170, 182, 252
  generalized, 168

Circuit field, 173, 219
Circuit wave, 185
  backward, 222
  forward, 222
Cleeton, C. E., 2
Cold circuit, 142
Cold mode, 143, 156, 164, 165, 171, 172
Collection of electrons, 14, 57
Concentric cylinders, 22, 31, 35
Concentric spheres, 25, 31, 35
Confined beam, 97–103
Confined flow, 43
Conservation, of energy, 68, 206
  of power, 222
Continuity, of charge, 63
  equation of, 71, 144, 155
Convection current, 72, 73, 121–123, 128, 139, 216
  entrance, 123
  exit, 123
Convection-current density, 71, 75, 78, 90, 145, 146
Converging beams, 34
Conversion of velocity modulation to density modulation, 11, 58
Conversion mechanism, 12
Coupled-mode analysis, 205
  equations, 216, 220
  theory, 222, 227
Couplers, fast-wave, 229
Coupling coefficient, 196
  constants, 143
Crestratron, 228
Crossed fields, 230, 236, 243, 250, 260, 263, 269, 281
  electric, 235
  magnetic, 235
  motion in, 266
  static, 232
Current, 54, 62, 64, 66, 250
  critical, 48
  induced, 250, 251
  limiting, 48
  r-f, 147
  starting, 282
Current density, 54, 71, 77
Current equations, 62–66

Current flow, 60
Current generator, 148
Cutler, C. C., 56n.
Cycloid, 234
Cyclotron frequency, 2, 97n., 233, 238, 242, 263, 264
Cyclotron waves, 258, 266
  fast, 267
  slow, 264, 267
Cylindrical cathode, 30

D

D, 277, 278
Density-modulation tube, 6
Depressed collectors, 57
Diocotron effect, 242, 269, 279, 282
Diode, 120, 135
  space-charge-limited, 19, 126, 127, 136
  temperature-limited, 126
Diode equations, 134
Diode oscillators, 137, 138
Directional coupler, 214
Displacement, transverse, 270, 280
Displacement current, 72, 73, 122, 147, 148, 157
Displacement current density, 71, 145, 146
Double-beam tubes, 103–112
Drift, steady, 242
Drift space, 4, 60
Drift tube, 214
  klystron, 205
Drift velocity, 234, 235
Driving current, 73, 75
Dunn, D. A., viii
Dushman, S., 17
Dynamics, Hamiltonian form of, 46n.

E

Eigenfunctions, 165
Eigenvalue, 165
Electrode shapes, 35
Electrodes, 31, 32

Electrodes, focusing, 31
Electrolytic tank, 33, 35
Electromagnetic field, 13, 59
Electromagnetic power, 208–210, 222, 224, 228
Electromagnetic power flow, 207, 218
Electron beams, 16–21, 142, 143, 149, 178
Electron emission, 16, 17
Electron guns, 30–37, 52
Electron motion, radial, 190
Electron transit time, 2
Electronic admittance, 109
Electronic curve, 152
Electronic equation, 20n., 74, 107, 108, 144, 150, 151, 161, 163, 169, 172, 181, 182, 256
Electrostatic lens, 34
Emde, F., 39
Emission, 17
  space-charge-limited, 20
Emission current, 21
Energy, 205, 206
  conservation of, 68, 206
Energy transfer, 13, 59, 66, 67
Epsztein, B., 4
Equation, circuit, 123
  of continuity, 71, 107, 108, 272
  electronic, 123
Equilibrium condition, 48
  radius, 47n., 51
Equipotentials, 32
Eulerian approach to hydrodynamics, 63, 70, 83, 283–285
  equations of motion, 255n., 272n.
  variables, 71, 92n., 112n., 114, 116, 121, 124, 128, 245
Exciting current, 74, 80

F

Fast wave, 99, 213
Ferrites, 178
Field, L. M., 89n.
Field, circularly polarized, 267
  crossed-electric, 235
  electric, 17

Field, electromagnetic, 13
  knife-edge, 196
  magnetic, 9, 17, 30, 42, 43, 47, 53,
    82, 83, 97, 112, 235
Field configuration, 142
  theory, 143
  waves, 98
Floquet's theorem, 181
Flow, Brillouin, 44, 45, 48–50, 84,
    113, 117, 118, 202, 237, 240,
    243n., 246, 270
  confined, 43
  Harris, 56
  immersed, 42–44
  slipping-stream, 240
  space-charge-balanced, 44, 46
Focusing, 16, 44, 47
  Brillouin, 202, 251
  magnetic, 11
  positive ions, 113
Focusing electrodes, 31
Folded line, 179, 180
Forward wave, 179, 218
Fourier analysis, 65, 66
Fourier integral, 194
Frequency, cyclotron, 2, 97n., 233,
    238, 242, 263, 264
  Doppler-shifted, 265
  Larmor precession, 46
  plasma, 40, 47, 51, 82, 86, 97n.,
    104, 106

G

Gain, 111, 142, 143, 156, 183, 229,
    268
Gain parameter, 154
Gap, 4
  finite, 195
  gridless, 190
  high-velocity, 72–80
  klystron, 196, 206
  modulating, 5
  nonplanar, 190
  plane parallel, 59
Gap factor, 78
Gap modulation, 202, 203

Gap spacing, 60
Gap voltage, 217
Gauss's theorem, 212
Ginzton, E. L., viii
Gould, R. W., 82n., 221n., 270n.,
    277n., 278–282
Green's theorem, 167, 287
Grid, 6
Grid loading, 68
Group velocity, 4, 178, 179, 181, 218,
    219
  negative, 222
Growing waves, 110, 111, 151, 155,
    156, 161, 184, 205, 223, 224, 260,
    261, 279

H

H, 259, 278
Habann, E., 2
Haeff, A. V., 103n.
Hahn, W. C., 115n.
Hansen, J. W., 57n.
Hansen, W. W., vii, viii, 3
Harman, W. A., 185
Harris, L. A., 56, 56n.
Haus, H. A., 210n., 212n., 268n.
Hay, H. G., 246n., 269n., 279n.
Hebenstreit, W. B., 103n.
Heffner, Hubert, viii
Heil, A. Arsenjewa-, 3
Heil, O., 3
Helix, 4, 142, 147, 185
High-velocity gap, 72
Hines, M. E., 56n.
Hull, A. W., 2
Hydronamics, Eulerian, 63, 70, 83,
    283–285
  Lagrangian, 62, 63, 70, 283–285

I

Immersed flow, 42–44
Impedance, coupling, 157, 169
  diode, 135, 138, 139
  external, 123
  normal interaction, 263

Induced current, 13, 68, 69, 148, 250, 251, 286–288
Induced field, 157
Infinite cross section, 96, 103
Infinitesimal generators, 149
Initial conditions, 99, 100
Injected velocity, 79
Input gap, 68
Interaction, backward-wave, 268
  backward-wave-tube, 179
  beam-circuit, 278
  multiple-stream, 235
  of r-f space current with electromagnetic field, 58, 59
  traveling-wave, 244
Interaction impedance, 229, 277
Interference effect, 184
Internal feedback, 183

J

Jackson, J. D., 143n.
Jahnke, E., 39
Jansen, M. J., 18n.

K

Kilgore, G. R., 2
Kinematics, 260
Kinetic energy, 207
Kinetic power, 207, 209, 210, 213, 216, 222, 224, 228
  negative, 211
  positive, 211
Kinetic power flow, negative, 214
  positive, 214
Kinetic voltage, 207, 217
  a-c, 210
Kino, G. S., viii, 164, 174n.
Klystron, 2, 3, 30, 59, 63, 64, 66, 68, 78, 191
  gridless, 190
  reflex, 3
  two-cavity, 4, 12
Klystron cavity, 59
Klystron gap, 196, 206
Kompfner, R., 3, 4, 221n., 222, 229
Kompfner dip, 221n., 222, 229

L

Lagrangian hydrodynamics, 62, 63, 70, 83, 283–285
Lagrangian treatment, 121
Lagrangian variables, 71, 92n., 112n., 124, 245
Laminar beam, 38
Langmuir, I., 23n., 24–26
Laplace's equation, 32, 33, 118
Laplacian, 95, 165
Large signals, 66
Larmor, J., 44n., 46, 237n.
Larmor precession frequency, 46
Leibnitz, G. W. v., 150n.
Lemmens, H. J., 18n.
Levi, R., 18n.
Linear dimensions, 52
Linear theory, 206
Llewellyn, F. B., 2, 81, 120–123, 122n., 125, 127, 131, 134, 137–140, 159, 284
Llewellyn coefficients, 131
Llewellyn's equation, 123, 134, 140, 159, 284
Local derivative, 92
Loosjes, R., 18n.
Loss, initial, 156

M

M-type device, 268, 279
MacColl, L. A., 209
McFarlane, G. G., 246, 269n., 279n.
Magnetic field, 9, 17, 30, 42, 43, 47, 53, 82, 83, 97, 112, 189, 230, 231, 233, 240, 257, 281
  axial, 231
Magnetic-flux density, 54
Magnetic focusing, 11
Magnetron, 2, 3, 8, 10, 17, 59
Magnetron amplifier, 12
Magnetron oscillator, 13, 230, 231
Malairov, D. D., 3
Manifold, M. Bowman-, 33n.
Maximum current, 41
Maxwellian distribution, 20, 21

Microperveance, 31
Mode, 142, 147
  cold, 142
  normal, 165, 167
  propagating, 146
  TE, 164, 165
  TM, 164, 165, 166
Modes of the circuit, 149
Modified plasma propagation con-
    stant, 203
Modulating gap, 5
Modulation, density, 12
  conversion to, 11, 58
  small-amplitude, 191
  velocity, 3, 5, 11, 12, 14, 58–61, 74,
    85, 192
Modulation factor, 78
Motion, 236
  axial, 191
  radial, 191
Müller, J., 138
Muller, M., 256n.

N

Negative power, 213
Neutralization by positive ions, 42,
    117, 189, 202
Nicoll, F. H., 33n.
Noise, 140, 281
Nörgaard, L. S., 130n.
Normal-mode approach, 164
  expansion, 163, 171, 174
  method, 143

O

O-type device, 268, 269
Okabe, K., 2
Orthogonality, 164
Oscillation conditions, 183
Oscillations, 187
  plasma, 14, 82, 104
Oscillator, backward-wave, 4, 141,
    183, 184, 221, 223, 225, 226, 241

Oscillator, Barkhausen, 6
  diode, 137, 138
  M-type backward-wave, 281, 282
  magnetron, 13
Output gap, 68
Overtaking of slow electrons by faster
    electrons, 63
Oxide-coated cathode, 18

P

Palmer, J. L., 43
Parallel planes, 21, 31, 59, 121
Parametric amplifier, 214n., 229
Particle derivative, 92, 201
Pentode, 6
Perturbed waveguide mode, 99
Perveance, 31, 40, 48
Peterson, L. C., 81, 122, 122n., 137,
    139, 140, 159, 284
Phase velocity, 4, 142, 178, 179, 181,
    182, 219
  negative, 268
Pierce, J. R., viii, 3, 21n., 31n., 32,
    35, 56n., 85n., 103n., 112n.,
    141n., 154n., 172n., 197n.,
    202n., 221, 226, 256n., 277
Pierce guns, 31, 32, 55
Planar configurations, 120
Plasma, 178n.
Plasma devices, 103
Plasma frequency, 40, 47, 51, 82, 86,
    101, 104, 106, 131, 238, 241
  reduction factor, 99, 119
Plasma oscillations, 14, 82, 104
Plasma propagation constant, modi-
    fied, 203
  reduced, 99
Plasma wave number, 40, 87, 110
Plasma wavelength, 40
Plate, 6
Poisson, 159
Poisson's equation, 20, 22, 25, 28, 49,
    53, 108, 159, 237, 239
Positive ion, 82, 85, 104
  focusing, 113, 118
  neutralization, 42, 117, 189, 202

Posthumus, K., 2
Potential, 19
  depression, 48
  minimum, 20, 21
Power, 54
  beam-loading, 216
Power density, 54
Power flow, 167
  theorem, 214
Power transfer, 206
Poynting vector, 167, 207
Propagation constant, 142, 143, 155
  beam, 260
  circuit, 260
  cold, 148, 149
Pulsed operation, 42

Q

Q, 172, 173
QC, 173, 185, 226
Quadratic correction, 77, 209
Quantum mechanics, 175, 176

R

Radial displacement, 114, 116
  modulation, 198
  velocity, 50, 51
Ramo, S., 68n.
Randal, J. T., 3
Rectilinear flow, 31, 32
Reduced plasma propagation constant, 99
Reduction factor, 78
  of plasma frequency, 99, 119
Reflex klystron, 3
Resistance, negative, 138
Resonant cavity, 4
Resonant circuit, 8
Richardson, O. W., 17, 26, 27
Richardson's equation, 17, 26, 27
Rigrod, W. W., 112n., 202n.
Rippled boundary, 204

S

Samuel, A. L., 35
Saturation current, 20
Scaling, 30, 52–55
Scalloped beam boundary, 115
Schiff, L. I., 176n.
Schottky, W., 27
Screen, 6
Separation of velocities, 110
Shockley, W., 68n.
Shunt resistance, 67
Slater, J. C., 166
Slipping stream, 246, 246n., 279, 280
Slow wave, 99, 213
Slow-wave circuit, 4, 8
Small signal, 144, 206, 211
  approximation, 91, 194
  kinetic power, 210, 212
    theorem, 207, 216
  plane diode, 121
  theory, 74, 208
Smullin, L. D., 84n., 120n.
Sole, 232, 244, 269, 281
Sorting, 12, 13
Space charge, 123, 162, 236, 237, 281
  electron flow, 140
Space-charge-balanced flow, 44, 46
Space-charge-control tubes, 1, 2
Space-charge effects, 11, 15, 31, 74,
    81, 120, 158, 159, 163, 172
  in plasmas, 40
Space-charge factor, 132, 136
  fields, 158, 171, 241, 242
    interaction with, 269
  forces, 66, 131, 158, 200, 273
Space-charge-limited diodes, 19
  emission, 20
  operation, 26, 27, 31
  regime, 28
Space-charge spreading, 31, 37–42
  theory, 279
Space-charge-wave amplifier, 89
  analysis, 81
  tube, 10
Space-charge waves, 83, 90, 96, 98,
    121, 189, 202, 203, 205, 206, 213,
    217, 251n.

Space-charge waves, fast, 211, 214, 215, 217, 227, 229
  general equations, 90–95
  solution of, 96–102
  particle equations of, 84–90
  slow, 185–187, 211, 214, 215, 217, 222, 227
  with transverse motion, 112–119, 189
Spatial harmonic, 178, 181, 182
Start-oscillation condition, 225, 226
Stiffness, 43
Structure propagating, 142, 144
Surface charge, 115, 116, 118, 204, 270, 271
Susskind, C., 43n., 57n.
Synchronous velocity, 153

T

Tantalum, 18
Temperature-limited operation, 31
Temperature saturation, 26
Tetrode, 28, 120
Theory, M-type, 278
  O-type, 278
Thin beam, 246, 269
Thoriated tungsten, 18
Tien, P. K., viii, 89n.
Total current, 70–73, 121–123, 145
Total current density, 71
Trajectory, 29, 52, 55
  curvilinear, 55, 56
  shape, 53, 54
Transfer of energy, 14
Transit angle, 7, 53, 54, 74
Transit time, 4n., 6, 60, 76–78, 132, 215
  d-c, 125, 127, 128
Transverse fields, 190, 271
Transverse motion, 191
Traveling-wave application, 178
Traveling-wave circuit, 8
Traveling-wave tube, 2, 3, 7, 10, 12, 30, 59, 84, 103, 141, 142, 144, 197, 205, 214, 218, 221–224, 227, 241, 256, 257, 282
  forward-wave, 184

Traveling-wave tube, O-type, 276
Traveling waves, 142
Triode, 6, 12, 59, 63, 68, 78, 120
Trivelpiece, A. W., 82n.
Tubes, backward-wave, 183
  density modulation, 6
  double-beam, 103–112
  M-type, 241, 242, 252
  microwave, 10
  multielement, 139
  O-type, 241, 242, 252, 256, 257, 259, 260, 279, 281
  space-charge-control, 1, 2, 6
  space-charge-wave, 10
  traveling-wave, 2, 3, 7, 10, 12, 30, 59, 84, 103, 141, 142, 144, 197, 205, 214, 218, 222–224, 227, 241, 256, 257, 282
Tungsten, 18

V

Vacuum tubes, high-frequency, 122
Varian, R. H., viii, 3
Varian, S. F., viii, 3
Velocities, separation of, 110
Velocity, 60, 89
  axial, 48, 49, 199
  electron-beam, 142
  entrance, 123
  exit, 123
  initial, 266, 267
  radial, 50, 51, 199, 200
  thermal, 55
Velocity modulation, 3, 5, 11, 12, 14, 58–61, 74, 85, 192, 266
Velocity vector, 266
Voltage gain, 182
  saturation, 27
Volume current, 204

W

Walker, L. R., 56n.
Watkins, D. A., viii

Wave, cold-circuit, 154
Wave equation, 91
    inhomogeneous, 168
Webster, D. L., 3
Wehnelt, 32
Wessel-Berg, T., 194
Whinnery, J. R., 163n.
Williams, N. H., 2
Work function, 17, 18

Y

Yagi, H., 2

Z

Žáček, A., 2
Zitelli, L. T., viii, 101n., 102n., 202n.